# ROYAL COMMISSION

## ON

# ENVIRONMENTAL

# POLLUTION

CHAIRMAN:
SIR JOHN HOUGHTON CBE FRS

## SEVENTEENTH REPORT

## INCINERATION OF WASTE

*Presented to Parliament by Command of Her Majesty
May 1993*

HMSO: LONDON
£18.60 net

Cm 2181

Recycled Paper

| | | |
|---|---|---|
| 1st report | First Report | Cmnd 4585, February 1971 |
| 2nd report | Three Issues in Industrial Pollution | Cmnd 4894, March 1972 |
| 3rd report | Pollution in some British Estuaries and Coastal Waters | Cmnd 5054, September 1972 |
| 4th report | Pollution Control: Progress and Problems | Cmnd 5780, December 1974 |
| 5th report | Air Pollution Control: an Integrated Approach | Cmnd 6371, January 1976 |
| 6th report | Nuclear Power and the Environment | Cmnd 6618, September 1976 |
| 7th report | Agriculture and Pollution | Cmnd 7644, September 1979 |
| 8th report | Oil Pollution of the Sea | Cmnd 8358, October 1981 |
| 9th report | Lead in the Environment | Cmnd 8852, April 1983 |
| 10th report | Tackling Pollution – Experience and Prospects | Cmnd 9149, February 1984 |
| 11th report | Managing Waste: The Duty of Care | Cmnd 9675, December 1985 |
| 12th report | Best Practicable Environmental Option | Cm 310, February 1988 |
| 13th report | The Release of Genetically Engineered Organisms to the Environment | Cm 720, July 1989 |
| 14th report | GENHAZ  A system for the critical appraisal of proposals to release genetically modified organisms into the environment | Cm 1557, June 1991 |
| 15th report | Emissions from Heavy Duty Diesel Vehicles | Cm 1631, September 1991 |
| 16th report | Freshwater Quality | Cm 1966, June 1992 |

# ROYAL COMMISSION ON ENVIRONMENTAL POLLUTION

## SEVENTEENTH REPORT

*To the Queen's Most Excellent Majesty*

MAY IT PLEASE YOUR MAJESTY

We, the undersigned Commissioners, having been appointed "to advise on matters, both national and international, concerning the pollution of the environment; on the adequacy of research in this field; and the future possibilities of danger to the environment";

And to enquire into any such matters referred to us by one of Your Majesty's Secretaries of State or by one of Your Majesty's Ministers, or any other such matters on which we ourselves shall deem it expedient to advise:

HUMBLY SUBMIT TO YOUR MAJESTY THE FOLLOWING REPORT.

Can a man take fire in his bosom, and his clothes not be burned?

*Proverbs 6,27.*

# CONTENTS

# CHAPTER 5

## Energy recovery

# CHAPTER 6

## Health issues

# CHAPTER 7

## Other forms of environmental impact

# CHAPTER 8

## The future of the technology

# CHAPTER 9

## The place of incineration in a waste management strategy

# CHAPTER 10

## Conclusions and recommendations

## GLOSSARY

## REFERENCES

## APPENDICES

# INDEXES

## PHOTOGRAPHS

*The photographs are inserted between pages 70 and 71.*

## INFORMATION BOXES

## TABLES

# FIGURES

# CHAPTER 1

# INTRODUCTION

**The scope of this study**

1.1  The Commission's view of waste management is that it must be based on a four-stage decision procedure:

**1st**, wherever possible avoid creating wastes

**2nd**, where wastes are unavoidable, recycle them if possible

**3rd**, where wastes cannot be recycled in the form of materials, recover energy from them

**4th**, when the foregoing options have been exhausted, utilise the best practicable environmental option to dispose of wastes.

1.2  This report deals with incineration and its role in relation to the 34 million tonnes of municipal waste, 30–40 million tonnes of sewage sludge and possibly 6 million tonnes of chemical and clinical wastes produced in the UK each year. There are differences of opinion about the general desirability of incineration. Government policy for waste management envisages that incineration and landfill both have a role. In a number of countries incineration is used much more extensively for municipal waste than in the UK, and some have adopted it as the primary method for future disposal of industrial and municipal wastes. On the other hand there has been some strong opposition to waste incineration from an environmental perspective on the grounds that it causes pollution and is likely to reduce the recycling of materials.[1] These arguments need to be carefully assessed.

1.3  As well as being a method of treatment and disposal, incineration can recover energy from wastes of suitable calorific value. In this respect it can substitute for fossil fuels, and have a beneficial influence on the greenhouse effect. Both the environmental impact and the economics of energy recovery need to be taken into account.

1.4  Legislation recently enacted or in prospect, at both European Community (EC) and national levels, has important implications for waste incineration. In particular stringent standards have now been set for emissions to air. We have considered the implications of the new limits on pollution from incineration plants, and whether they ought to be made more stringent.

1.5  A high proportion of existing UK plants, especially those for municipal or clinical wastes, do not meet the new standards, and will either have to be closed or expensively rebuilt. We have based our assessment of the role of incineration on the standards that will apply for the future, together with studies of the impact of older plants.

1.6  We have considered the extent to which new plants meeting the new standards are likely to be constructed. Only a few major incinerators have been authorised in the UK in the last 20 years. Planning permission has been sought for other new incinerators, but some of these have aroused strong public opposition. If new plants are not built, the relative importance of incineration in the UK will decline considerably over the next few years as older plants close, with a corresponding increase in the use of landfill.

1.7  In 1985 the Commission published a comprehensive study of waste management in its Eleventh Report[2], which was accompanied by an analysis by consultants of the scope for recycling.[3] Recommendations made in the Eleventh Report about the management and aftercare of landfill sites have been incorporated in legislation. We have had due regard to this and other subsequent developments. The present report is not another comprehensive study of waste management. Nor does it aim to establish rigorously the best practicable environmental options for particular waste streams. We have taken a general view about the advantages and disadvantages of incineration in comparison with other techniques for waste management, including recycling and landfill.

**1.8 For municipal waste, a fundamental feature of incineration is that it complements other forms of treatment, rather than being a complete alternative. Incineration of municipal waste leaves solid residues which will usually be disposed of by landfill. These are stabilised and substantially reduced in volume. Decisions about the future role of waste incineration turn largely on the view taken about the benefits of that transformation.**

## The form of this report

1.9 Chapters 2–7 of this report present and analyse information about how incinerators work, the numbers and types of plants in operation or planned, how these are regulated, the health implications of the pollutants produced, and the other environmental impacts of plants. The main emphasis is deliberately on the major plants for municipal or industrial wastes or for sewage sludge, and on clinical wastes, rather than on the smaller incinerators serving individual industrial plants or farms. There are certain related topics we have not attempted to cover: these are the emissions from crematoria; the control of radioactive substances; and the incineration of wastes at sea, which is now prohibited by international convention.

1.10 We start by describing in **chapter 2** the present legal and administrative framework for waste incineration, including relevant EC legislation, and likely changes. To place this in context, the latter part of the chapter summarises the present and proposed systems for planning and co-ordinating the provision of waste disposal facilities.

1.11 **Chapter 3** describes the size and nature of the main waste streams, and the proportion of these for which incineration is at present used in the UK; and brings together the available information about existing and proposed plants. We have noted recent and projected trends in the quantities of different types of waste and the proportions incinerated; and compared the position in the UK with that in other major developed countries. We have also covered the importation of waste into the UK for treatment.

1.12 **Chapter 4** outlines the technology of incineration, and the ways in which various pollutants arise and are monitored. It compares emissions to air from existing plants with the new standards; and assesses the pollution load these older incineration plants have created, and how this is likely to change in future. It summarises the techniques available for controlling pollution, and considers whether they are capable of achieving present and proposed standards for emissions.

1.13 **Chapter 5** deals with waste incineration as a source of energy, including the potential for conflict between energy recovery and minimising pollution. In this respect too we have compared the position in the UK with that in other major developed countries. We have then assessed what relevance incineration of municipal waste has for global warming.

1.14 In **chapter 6** we examine the possible health implications of incineration, the policy relevance of studies carried out in the areas surrounding older plants, and the role of risk analysis.

1.15 **Chapter 7** considers whether new incineration plants are likely to have other forms of environmental impact that would make them unacceptable.

1.16 The final part of the report turns to wider issues and provides an assessment of the future role of incineration in UK waste management, against the background of the factors identified and analysed in earlier chapters.

1.17 **Chapter 8** investigates whether developments are likely in technology or management within the next 10 years or so which would supersede waste incineration or bring about significant further changes in its environmental impact. We review briefly the possible alternative technologies for waste destruction and their present status. We discuss whether it would be justifiable to place still more stringent limits on emissions from incineration plants, and the scope for improving the way these are managed and operated. We then consider the scope for reducing the quantities of waste requiring incineration or for removing from waste streams the substances which cause most difficulty in terms of pollution.

1.18   On the assumption there will continue to be a need for waste incineration using broadly the present technology, **chapter 9** discusses what we regard as the crucial policy issues about it. Our conclusions and recommendations are brought together in **chapter 10**.

1.19   **Appendix A** gives a concise description of the main combustion systems at present used in the UK to burn waste. **Appendix B** examines how the costs of incineration compare with the costs of landfill in the UK, and **appendix C** is an extract from the Dutch government's waste management programme.

### Acknowledgements

1.20   We requested written evidence, and in some cases oral evidence, from a large number of organisations; and also published a general invitation to submit evidence, the text of which is at **appendix D**. Commissioners made visits to several modern incinerators either operating or under construction in the UK and Germany, and to the German government's research centre at Karlsruhe. They also held discussions with government bodies in Germany and the Netherlands. Dr Wakeford of the secretariat attended the Twelfth US Incineration Congress. We are grateful to many organisations and individuals for providing us with information and views for the purposes of this study, and they are listed in **appendix E**.

1.21   The Commission had as its special adviser on technical issues Mr R Taylor BSc CEng, formerly of Waste Technical Division in the Department of the Environment (DOE). Warren Spring Laboratory (WSL) and Aspinwall & Co Ltd were contracted to carry out studies: the material provided by WSL was the basis for much of the factual description in the text and for appendix A, while the report by Aspinwall & Co Ltd forms appendix B.

1.22   The members of the Commission's secretariat with primary responsibility for this study were Mr R B Adams and Dr R Wakeford. Other members of the secretariat who made a particular contribution were Mr D A Benson, Dr L M Hole and Mrs V A Woodyer.

1.23   This report was prepared by a group of Commissioners chaired by Mr D A D Reeve, and including Sir Geoffrey Allen, Professor H Charnock, Professor Dame Barbara Clayton, Sir John Houghton and Professor J G Morris. Dr C W Suckling, then a Member of the Commission, also contributed to its early thinking about incineration. Drafts of the report were discussed in detail, revised and approved by the full Commission, and the published report represents its views.

# CHAPTER 2

# THE REGULATION OF WASTE INCINERATION

## Introduction

2.1   This chapter summarises the present arrangements for regulating waste incineration, including some modifications already in train. Having distinguished the different contexts in which incineration plants are regulated (2.2–2.9), it describes first how the legislation applies to individual plants (2.10–2.39); and then the present and proposed systems for planning and co-ordinating the provision of waste disposal facilities (2.40–2.48).

2.2   Waste incineration plants in England and Wales are controlled by public authorities from four main aspects:

   a.   by the local planning authority (for this purpose, the county or metropolitan district council in England and the district council in Wales), as a development of land

   b.   by the waste regulation authority (the county or metropolitan district council in England and the district council in Wales), as a form of waste management

   c.   by Her Majesty's Inspectorate of Pollution (HMIP), or for smaller plants by the district council and other authorities, as a source of pollution

   d.   by the Health and Safety Executive (HSE) where there is a potential hazard to workers on the site and persons outside it.

2.3   The Secretaries of State for the Environment and for Wales decide appeals under a, b and c above, and their Departments provide advice and guidance to local authorities. In important respects the legal provisions applying to incineration plants are now, or will probably in future be, contained in EC legislation, rather than purely national legislation. If a plant is designed to produce electricity for public supply and has a net capacity of more than 50 MWe, its construction and operation require the consent of the President of the Board of Trade.

2.4   In Scotland the legislation is broadly similar. The planning authority may be the regional, district or islands council; the waste regulation authority is the district or islands council. There is no direct Scottish equivalent to HMIP but Her Majesty's Industrial Pollution Inspectorate (HMIPI) controls emissions to air from larger incineration plants; the district or islands council is responsible for smaller plants. Discharges of liquid effluents to the environment are controlled by the river purification authorities. References in this report to particular functions of regulatory authorities or Ministers should normally be taken to include the arrangements in Scotland.

2.5   Although legislation and organisation differ in Northern Ireland, the same principles are applied, and it can be assumed that emission standards, technical guidance and other criteria are identical. The government has published proposals for a new pollution control system modelled on that in Great Britain.

2.6   One approach used in the past was to incinerate certain liquid chemical wastes at sea.[4] Although several ships were designed and operated for that purpose, the practice is now banned internationally.[5] On the assumption that this ban will remain in force for the foreseeable future, we have not reconsidered in this report under what conditions, if any, incineration of wastes at sea would be environmentally acceptable, or whether it might represent the best practicable environmental option for some types of waste.

2.7   In examining the present system for regulating incineration plants our main concern has been to establish not only whether each of the four codes mentioned in 2.2 is satisfactory in its own terms but also whether there is a coherent relationship between them. If they were not properly related to each other, there would be, at best, a risk of duplication and confusion. At worst a defective regulatory

4

framework could be a serious obstacle to identification and adoption of the best practicable environmental options.

2.8    Much of the present framework is of recent origin. For example the introduction of integrated pollution control (2.19, 2.23) represents a considerable improvement on the previous legislation under which the incineration plants now in existence were designed, constructed and brought into operation. We have not attempted however to provide a history of the relevant legislation, but rather to consider what basis it provides for the future control of waste incineration.

2.9    Over the next few years the bodies responsible for regulation are likely to change. The government is committed to legislation that will bring together in a new Environment Agency the functions of HMIP, the National Rivers Authority (NRA) and waste regulation authorities. In Scotland a Scottish Environment Protection Agency will replace HMIPI and the river purification authorities, and take over the waste regulation and local air pollution functions of district and islands councils. There are reviews of the structure of local government in each part of Great Britain. The creation of the two Environment Agencies will provide an opportunity for remedying any deficiencies in the present legislation. With that in mind, the final section of this chapter (2.49–2.51) assesses the adequacy of the present regulatory framework.

## Regulation of incineration as land use

2.10    Constructing an incineration plant or modifying an existing one will usually be regarded as development and require planning permission, although specific planning permission is not necessary for smaller incinerators on farms which are ancillary to the agricultural operations. In deciding whether to give planning permission, the planning authority must have regard to the development plan for the area and any other material considerations. The Planning and Compensation Act 1991 has enhanced the status of the development plan as the prime consideration.

2.11    DOE has published draft guidance on planning and pollution control.[6] The factors that particularly need to be taken into account when considering a planning application for an incineration plant are identified as:

>    storage facilities
>
>    emissions (insofar as these might affect land use)
>
>    disposal of the ash residue
>
>    transport requirements
>
>    location in relation to:
>
>>        the source of the waste, and
>>
>>        the disposal site for ash
>
>    the cumulative impact if an incinerator were to be built in close proximity to other sources of pollution (insofar as this might affect land use).

The requirements about preparation of an environmental statement to support a planning application are discussed later in this chapter (2.37–2.39).

2.12    The government regards[7] some overlap as inevitable both in the matters taken into account by the various regulatory authorities and in the content of conditions they impose. It believes that planning conditions are widely employed to deal with matters which are outside the legitimate scope of the planning system. It also believes that, as a result of improved pollution control legislation and the proposed Planning Policy Guidance, instances of overlap will be considerably reduced.

## Regulation of incineration as waste management

2.13    There is an EC Framework Directive on waste[8] which has four main mandatory elements:

>    a.    each member state must have a competent authority or authorities with responsibility for waste
>
>    b.    the competent authorities must prepare waste management plans

    c.  undertakings handling waste must have a permit from the competent authority

    d.  the polluter pays principle must be applied.

An amending Directive[9] has recently clarified the definitions in the Framework Directive. Other EC Directives deal with disposal of:

waste oils[10]

polychlorinated biphenyls (PCBs) and polychlorinated terphenyls (PCTs)[11]

toxic and hazardous waste[12]

animal waste.[13]

2.14  In May 1991, under the Environmental Protection Act 1990[14] ("the 1990 Act"), the operational responsibilities of county and metropolitan district councils as waste disposal authorities were separated from their functions as waste regulation authorities. Waste disposal authorities had to make arrangements to cease direct operation of disposal facilities, and must instead award a contract or contracts on a competitive basis either to a private contractor or at arm's length to a local authority waste disposal company (LAWDC) in which there may be a private sector holding.

2.15  A number of forms of waste management, including fixed and mobile incinerators, require a licence from the waste regulation authority. The licence permits an operator to treat or dispose of specified kinds of controlled wastes, and may impose conditions; at a fixed incinerator the operator may also be licensed to store controlled wastes. Waste treatment processes authorised under integrated pollution control, such as large incinerators (see 2.19), have been exempted from waste management licensing.[15] However, the storage of wastes at the sites of authorised incinerators is not covered by the authorisation and still requires a licence.

2.16  The waste regulation authority may refuse a licence for a waste facility:

    a.  if its operation would pollute the environment or harm human health

    b.  if it would cause serious detriment to the amenities of the locality (in those cases where its construction and operation do not require planning permission)

    c.  if the applicant is not a fit and proper person (for example if he is not technically competent).

If planning permission is needed it has to be obtained before a waste management licence can be granted.

2.17  Some important amendments to the legislation come into force in June 1993. They are directed primarily towards landfill rather than incineration: an applicant for a licence will have to demonstrate that he has the financial capacity to meet the obligations; and a licence-holder will not be allowed to surrender his licence after operations have ceased until the waste regulation authority is satisfied there is no likelihood of pollution or harm to health arising from the site, and until NRA is satisfied the proposed surrender is acceptable. The surrender provisions meet a recommendation in the Commission's Eleventh Report.[16]

2.18  The movement of wastes across national frontiers has caused controversy, both in the UK and in other countries. The EC Directive on the Transfrontier Shipment of Hazardous Wastes[17] requires such shipments to be notified in advance to the competent authorities in the countries concerned. Those authorities are entitled to object to the import or export of the wastes if it would result in unsuitable or illegal disposal or otherwise contravene national legislation (where that implements EC Directives) or international conventions. An EC Regulation agreed in October 1992[18] will implement the Basel Convention on transfrontier movements of waste, and applies to all wastes. It considerably widens the grounds for objection to the import of waste for disposal, and allows a country to act unilaterally in banning imports.

**Regulation of incineration as a source of pollution**

2.19  Until 1989 the only incineration plants regulated by HMIP, rather than by the district council, were those for chemical waste. The new system of integrated pollution control now operated by HMIP covers larger incineration plants of all types. In the last two years standards have been set for a wide range of pollutants in emissions to air from incineration plants. These standards differ however depending on the capacity of a plant, whether it is regarded primarily as providing energy or disposing of waste, and the type of waste burnt.

2.20   HMIP regulates as *part A processes* for waste disposal[19] the incineration of:

   a.   wastes arising from the manufacture of chemicals or plastics

   b.   specified waste chemicals (bromine, cadmium, chlorine, fluorine, iodine, lead, mercury, nitrogen, phosphorus, sulphur, zinc)

   c.   any substances, if the incinerator is rated at 1 tonne an hour or more

   d.   chemicals contaminating reusable metal containers.

Other processes involving wastes are regarded by HMIP as having the primary purpose of providing energy. These include combustion processes with a net rated thermal input of 3MWth or more involving waste-derived fuel, waste or recovered oil, tyres, wood waste, straw or poultry litter.

2.21   The 1990 Act also made improvements in the legislation on local authority control of air pollution. District and metropolitan district councils regulate emissions to air from smaller incineration and combustion plants and from crematoria (*part B processes*). However incinerators not regulated by HMIP and designed to dispose of 50 kg an hour or less of substances other than clinical waste, sewage sludge, sewage screenings and municipal waste, do not require an authorisation from the local authority.

2.22   The timetable for introducing the present system as it affects incineration plants is as follows:

|  | *part A processes* | *part B processes* |
|---|---|---|
| new or substantially altered processes required prior authorisation | from 1 April 1991 | from 1 April 1992 |
| applications had to be made for authorisation of existing processes | by 31 October 1992 | by 31 October 1992 |
| existing processes should meet the standards for new processes unless there are exceptional circumstances | by 1 December 1996 | by 1 October 1995. |

2.23   An authorisation (which must be reviewed every four years) lays down conditions for the operation of a plant including limits on emissions, together with provisions about materials handling and good housekeeping. The conditions must be designed to ensure the use of the best available techniques not entailing excessive cost (BATNEEC) to prevent the release of prescribed substances; or, where prevention is not practicable, to minimise releases and render any substances released harmless. In the case of part A processes they should also ensure that, if the process is likely to involve releases into more than one medium, the means adopted represents the best practicable environmental option (BPEO). The Commission's Twelfth Report was devoted to the BPEO concept.[20] The main features of the BATNEEC concept are described in box 2A. The government expects that for new plants BATNEEC and "best available techniques" will often be the same.[21]

2.24   The Chief Inspector of HMIP, and the Secretaries of State for part B processes, have issued guidance notes (listed in box 2B) for the processes with which we are concerned. The performance standards for combustion conditions and emissions to air set for incineration plants in the Chief Inspector's guidance notes mark an important advance in pollution control and are referred to in this report as "the new HMIP standards". It is the responsibility of the individual HMIP inspector, or the district council, to interpret the BATNEEC concept and decide what standards a particular plant should be required to achieve and by when. Authorisations must however contain the conditions required

---

**BOX 2A**                                                          **BATNEEC**[22a]

Best available techniques not entailing excessive cost

"Techniques" covers not only the hardware but also the way in which a particular process is operated, including such factors as operational management and staff training.

"Best available" is generally taken to mean demonstrably the most effective techniques, proven in operation at the appropriate scale and commercially available, even if they are not in general use, or have not been used in the UK.

"Not entailing excessive cost" indicates that the benefits gained by using the best available techniques should bear a reasonable relationship to the costs of obtaining them. For example it may not be justifiable to obtain small reductions in emissions at a high cost unless the emissions affected are particularly toxic. It may be necessary to take into account, not only the costs for individual plants, but the overall implications for the industry using the process.

Judgements about what constitutes BATNEEC may well differ as between new and existing plants:

> the *costs* of adopting given techniques at an existing incineration plant will depend on its technical characteristics, and are likely to be about 50% higher than at a new plant[22b]

> the *benefits* from adopting those techniques may be less at an existing plant, depending on its remaining life and likely utilisation.

---

to meet EC requirements (2.30–2.34). The annexes to the guidance notes refer to various techniques which the Chief Inspector or the Secretary of State believes fulfil the criterion of BATNEEC and would enable the performance standards to be met with a good measure of confidence. This is not intended to hinder the development of new techniques. The guidance notes also deal with the monitoring to be carried out by the operator.

2.25   The Chief Inspector's guidance notes also cover releases to land and water; and require limits to be set on the annual mass of each pollutant released from a plant by all routes. Waste streams producing solid residues must be analysed by the operator at least once a year for likely substances from a list prescribed for each process. HMIP does not have power to place conditions on the disposal of solid residues by landfill, as this is controlled by the waste regulation authority. HMIP may however seek to place conditions on the quantity and nature of the residues produced.

2.26   In addition to authorisation by HMIP, discharges of liquid effluent require the consent of the sewerage undertaker if they are made to a public sewer. If they are made to other water bodies, the NRA stipulates limits on particular pollutants in the light of its environmental quality objectives for the relevant waters, and those limits are incorporated in the authorisation issued by HMIP. HMIP sets certain standards for pollutants in liquid discharges: in the case of waste incineration, these are for cadmium, mercury, PCBs and some pesticides. Any discharge of liquid effluent from a part B process to the environment is regulated by the NRA, not the local authority.

2.27   The new HMIP standards for emissions to air are shown:

> for plants incinerating **municipal** waste, in the final column of table 2.1
> for plants incinerating **chemical** waste, in the first column of table 2.3.

The units of measurement used in the tables are explained in box 2C. For other types of incineration plant, the new HMIP standards are in most respects identical to the standards for municipal waste plants, except that:

> for **clinical** waste plants a higher combustion temperature is required

> for **sewage sludge** plants a more stringent limit is set for emissions of particulates to air and a less stringent limit for nitrogen oxides

---

**BOX 2B**        **GUIDANCE NOTES ISSUED FOR RELEVANT PROCESSES**[23]

*Process Guidance Notes issued by the Chief Inspector of HMIP (1991–92)*

|  |  |  | *capacity of plant* |
|---|---|---|---|
| **Waste disposal and recycling:** | | | |
| IPR | 5/1 | merchant and in house chemical waste incineration | all |
| | 5/2 | clinical waste incineration | |
| | 5/3 | municipal waste incineration | 1 tonne an hour or more |
| | 5/4 | animal carcass incineration | |
| | 5/11 | sewage sludge incineration | |
| **Combustion:** | | | |
| IPR | 1/1 | large boilers and furnaces | 50MWth or more |
| | 1/4 | combustion of waste oil and recovered oil | |
| | 1/5 | combustion of solid fuel from municipal waste | net rated thermal input of 3MWth or more |
| | 1/6 | combustion of tyres, tyre rubber etc | |
| | 1/7 | combustion of poultry litter | |
| | 1/8 | combustion of wood waste or straw | |

*Secretary of State's Guidance (1991–92)*

| | | | |
|---|---|---|---|
| **Incineration:** | | | |
| PG | 5/1 (91) | clinical waste incineration | less than 1 tonne an hour |
| | 5/3 (91) | animal carcase incineration | less than 1 tonne [but more than 50 kg] an hour |
| | 5/4 (91) | general waste incineration | less than 1 tonne [but more than 50 kg] an hour |
| | 5/5 (91) | sewage sludge incineration | less than 1 tonne an hour |
| **Combustion:** | | | |
| PG | 1/1 (91) | waste oil and recovered oil burners | less than 0.4MWth |
| | 1/2 (91) | waste oil and recovered oil burners | |
| | 1/6 (91) | tyre and rubber combustion | 0.4MWth - 3MWth |
| | 1/7 (91) | straw combustion | net rated thermal input |
| | 1/8 (91) | wood combustion | |
| | 1/9 (91) | poultry litter combustion | |
| | 1/10 (92) | waste derived fuel burning | less than 3MWth [but at least 0.4 MWth] |

Guidance issued by the Secretary of State is applicable to Scotland as well as to England and Wales. HMIPI takes full account of the guidance notes issued by HMIP, but is not bound by them, and may decide in due course to issue its own guidance.

---

for **animal carcass** plants a less stringent limit is set for hydrogen fluoride and no limits are set on concentrations of metals.

Other plants using wastes as fuel, which are regarded by HMIP as having the primary purpose of providing energy (2.20), are subject to less stringent standards. The discrepancy is discussed later in this report (8.14).

2.28 The standards set by the Secretary of State for smaller incinerators are also less stringent than the new HMIP standards for incineration plants. A direct comparison can be made between plants for

| BOX 2C | | UNITS OF MEASUREMENT |
|---|---|---|
| mg | milligram - a thousandth of a gram ($10^{-3}$g), a millionth of a kilogram | |
| μg | microgram - a millionth of a gram ($10^{-6}$g) | |
| ng | nanogram - a thousand millionth of a gram ($10^{-9}$g), a millionth of a milligram | |
| pg | picogram - a thousand billionth of a gram ($10^{-12}$g), a thousand millionth of a milligram, a thousandth of a nanogram | |
| Nm³ | a cubic metre of gas measured under standard (normal) conditions. These conditions are temperature 273° kelvin (0°C); pressure 101.3 kilopascals {equivalent to 760 mm mercury}; 11% oxygen or 9% carbon dioxide; dry gas | |
| MWe | a million watts of electricity generated | |
| MWth | a million watts of heat generated | |
| TEQ | toxic equivalent. See box 6A | |

clinical waste rated at less than 1 tonne an hour and those rated at 1 tonne an hour or more (table 2.2, which also shows the standards for plants incinerating less than 1 tonne an hour of general waste). The discrepancy is discussed later in this report (9.72).

2.29   Incinerators operated by the National Health Service (NHS) for clinical waste were formerly exempt from pollution control and waste management legislation because they were regarded for legal purposes as being operated by the Crown. Following a recommendation in the Commission's Eleventh Report[26], this exemption was removed in April 1991.[27] The dates by which existing plants must reach the standards for new plants are now the same for NHS incinerators as for merchant incinerators (2.22).

## EC legislation on pollution from incineration

2.30   The European Commission is expected to publish shortly a draft Framework Directive on integrated pollution prevention and control, which is likely to be compatible with the UK system. The existing EC legislation relevant to pollution from incineration is principally:

the Framework Directive on combatting air pollution from industrial plants[28], under which prior authorisation is needed for the operation of a plant and the operator is required to use BATNEEC (see box 2A)

the Directive on air pollution from **new** municipal waste incineration plants[29], which requires the emission limits and combustion conditions shown in table 2.1. The new HMIP standards for such plants, shown in the same table, go beyond EC requirements by setting limits on emissions of nitrogen oxides and dioxins, and setting more stringent limits for hydrogen chloride and metals

the Directive on air pollution from **existing** municipal waste incineration plants[30], which requires the emission limits and combustion conditions shown in table 2.1.

The Directives on incineration plants also contain requirements about monitoring (see 4.35).

2.31   The Directive on existing municipal waste plants sets time-limits for compliance, which are reflected in the relevant HMIP guidance note. Existing plants burning 6 or more tonnes of waste an hour must comply with the standards for new plants by 1 December 1996. If there are major technical difficulties however the requirement to sustain a temperature of 850°C for at least two seconds must be implemented at the latest when the furnaces are replaced. Smaller existing plants must achieve the much less demanding standards in the Directive on existing municipal waste plants by 1 December 1995: the HMIP guidance note says that the retention time may be "a sufficient period ... determined by the Inspector". The Directive requires such smaller plants to achieve the standards for new plants by 2000.

2.32   The European Commission has said it is now reviewing the Directives on municipal waste incineration.[31]

2.33   A draft Directive on the Incineration of Hazardous Waste[32] is being discussed by the Council of

**Table 2.1**
**EC and new HMIP standards for emissions to air: incineration of municipal waste**

Pollutant concentration (mg/Nm³)

| Plant size (tonnes/hour) | EC Directive 89/429/EEC (applies to existing plants) | | EC Directive 89/369/EEC (applies to new plants) | | | New HMIP standards IPR5/3 (apply to new and existing plants) 1992 |
|---|---|---|---|---|---|---|
| | less than 1 | between 1 and 6ᵃ | less than 1 | between 1 and 3 | 3 or more | more than 1 |
| Total particulate matter | 600 | 100 | 200 | 100 | 30 | 30 |
| Carbon monoxide | 100 | 100 | 100 | 100 | 100 | 100 |
| Volatile organic compounds (excluding particulates; expressed as total carbon) | - | - | 20 | 20 | 20 | 20 |
| **Acidic gases:** | | | | | | |
| Sulphur dioxide | - | - | - | 300 | 300 | 300 |
| Hydrogen chloride | - | - | 250 | 100 | 50 | 30 |
| Hydrogen fluoride | - | - | - | 4 | 2 | 2 |
| Nitrogen oxides (as $NO_2$) | - | - | - | - | - | 350 |
| **Heavy metals:** | | | | | | |
| Cadmium and mercury | - | - | - | 0.2 | 0.2 | 0.1 each |
| Nickel and arsenic | - | - | - | 1 | 1 | 1 |
| Other metalsᵇ | - | - | - | 5 | 5 | |
| | | | | | | (ngTEQ/Nm³) |
| Dioxins | - | - | - | - | - | 1ᶜ |

a  existing plants with a capacity of 6 tonnes/hour or more have to meet the standards for new plants (2.31)
b  total of chromium, copper, lead and manganese plus (in the HMIP standard but not in the EC Directive) tin
c  HMIP's guidance note says that the emission of dioxins should be reduced as far as possible by progressive techniques with the aim of achieving a guide value of 0.1 ng/Nm³.

*Combustion conditions specified in EC Directives and HMIP's guidance note:*

i)   for new municipal waste incineration plants and existing plants with a capacity of at least 6 tonnes/hour: at least 850°C for at least 2 seconds in the presence of at least 6% oxygen, or other equally effective techniques for reducing emissions of dioxins

ii)  for existing plants with a capacity of less than 6 tonnes/hour: at least 850°C in the presence of at least 6% oxygen for a sufficient period of time determined by the regulatory authority, or other equally effective techniques for reducing emissions of dioxins.

Where alternative techniques are accepted, the European Commission must be informed.

**Table 2.2**
**UK standards for emissions to air:  new HMIP standards for waste incineration compared with Secretary of State's standards for part B processes**

Pollutant concentration (mg/Nm³)

| | Clinical Waste<br>New HMIP standards 1992 (IPR 5/2) | Clinical Waste<br>Secretary of State's standards 1991 (PG 5/1) | General Waste<br>Secretary of State's standards 1991 (PG 5/4) |
|---|---|---|---|
| Total particulate matter | 30 | 100 | 200 |
| Carbon monoxide | 100 | 100 | 100 |
| Volatile organic compounds (excluding particulates; expressed as total carbon) | 20 | 20 | 20 |
| **Acidic gases:** | | | |
| Sulphur dioxide | 300 | 300 | 300 |
| Hydrogen chloride | 30 | 100 | 250 |
| Hydrogen fluoride | 2 | - | - |
| Nitrogen oxides (as $NO_2$) | 350 | - | - |
| **Heavy metals:** | | | |
| Cadmium | 0.1 | } 5[b] | 5[b] |
| Mercury | 0.1 | | |
| Others | 1[a] | | |
| | | | (ngTEQ/Nm³) |
| Dioxins | 1[c] | - | - |

a     Total of arsenic, chromium, copper, lead, manganese, nickel and tin.

b     Total of cadmium, mercury and all the metals listed above except tin.

c     HMIP's guidance note says that the emission of dioxins should be reduced as far as possible by progressive techniques with the aim of achieving a guide value of 0.1 ng/Nm³.

Note:   The standards set by the Secretary of State for incineration of animal carcasses (PG 5/3) and sewage sludge (PG 5/5) differ from those for clinical waste in not placing any limit on heavy metals and in setting a limit of 4 mg/Nm³ for hydrogen fluoride.

Ministers. Table 2.3 compares the requirements of the draft with the new HMIP standards for chemical waste incineration and the present German legislation.[33] The justification for the further tightening of standards this draft Directive would entail is discussed later in this report (8.12–8.25).

2.34    The European Commission has issued a BAT Note[34] on the incineration of hazardous waste. This type of advisory note is intended to identify the best available technologies for controlling releases and their characteristics, so that these can become the main criteria used by member states when dealing with applications for authorisations for new or substantially modified plants. This note provided the basis for the annexes to the draft Directive mentioned in the previous paragraph.

**Regulation of incineration plants as a potential hazard**

2.35    Licensed waste disposal sites were exempted from the Control of Industrial Major Accident Hazards Regulations 1984[35] on the ground that the waste management licensing provisions of the Control of Pollution Act 1974 represented adequate implementation of the EC "Seveso" Directive.[36] The exemption is likely to be removed in the near future. The Regulations apply to sites which contain dangerous substances in more than specified quantities for either process purposes or storage. There are arrangements for the local planning authority to consult HSE about any planning

**Table 2.3**
**Proposed EC, German and new HMIP standards for emissions to air:**
**incineration of chemical waste**

| | Pollutant concentration (mg/Nm³) | | |
|---|---|---|---|
| | New HMIP standards (IPR 5/1) 1992 | German standards 17.BlmSchV 1990[24] | Proposed EC standards [25] |
| Total particulate matter | 20 | 10 | 5 |
| Carbon monoxide | 50 | 50 | 50 |
| Volatile organic compounds (excluding particulates; expressed as total carbon) | 20 | 10 | 5 |
| **Acidic gases:** | | | |
| Sulphur dioxide | 50 | 50 | 25 |
| Hydrogen chloride | 10 | 10 | 5 |
| Hydrogen fluoride | 2 | 1 | 1 |
| Nitrogen oxides (as $NO_2$) | 350 | 200 | - |
| **Heavy metals:** | | | |
| Cadmium and thallium | 0.1 (Cd) | 0.05 | 0.05[d] |
| Mercury | 0.1 | 0.05 | 0.05[d] |
| Others[a] | 1 | 0.5 | 0.5[d] |
| | | | (ngTEQ/Nm³) |
| Dioxins | 1[b] | 0.1 | 0.1[c][e] |

a    Total of antimony, arsenic, chromium, cobalt, copper, lead, manganese, nickel, tin and vanadium.

b    HMIP's guidance note says that the emission of dioxins should be reduced as far as possible by progressive techniques with the aim of achieving a guide value of 0.1 ng/Nm³.

c    Guide value.

d    Average value over the sample period of a minimum of half an hour and a maximum of 4 hours.

e    Average value over the sample period of a minimum of 6 hours and a maximum of 16 hours.

Apart from d and e all standards represent daily averages except that, if monitoring is not continuous, the new HMIP standards apply to any sample.

application which could lead to such a situation or which would involve development in the vicinity of a major hazard.

2.36   The Regulations have two levels of requirements, depending on the quantities of dangerous substances involved. The bottom-tier requirements are similar to those imposed on all employers by the Health and Safety at Work etc. Act 1974.[37] A few incineration sites handling toxic wastes may attract the top-tier requirements, under which the operator must:

a.   notify HSE of his activity

b.   prepare a comprehensive safety report

c.   prepare an on-site emergency plan

d.   provide the county council with information about any possible off-site consequences of a major accident occurring on the site so that the council can draw up an off-site emergency plan

e.   inform people in the vicinity about accident hazards, action to be taken in an emergency, and how they would be alerted.

**Role of environmental assessment**

2.37    The UK has implemented the EC Directive on environmental assessment[38] within the framework of existing legislation on development control by requiring an applicant for planning permission to submit an environmental statement to the local planning authority where appropriate.

2.38    The categories of project for which an environmental statement is required are set out in the Directive and the Regulations made to implement it.[39] They include all installations that incinerate, treat or landfill special waste (see 3.9). In the case of incineration or landfilling of other kinds of waste an environmental statement is required if the proposed installation would be likely to have significant effects on the environment. DOE Circular 15/88[40] suggests that installations for waste transfer, treatment or disposal which have a capacity of more than 75,000 tonnes a year (including landfill sites) are likely to meet this criterion.

2.39    The Regulations prescribe subjects which must be covered in an environmental statement. No specific guidance has been given at national level however about the content or approach. Some environmental statements were included in evidence submitted for this study and showed wide variations in scope, depth and level of detail.

**Planning and co-ordination of waste disposal facilities**

2.40    There are statutory requirements on both the waste regulation authority and the local planning authority (normally these are the same local authority) to draw up overall plans for waste disposal incorporating whichever types of disposal facility exist within, or are considered appropriate for, that particular area.

2.41    Under section 50 of the 1990 Act each waste regulation authority must prepare a *waste disposal plan*. The Secretary of State has power to give directions about the timetable for preparing plans and has proposed that authorities should do so by "around the end of 1994".[41] A plan must include the following information:

>    types and quantities of controlled waste arising in, and expected to be imported to, or exported from, the authority's area over the period of the plan

>    the authority's view on the priorities for different methods of waste disposal and treatment in its area, having particular regard to the desirability of giving priority to recycling waste

>    the authority's policy on waste disposal licensing

>    the waste disposal sites and facilities available and proposed

>    estimated cost of the disposal or treatment methods provided for in the plan.

The original requirement to produce a waste disposal plan was in the Control of Pollution Act 1974.[42] Progress had been slow up to 1985 and in its Eleventh Report[43] the Commission recommended that all plans should be completed at an early date and regularly updated. By 1991 all but one of the waste regulation authorities in England and Wales had produced such a plan (although in some cases only in draft). Unfortunately the 1990 Act does not explicitly oblige an authority to work to its plan.

2.42    The Secretary of State has powers to set up regional authorities for waste regulation: these powers have not so far been exercised, but eight regional groupings in England and three in Wales have been established informally to advise their constituent authorities on policies and standards. Statutory joint arrangements operate under previous legislation in Greater London and some other metropolitan areas. The stated purpose of transferring waste regulation functions to the Environment Agency (2.9) is to harness greater collective expertise and ensure uniform regulatory standards across the country.

2.43    As part of the land use planning system the Planning and Compensation Act 1991[44] requires county councils and national park authorities in England to draw up *waste local plans*, or combined waste and minerals plans. These plans must be based on the strategic policies in the structure plan previously adopted by the council, which must in turn have regard to any relevant national or regional guidance issued by the Secretary of State. In Wales and metropolitan areas of England the planning authority must include waste policies in its local or unitary development plan, and these must also have regard to any guidance issued by the Secretary of State. In all cases the local planning authority must have regard to the policies in the corresponding waste disposal plan (2.41). The government expects local planning authorities to draw up waste local plans as soon as possible in the light of the availability of waste disposal plans, so that substantially complete coverage will be achieved by 1997.

2.44   Draft Planning Policy Guidance[45] states that waste local plans should:

in calculating the extent of waste disposal requirements, take account of the need for self-sufficiency, waste minimisation and recycling

identify existing disposal, storage and treatment sites with spare capacity

identify broad areas of search which will allow sufficient sites for whatever method of recycling, treatment or disposal is required to meet demand in the plan period

set out criteria against which applications for planning permission will be considered.

2.45   Waste disposal plans are intended to deal with the need for waste disposal facilities and the type of facility; waste local plans are intended to complement them by dealing principally with the location of such facilities, in order to indicate which areas are suitable for them and what criteria (for example, geological and hydrological factors) will be applied in determining planning applications. The local planning authority is expected to obtain information about the future need for waste disposal facilities from the waste disposal plan, and to justify any inconsistencies between the two plans. Because of this close link at the plan preparation stage, and in order to deal with casework more effectively, a number of local authorities have brought their responsibilities for waste regulation and land use planning together in one department; in other areas the two responsibilities remain separate.

2.46   The government has proposed that, following creation of the Environment Agency, waste disposal plans should be replaced by a national statement of waste policies and priorities prepared by the Secretary of State with the advice of the Agency.[46] This statement would cover waste disposal needs down to the regional level over the next 10–15 years. It would be reviewed probably every 5 years (to match the recommended interval for reviewing local development plans). It is envisaged the Agency would initiate preparation of the national statement by providing local authorities with data from its periodic survey of waste arisings and seeking their advice (preferably through regional arrangements) about future waste disposal requirements, in particular from major new developments. After the Agency had collated the responses and submitted advice to the Secretary of State, he would issue the draft national statement for wide consultation.

2.47   Further procedures would be established to ensure that:

a.   after the national statement has been issued, local planning authorities will have sufficiently detailed information about waste disposal needs to draw up their structure plans and waste local plans

b.   the plans of neighbouring authorities will be compatible.

Local planning authorities in England (possibly through some form of regional co-operation) would be expected to provide advice to the Secretary of State on waste planning issues as these affect their respective areas. In the light of this advice and the national statement, the Secretary of State would then issue regional planning guidance (2.43) about waste. Corresponding arrangements would be made in Wales.

2.48   It is also proposed that the national statement should place an obligation on all planning authorities to "recognise cross-boundary issues" and "give full and proper consideration to their role in meeting national needs and the special needs of other regions". The government does not wish to see formal regional bodies established. It believes the combination of the national statement, regional planning guidance and waste local plans will meet the EC requirement that member states must have waste management plans (2.13).

### Adequacy of the present regulatory framework

2.49   It will be apparent from the description in this chapter that the present regulatory framework for waste incineration is an involved one. A number of bodies are concerned: the local planning authority

(2.10–2.12), up to three environmental regulatory authorities (2.15, 2.20–2.21, 2.25–2.26); and in certain circumstances HSE (2.35–2.36) or the Department of Trade and Industry (2.3). There are provisions in the legislation designed to prevent duplication or conflict: planning permission (if required) is a precondition for the grant of a waste management licence, facilities authorised under integrated pollution control are exempt from licensing, and the waste regulation authority is not permitted to take into account whether an incinerator would cause detriment to amenities except in cases where its construction and operation do not require planning permission. Problems remain however. The dividing lines between the factors that can legitimately be taken into account under the different codes are far from clear. DOE believes that planning conditions are widely used to cover matters which ought now to be covered under pollution control legislation (2.12), and hopes to resolve the problem by issuing Planning Policy Guidance. In practice some facilities subject to integrated pollution control may also require a waste management licence (2.15). Last but not least, the relationship between waste disposal plans and waste local plans (2.40–2.45), however clear in principle, has caused a good deal of confusion in practice.

2.50    Stringent standards for emissions to air from incineration plants have recently been set (2.27): they go beyond present EC requirements (2.30, table 2.1), and will be progressively applied to existing plants as well as new plants (2.22, 2.31). For most incineration processes standards are also set for cadmium and mercury levels in liquid discharges. In chapter 4 we analyse the data on measured emission levels from existing incineration plants in the light of the new standards (4.14 and table 4.1). In chapter 8 we consider the justification for the even more stringent standards now being proposed by the European Commission (8.12–8.25). The new HMIP standards represent a major advance, but nevertheless give rise to some undesirable discrepancies, to which we return later in the report (8.14, 9.72).

2.51    In chapter 9 we consider how the co-ordinating and regulatory mechanisms can be rationalised and improved (9.1–9.3, 9.64–9.80).

# CHAPTER 3

# PRESENT AND PLANNED USE OF INCINERATION

**Introduction**

3.1  This chapter provides an overview of waste management in the UK from three aspects:

  i.   the size and nature of the relevant waste streams, including imports of waste (3.3–3.16)

  ii.  existing incineration plants and the proportions of the main waste streams which these handle (3.17–3.25)

  iii. present plans for the future use of incineration (3.26–3.34).

Unless otherwise indicated all statistics are for the UK as a whole. The chapter concludes (3.35–3.53) by making comparisons with the situation in other developed countries.

3.2  There is a shortage of reliable information on this subject. The available statistics have been brought together for the purposes of this report by WSL. Many of these are based on estimates, and may well be overestimates.[47] The government has undertaken to monitor the availability of waste disposal facilities across the country and compile information on trends in volumes, types and costs.[48] To achieve this, a review of waste disposal statistics and information has been launched, and consultants employed to develop a site record system. Statistics about waste arisings also need to be improved. DOE has commissioned WSL to carry out new surveys of domestic wastes and general industrial wastes. DOE is also working with the Chartered Institute of Public Finance and Accountancy (CIPFA) to improve the flow of information from local authorities; and is planning to improve the collection of statistics about special waste (3.9).

**The waste streams**

3.3  The main waste streams which are relevant in considering the role of incineration are:

  municipal waste
  sewage sludge
  clinical waste
  chemical waste
  agricultural waste.

These are dealt with separately below. Incineration is not an appropriate treatment for stable wastes such as demolition rubble, mining and smelting wastes, or fly ash from power stations.

3.4  Rough estimates of the **municipal waste** arising each year are given in table 3.1. Each household in the UK is thought to generate on average 600kg of waste a year. However there is considerable variation from place to place, with the amount of waste collected and its composition affected by such factors as the method of collection (bin or plastic bag or wheeled bin), the method of domestic heating and the size of gardens, as well as lifestyle and purchasing habits. A typical composition for domestic waste, as measured in a recent study, is given in table 3.2.

3.5  None of the available statistics shows clear trends in arisings over time. When solid fuel was used widely for domestic heating, ash formed a substantial part of domestic waste. More recently the pattern has been for amounts of waste per person to increase, and it has been suggested this parallels increases in gross domestic product. UK arisings (about 350kg per person a year in the late 1980s) are considerably below those reported for the USA (about 750kg) or some developed Pacific countries. However, any upward tendency could be balanced, or even reversed, by policies for reducing the materials used in packaging and promoting recycling.[52]

17

**Table 3.1**
**Municipal waste: annual arisings**

| | million tonnes |
|---|---|
| Collected from households [49] | 15 |
| Civic amenity sites and special collections [49] | 4 |
| Similar commercial/trade wastes [50] | 15 |
| **TOTAL** | **34** |

**Table 3.2**
**Typical composition of domestic waste[51]**

| Component | %weight as received | %dry weight |
|---|---|---|
| Paper | 33 | 35 |
| Plastic | 6 | 7 |
| Textile | 4 | 4 |
| Glass | 9 | 12 |
| Ferrous metal | 7 | 9 |
| Non-ferrous metal | 1 | 1 |
| Putrescible | 20 | 11 |
| Misc. combustible | 5 | 6 |
| Misc. non-combustible | 5 | 6 |
| Material less than 10 mm | 10 | 9 |
| **TOTAL** | **100** | **100** |

3.6　**Sewage sludge** arises at two points in the sewage treatment process[53]:

through the removal of solids (organic and inorganic) from raw sewage

through the settlement of organic solids produced during biological treatment processes.

Initially it has a high water content, and its weight depends on how much of this water has been removed. The sewage sludge at present produced each year in the UK contains about 1 million tonnes of dry solids, equivalent to 30–40 million tonnes of wet sludge.[54]

3.7　This figure will increase considerably in future. There appears to have been an increase of about 60,000 tonnes dry solids in annual arisings of sewage sludge between 1985 and 1990.[55] A large number of sewage treatment works will be constructed or extended in order to meet more stringent effluent standards and provide for an increased population. Forecasts by water companies show an increase in annual arisings to 1.7 million tonnes by 1999 and 2.1 million tonnes by 2005, although these may be overestimates.[56]

3.8　Annual UK arisings of **clinical waste** (see glossary) are thought to be in the region of 300,000–400,000 tonnes a year from all sources.[57] There is no reliable information about trends in arisings of clinical waste, either past or future. The amounts of waste requiring incineration will be affected considerably by decisions about management methods (8.49).

3.9　**Chemical waste** is not a legally defined category: UK legislation[58] uses the term **special waste** for controlled wastes (see glossary) which represent an immediate hazard to human health. From returns made by waste disposal authorities DOE[59] has estimated that arisings of special waste in the year 1990/91 were about 2.5 million tonnes; but this estimate has a wide margin of error.

3.10　In the European Community the wider concept of *hazardous waste* (see glossary) is used. The EC Hazardous Waste Directive[60] has as one of its objectives the development of a consistent definition of such waste. The European Commission is producing a European Waste Catalogue, which will indicate those wastes regarded as hazardous in terms of the criteria in the Directive. Within the UK it has been estimated that arisings of other types of hazardous waste are larger than the arisings of special waste.[61] The government plans consultation later this year on regulations to bring the definition of "special waste" into line with the agreed Community definition of "hazardous waste".

**Table 3.3**
**Agricultural waste: annual arisings[67]**

|  | million tonnes |
|---|---|
| Excreta in buildings: | |
| cattle | 64 |
| pigs | 9 |
| poultry | 5 |
| Poultry litter (excreta and wood shavings) | 1 |
| Straw waste | 13 |
| Plastics | 0.1 |
| Carcasses | 0.1 |
| Silage liquor | 2 |
| **TOTAL** | **94** |

Note: These figures are subject to a large margin of error. Moisture content of the waste is not specified. No data are available for waste chemicals and containers, nor for poultry carcasses.

3.11    There is a general belief that arisings of special waste are increasing. However there are large year-to-year fluctuations in the statistics, apparently caused by isolated disposals of contaminated soil and similar materials.

3.12    Agricultural waste is not included in the definition of controlled waste. Estimates of the approximate scale of the main categories of **agricultural waste** are given in table 3.3. Although a figure of 250 million tonnes is often quoted for annual UK arisings, this would include in addition over 100 million tonnes of excreta deposited by animals in fields.[62] For some wastes, such as straw, there are possibilities for beneficial use within agriculture. Animal carcasses have been recycled: firms of knackers have taken them from farms, removed skins and hides, and passed on the remaining parts to firms of renderers, which have produced bonemeal and tallow and sold the meat for petfood.

3.13    Future trends in quantities of agricultural waste will be determined largely by the numbers of animals kept and the amount of land in cultivation. These factors are likely to lead to moderate declines.[63]

**Imports of waste**

3.14    On the basis of consignment notes received by HMIP, it is estimated that imports of hazardous waste to England and Wales in the year 1990/91 were 44,000 tonnes (compared with about 35,000 tonnes the previous year, the first complete year for which records are available). In broad terms it is likely that a further 1,000 tonnes was imported into Scotland in 1990/91.[64] No hazardous waste is imported into Northern Ireland for incineration.[65] Of the waste imported into England and Wales in 1990/91, 38% was classified as "miscellaneous" and a further 18% was classified in ways which also gave no information about chemical composition.

3.15    It is difficult to forecast future trends, but the Basel Convention (2.18) will restrict transboundary movements of wastes; this accords with the UK government's policy.

3.16    At least 2,500 tonnes of clinical waste is imported into the UK each year for incineration.[66] So far as is known, there are no imports of waste in the other categories discussed here. Exports of waste from the UK are negligible.

**Table 3.4**
**Municipal waste incinerators: capacity and year of opening**

| Location[70] | Design capacity[70] (tonnes/year) | Year of opening[71] |
|---|---|---|
| Alloa | 15,000 | 1975 |
| Altrincham | 40,000 | 1973 |
| Basingstoke | 43,000 | 1969 |
| Belfast | 3,000 | 1973 |
| Bolton | 80,000 | 1971 |
| Bristol | 160,000 | 1972 |
| Chinglebraes, Orkney [72] | 14,000 | 1980 |
| Coventry | 160,000 | 1975 |
| Derby | 80,000 | 1969 |
| Dudley | 80,000 | 1969 |
| Dundee | 70,000 | 1979 |
| Edmonton, London | 400,000 | 1970 |
| Exeter | 60,000 | 1970 |
| Havant | 90,000 | 1974 |
| Huddersfield | 50,000 | 1975 |
| Linwood, Glasgow | 75,000 | 1970 |
| Nottingham | 120,000 | 1973 |
| Portrack, Cleveland | 200,000 | 1972 |
| Rochdale | 40,000 | 1974 |
| Rova Head, Shetland [72] | 20,000 | 1981 |
| St Mary's, Isles of Scilly [73] | 1,500 | 1978 |
| Sheffield | 120,000 | 1976 |
| Southampton | 50,000 | 1975 |
| Stoke on Trent | 100,000 | 1977 |
| Sunderland | 100,000 | 1972 |
| Tynemouth | 125,000 | 1971 |
| Tyseley, Birmingham | 150,000 | 1978 |
| Winchester | 43,000 | 1972 |
| Wolverhampton | 170,000 | 1973 |
| Worcester | 16,000 | 1972 |

## Present use of incineration

3.17   In 1991 there were over two hundred incineration plants in the UK licensed by waste regulation authorities.[68] In general each of these handles only one of the major waste streams identified above. They vary considerably in size and design. They include 30 for municipal waste. Most of the remainder are clinical waste incinerators and privately owned general waste incinerators.

3.18   Most of the **municipal waste** plants were built in the late 1960s and early 1970s. They are listed in table 3.4, with their capacity and the year in which they were opened.

3.19   At present the UK incinerates about 2.5 million tonnes of municipal waste a year, about 7% of arisings.[69]

3.20   There are 6 incineration plants for **sewage sludge** operating in England (listed in table 3.5). There is one plant in Scotland (at Alloa), which also incinerates shredded municipal waste (in a multiple hearth furnace); and none in Wales or Northern Ireland, although the possibility of building one in Belfast is being considered.[74]

3.21   All the plants in table 3.5 are operated by water companies. With the opening of new plants the

**Table 3.5**
**Sewage sludge incinerators: capacity and year of opening[75]**

| Location | Design capacity (tonnes/year) | Year opened |
|---|---|---|
| Blackburn Meadows, Sheffield[a] | 15,000 | 1990 |
| Calder Valley, Huddersfield[a] | 24,000 | 1993 |
| Esholt, Bradford[a] | 15,000 | 1989 |
| Peel Common, Fareham[a] | 21,000 | 1980 |
| Coleshill, near Birmingham[b] | 30,000 | 1976 |
| Douglas Valley, Wigan[b] | 7,500 | 1977 |

a    Fluidised Bed (see description in appendix A, A.4-A.6)
b    Multiple Hearth (see description in appendix A, A.13-A.15)

amount of sewage sludge incinerated in the UK each year has risen from about 45,000 tonnes dry solids in 1980 (4% of arisings)[76] to 75,000 tonnes dry solids in 1990 (7% of arisings).[77]

3.22   It has been suggested that as many as 700–800 incinerators for **clinical waste** were operating in the UK in 1991[78]; and that the annual throughput was in the range 300,000–400,000 tonnes.[79] Inciner-ation is the predominant method of disposal. Nearly all clinical waste incinerators are owned by NHS hospitals or trusts and located in hospital grounds, although a small number are owned by merchant operators.

3.23   There are 4 plants owned by merchant operators at present incinerating **special waste**[80] (see table 3.6). Of the 40 or so plants owned by chemical companies, 6 have the capacity to burn more than 5,000 tonnes of waste a year, and 18 can burn between 1,000 and 5,000 tonnes a year. Twenty three private plants commenced operation before 1980; most of the rest have come into operation since 1985.[81] Some private plants have ceased operation because waste arisings were reduced or because it proved more attractive to use an outside operator.

3.24   It is estimated that about 80,000 tonnes of special waste is incinerated in England and Wales each year, which represents about 3% of the total.[83] About 25% of the waste incinerated has been imported[84],

**Table 3.6**
**Merchant special waste incinerators: capacity, year of opening and subsequent modifications[82]**

| Location | Design capacity (tonnes/year) | Year opened | Subsequent modifications |
|---|---|---|---|
| Ellesmere Port, Cheshire | 60,000 | 1990 | Second scrubber to replace ESP; new filters (1993) |
| Fawley, Hampshire | 35,000 | 1978 | Replacement rotary kiln; gas cleaning system (1989) |
| Killamarsh, Yorkshire | 15,000 | 1988 | No major changes |
| Pontypool, Gwent | 25,000 | 1974 | Gas cleaning system (1986); ESP, rotary kiln (1993) |

Rotary kiln        see description in appendix A, A.19 - A.20
Gas-cleaning system   see 4.20
ESP               Electrostatic precipitator

and that in turn represents about half the 40,000 tonnes or so of hazardous waste which has been imported each year (3.14).

3.25    Incineration of **agricultural waste** has been a small-scale operation. Most poultry farms have had a small incinerator for burning offal or litter. Although there are some purpose-built plants for other carcasses, the National Farmers' Union regards open burning on the farm as the most usual method of disposing of them, and of low-grade packaging.[85] In addition, about 160,000 tonnes a year of straw are burned, mostly in whole-bale boilers to heat farm buildings.[86] It is even more difficult than with other categories to obtain an estimate of the total quantity of agricultural waste incinerated at present: but it would represent only a very small proportion of agricultural waste.

**Planned future use of incineration**

3.26    Installed capacity for incinerating **municipal waste** has shown a recent decline which is expected to gain pace. Existing plants will not comply with the new HMIP standards without new pollution abatement equipment, which may be prohibitively expensive in some cases. A number are likely to close, reducing the capacity of the remaining plants to less than two million tonnes a year.[87] The plants most likely to survive beyond 1996 are those which recover energy in order to generate electricity, to provide heat, or both (5.9), and can finance upgrading from the income received. It may be possible to obtain private sector finance for the upgrading of some other existing plants by installing energy recovery.[88]

3.27    Upgrading to comply with limits on emissions may involve some increase in capacity at those plants which survive. However increases in capacity will come mainly from new plants. Approval has been given for a major new plant at Deptford (London), and there are other proposals at Belvedere (London) and Newport (Isle of Wight).[89] WSL[90] estimates that total capacity for incineration of municipal waste could regain the 1980 level of 5 million tonnes a year by 2001, and possibly reach about 5.4 million tonnes a year by 2005. The latter figure represents 15% of present arisings.

3.28    A plant is being built at Wolverhampton to generate about 25MWe from incinerating about a quarter of the annual total of scrap tyres in England and Wales. Another, smaller plant is planned in the West Midlands and a 6MWe one in Scotland.[91]

3.29    Incineration of **sewage sludge** is expected to show a considerable increase as a result of the ban on disposal to sea which will come into effect at the beginning of 1999.[92] Taking into account also the expected increase in arisings (3.7), the amount of sludge incinerated could increase more than sixfold, to nearly 500,000 tonnes dry solids a year (about 30% of all sludge), or even tenfold.

3.30    The present disposal routes for sewage sludge in the UK are shown in table 3.7. The sludge disposed of at sea in 1990 was equivalent to about 274,000 tonnes dry solids.[93] Apart from incineration, the alternatives to sea disposal have only limited potential for expansion (see 8.45–8.48). In practice it is likely that firms providing sewage disposal services will want to maintain a diversified strategy by substantially increasing the proportion of sludge incinerated.

3.31    The two oldest plants incinerating sewage sludge will not be able to meet the new HMIP standards[95]: the operators plan to replace them with larger fluidised bed plants. Planning permission

**Table 3.7**
**Sewage sludge: disposal methods in 1990[94]**

|  | % |
| --- | --- |
| Farmland | 46 |
| Sea disposal | 28 |
| Landfill | 13 |
| Incineration | 7 |
| Other | 6 |
| **TOTAL** | **100** |

has been given for new plants at Knostrop (Leeds), due to come into operation in 1995, and at Beckton and Crossness (London), due to come into operation in 1997. To deal with the expected demand, a number of other new plants will be required. Opportunities for co-incineration with municipal or industrial waste may be adopted at some of them.

3.32   The majority of incinerators for **clinical waste** will not be able to meet the new HMIP standards and will have to close. Planning permission has been granted for new plants at Knostrop (14,000 tonnes a year to serve the Yorkshire health region), Pontefract (3,500 tonnes a year), Oldham (5,250 tonnes a year) and Bolton (5,250 tonnes a year). There are proposals for at least 16 more clinical waste incinerators in England, some of which involve co-incineration with other types of waste. If the proposed plants were all constructed and brought into operation, they would provide a substantial proportion of the required capacity.

3.33   No clear trends have been identified in the incineration of **special waste**. Planning permission has recently been granted to a merchant operator following a public inquiry for a new plant at Seal Sands (Cleveland), and to several plants proposed by chemical firms for their own use. Planning permission has been refused, in most cases following public inquiries, for new plants proposed by merchant operators at Doncaster and Manchester; and for two plants for co-incineration with sewage sludge. A decision has not yet been given on an application to construct a plant at Salt End, Hull.

3.34   Developments in the incineration of **agricultural waste** fall mainly into two categories:

    a.   small plants for animal carcasses and offal

    b.   plants to generate electricity from poultry litter.

The first large plant of the latter kind has recently opened at Eye (Suffolk) with an output of 12.6MWe. A further large plant (13.5MWe) is being built and another (8MWe) is planned.[96] In total they will burn about 0.33 million tonnes a year of poultry litter, just under a quarter of estimated arisings.[97] WSL suggests there could be scope for a further 7–8 such schemes over the next 10–15 years. That could raise the proportion of poultry litter incinerated to almost two-thirds.

### Waste incineration in other countries

3.35   Table 3.8 compares the proportion of municipal waste incinerated in Great Britain with that incinerated in other developed countries. Even before the reduction expected in the next few years (3.26), Britain makes much less use of incineration for municipal waste than the other countries listed, with the exception of Spain. The position in five selected countries (Netherlands, Germany, Sweden, USA and Japan) is summarised below. Energy recovery from waste in other countries is discussed further in chapter 5 (5.13–5.15, 5.18).

**Table 3.8**
**Proportion of municipal waste incinerated in developed countries[98]**

| Country | Municipal waste incinerated (%) | Population (million) | Number of municipal waste plants | Amount incinerated (million tonnes/year) |
|---|---|---|---|---|
| Japan | 72 | 123 | 1,893 | 32 |
| Denmark | 65 | 5 | 38 | 1.7 |
| Sweden | 55 | 9 | 23 | 1.8 |
| France | 42 | 56 | 170 | 7.6 |
| Netherlands | 40 | 15 | 12 | 2.8 |
| Germany (West) | 30 | 61 | 47 | 9.2 |
| Italy | 18 | 58 | 94 | 2.7 |
| USA | 16 | 248 | 168 | 28.6 |
| Great Britain | 7 | 57 | 30 | 2.5 |
| Spain | 6 | 38 | 22 | 0.7 |
| Canada | Not known | 23 | 17 | 1.7 |

*Netherlands*

3.36    The Netherlands is a densely populated country with limited landfill capacity. One of the largest landfill sites is likely to be full by 2000. Incineration is the preferred method of disposal for municipal waste, despite being more expensive than landfill. Most of the plants were commissioned in the early 1970s. They are owned by the municipalities, located in industrial areas and have a total capacity of about 3 million tonnes a year. Two-fifths of municipal waste produced in the Netherlands each year is incinerated, one-third is landfilled and one-third recycled.[99]

3.37    The Dutch government has produced a ten-year programme for waste management, extracts from which are reproduced in appendix C. The policy aims are first to minimise the production of waste, second to re-use as much as possible for its original purpose, third to recover materials for recycling, fourth to incinerate, and only to landfill wastes that are non-combustible and not suitable for composting. Incineration capacity in the Netherlands is expected to increase to 5.3 million tonnes in 2000 (appendix C, C.10). It is expected that a large increase (to about 1 million tonnes) will also be needed in the capacity for composting (C.11), although testing of an anaerobic technique has not yet been completed (C.17). Considerable increases in landfill capacity will still be needed so that all regions can be self-sufficient in dealing with other categories of waste such as construction and demolition waste (C.35).

3.38    There are two chemical waste incinerators of rotary kiln design in Rotterdam. These are owned jointly by the municipality and industrial companies (which is also a common pattern in Germany). Several companies have their own chemical waste incinerators. Contaminated clinical waste has usually been incinerated with chemical waste. Most hospital incinerators have closed over the last ten years. A clinical waste incinerator has recently come into operation; another is being built at Dordrecht, as is a sewage sludge incinerator.[100]

*Germany*

3.39    The former West Germany has 47 incineration plants for municipal waste, most of which burn 200,000–300,000 tonnes a year and generate electricity or heat water. Because a substantial proportion of the inorganic material is removed beforehand for recycling, the waste burnt has a high calorific value (see glossary). The recovery of energy reduces the costs of waste disposal by 20–40%.[101]

3.40    Because of a requirement that landfilled wastes must contain less than 10% organic carbon, landfilling of unsorted municipal waste is likely to cease in Germany. Despite an active programme of waste minimisation and recycling, about 50% of municipal waste will still need to be disposed of (as in the Netherlands), and the demand for incineration will increase.

3.41    About 2.7 million tonnes of slag and ash (30% of the weight of the raw waste) are produced each year from municipal waste incineration. Roughly half goes to landfill. The rest is used as in the construction of roads and dams, after ferrous metals have been removed.[102]

3.42    About 10% of sewage sludge in the former West Germany (0.7 million tonnes a year dewatered) is incinerated, some of it at combined municipal waste/sludge plants.[103]

*Sweden*

3.43    In 1990 just over half Swedish municipal waste was incinerated, 40% landfilled and 5% composted. Of the 23 municipal waste incinerators, mostly in the south, 21 are owned by the municipality. All recover energy. Their capacities range from 26,000 to 130,000 tonnes of waste a year. The high paper content, increasing proportion of plastics and decreasing metal content result in a high average calorific value of 10–12 GJth/te. About 300,000 tonnes of industrial waste is also incinerated in waste-to-energy plants, making a total of 1.8 million tonnes of waste a year incinerated with energy recovery.[104]

3.44    Sweden places a high priority on reusing and recovering materials. Nevertheless the proportion of paper in municipal waste is forecast to increase in future. Each municipality must draw up a plan for solid waste covering origins and amounts of wastes and the planned disposal methods.

3.45   Between 1980 and 1989 the amount of household and industrial waste incinerated doubled. Public opposition to incineration has been lessened by a policy of keeping different waste types separate, in order to make combustion and emissions more predictable.

3.46   There is increasing interest in biological processing of the wet organic component of municipal waste. After treatment this will be landfilled and will produce methane. As from 1994 there is a legal requirement that such methane must either be used for energy recovery or flared off (see 5.26–5.28 below). The effect would be a further increase in the calorific value of the remaining waste going to incineration.

3.47   About 20% by weight of municipal waste incinerated comes out as slag or ash and goes to landfill. Its use as a construction material elsewhere is prohibited. It includes about 60,000 tonnes of fly ash.[105]

3.48   No sewage sludge is incinerated in Sweden: 65% is landfilled and 35% spread on land.[106]

*USA*

3.49   The number of municipal waste incineration plants in the USA has risen from 50 in 1983 to about 170 in 1991, of which 137 recovered energy. One sixth of municipal waste is incinerated.[107]

3.50   The expectation is that recycling will reduce the amounts of municipal waste going to incineration and stimulate the building of smaller plants or regional plants covering a wider area. About 80% of incineration plants recover ferrous metals, and 25% recover aluminium. More than 80% of the plants being built and at the planning stage will be sited in communities with active recycling programmes.

3.51   Recent public controversy over incineration in the USA has focused particularly on the test burns supervised by the Environmental Protection Agency (EPA) at new plants for chemical waste at East Liverpool (Ohio) and Little Rock (Arkansas).[108]

*Japan*

3.52   There are about 1900 incinerators for municipal waste in Japan, over 100 of which are of the fluidised bed design (appendix A, A.4–A.6). Nearly three-quarters of municipal waste is incinerated.[109] Virtually all the incinerators recover energy and over 100 generate electricity. The emphasis is now on building larger plants of fluidised bed design which will generate electricity and meet more stringent limits on emissions. This design of plant requires bulky wastes to be crushed beforehand: metals are then recovered prior to incineration.

3.53   Japan, like other countries, places priority on waste avoidance, minimisation, reuse and recycling. There are legal requirements about the reuse and recycling of industrial wastes, including slag and ash from incinerators. As in Sweden, each municipality in Japan is responsible for disposing of its own waste and must prepare a waste disposal plan. Japan has little landfill capacity, and incineration remains the preferred disposal method. The target is to increase the proportion of municipal waste incinerated to the even higher figure of 80%.

# CHAPTER 4

# EMISSIONS FROM INCINERATION PLANTS

## Introduction

4.1   This chapter begins by outlining the basic principles of incineration (4.2–4.7) and the essential elements of an incineration plant (4.8–4.11).[110] It then goes on to discuss, against the background of the regulatory requirements described in chapter 2:

the types and amounts of pollutants produced by incineration (4.12–4.18)

the techniques used to remove those pollutants (4.19–4.26)

the monitoring of the process and the pollutants (4.27–4.35)

the capability of available techniques to achieve the new HMIP standards and proposed EC standards, and the implications of doing so ( 4.36–4.43).

## Basic principles of incineration

4.2   Incineration generally consists of two stages. In the first stage the waste burns at a sufficiently high temperature to turn some of the substances present into gases and release others as an aerosol of fine particles. In the second stage this mixture of gases and particles (*combustion fumes*) burns at a higher temperature. Some wastes may need supplementary energy in the form of recovered heat or oil to sustain combustion.

4.3   The essential conditions for effective gas-phase incineration are that the gas or aerosol must remain in the combustion chamber for an adequate time (*retention time*), at a high enough temperature, and in the presence of a sufficient supply of air. The process is most efficient if there is enough turbulence to mix the combustion fumes thoroughly and eliminate cooler, stationary zones. Satisfactory turbulence depends on the geometry of the combustion chamber and of the air supply.

4.4   Representative retention times are 30 minutes for solid waste at the first stage and 2–3 seconds for the combustion fumes at the second stage. The design temperature for gas-phase combustion is normally between 750°C and 1200°C. A gas-phase retention time of not less than 2 seconds and a temperature of not less than 850°C are specified in the EC Directives on air pollution from municipal waste incineration plants[111] and in the new HMIP standards for most types of incineration plant[112], together with a residual oxygen concentration at the outlet from the combustion chamber of not less than 6%.

4.5   The process is affected by variations in the characteristics of the waste fed into the incinerator (*feedstock*). It is easier to achieve efficient incineration with a homogeneous feedstock like sewage sludge and more difficult with municipal waste or clinical waste. With types of waste that are not homogeneous the feedstock has to be carefully selected and balanced: plate VI shows how chemical waste is assembled for feeding into an incinerator and plate V shows the crane operator's cabin at a plant for municipal waste.

4.6   Non-combustible material and the burnt out residues of combustible material form a loose ash which has to be collected from the grate of the incinerator. A smaller quantity of fine particles is carried out of the combustion chamber by the *exhaust gases* and collected as *fly ash*.

4.7   Wastes vary considerably in the amount of solid residue they leave. Liquid organic solvents leave a negligible amount of ash. Incineration of municipal waste leaves a significant solid residue; but this typically represents a reduction of up to 90% in the volume of the original waste and a reduction of about 70% in dry weight. The true reduction achieved in the volume of waste originally collected may well be less than 90% because large bulky items are not incinerated but removed for disposal elsewhere.

# Table 4.1
## Emissions to air: performance of typical existing plants burning different types of waste

Chapter 4

Pollutant concentration (mg/Nm³)

| | new HMIP standards | municipal waste UK mean[115] | sewage sludge pre-1985 plant[116] | sewage sludge post-1985 plant[117] | clinical waste pre-1985 plant[118] | clinical waste post-1985 plant[119] |
|---|---|---|---|---|---|---|
| Total particulate matter | 30 d | 500 | 25 | 3.7 | 210 | 140 |
| Carbon monoxide | 100 | 220 | 2,700 | 14.0 | 600 | 210 |
| Volatile organic compounds (excluding particulates; expressed as total carbon) | 20 | b | 260 | 8.6 | b | 14 |
| **Acidic gases:** | | | | | | |
| Sulphur dioxide | 300 | 340 | 450 | 216 | 60 | 16 |
| Hydrogen chloride | 30 | 690 | 65 | 1.10 | 460 | 23.0 |
| Hydrogen fluoride | 2 | 1.1 | c | 1.20 | b | 0.44 |
| Nitrogen oxides (as NO$_2$) | 350 d | b | b | 130 | 160 | 120 |
| **Heavy metals:** | | | | | | |
| Cadmium | 0.1 | 0.60 | 0.19 | 0.18 | 0.70 | 0.65 |
| Mercury | 0.1 | 0.26 | 0.08 | 0.029 | 0.08 | 0.82 |
| Lead | 1 | 10.40 | 0.26 | a | 9.00 | 4.90 |
| Copper | 1 | 1.50 | 0.07 | a | 0.66 | 0.23 |
| Chromium | 1 | 1.10 | 0.01 | a | 0.02 | 0.044 |
| Nickel | 1 | 0.70 | 0.01 | a | 0.01 | 0.008 |
| Manganese | 1 | 0.43 | a | a | 0.015 | 0.062 |
| Arsenic | 1 | 0.20 | 0.01 | a | a | 0.0073 |
| Tin | 1 | b | b | b | b | b |
| Dioxins | 1 | 45 | 7 | 0.85 | 20 | 4.4 |

(ngTEQ/Nm³)

a   Measured concentration was 0.001 mg/Nm³ or less.
b   No data available.
c   Data not considered reliable.
d   For plants incinerating sewage sludge the standard for particulates is 20 mg/Nm³.

Measurements made by WSL at 20 municipal waste incinerators (with the exception of volatile organic compounds, hydrogen fluoride, mercury, arsenic and dioxins, which were measured at between three and five plants only); one old-style multiple hearth and one new-style fluidised bed sewage sludge incinerator; and two old-style and three new-style clinical waste incinerators.

Concentrations of pollutants in the emissions from a particular plant are affected not only by the operation of the gas-cleaning system but also by the characteristics of the waste incinerated in that plant.

27

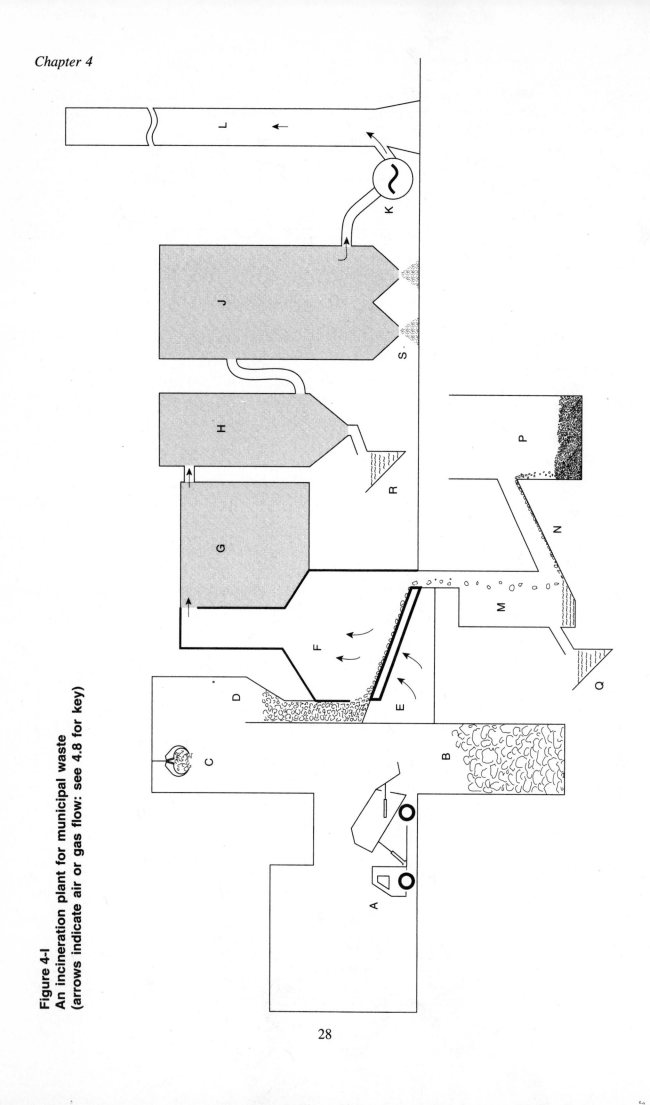

**Figure 4-I**
**An incineration plant for municipal waste**
**(arrows indicate air or gas flow: see 4.8 for key)**

**Essential elements of an incineration plant**

4.8    The essential elements of a modern incinerator are illustrated in figure 4-I, which is a diagram of a plant for municipal waste:

   i.    **facilities for handling, storing and mixing feedstock** without creating a hazard or a nuisance. In the diagram vehicles enter the tipping hall (A) and unload waste into a bunker (B), from which a grab on a crane (C) transfers it to a hopper (D) leading to the grate

   ii.    a **combustion chamber** (F) which is designed to achieve very efficient combustion in both the solid/liquid (*primary*) and gas/aerosol (*secondary*) phases. In the plant illustrated the waste is agitated mechanically as it moves over the **grate** (E) in order to expose it to air and maintain a free flow through the grate bars

   iii.    a **heat recovery system** (G) for cooling the exhaust gases prior to cleaning them. This minimises corrosion, thermal stress and the formation of undesirable compounds such as dioxins. It also opens up the opportunity of utilising the energy recovered

   iv.    a **gas-cleaning system**, typically consisting of a scrubber (H) and an electrostatic precipitator (J)

   v.    a **fan** (K) to draw the cleaned gases out of the plant so that they can be dispersed from the **stack** (L)

   vi.    facilities for the collection, handling, and where necessary **treatment of solid residues**. Ash and clinker from the grate fall into a water-filled quench tank (M) and are moved by conveyor (N) to a bunker (P); and fly ash is collected from the electrostatic precipitator (S)

   vii.    facilities for the collection and **treatment of liquid effluents** (Q, R) from the scrubber and quench tank.

Elements iii and iv can also be clearly seen in a photograph of a sewage sludge plant (plate IV); and element iv in a photograph of a chemical waste plant (plate III).

4.9    There are a number of combustion systems available: different designs suit different waste streams. Box 4A shows which designs are used in the UK for which waste streams. The designs are explained in appendix A.

4.10    Pollution abatement systems (elements iv, vi and vii in 4.8) are large and expensive, and may well represent one-third or more of the capital cost of a new plant. They are described in more detail below (4.19–4.26).

| BOX 4A | COMBUSTION SYSTEMS[113] |
|---|---|
| *Waste type* | *Combustion system* |
| **Municipal** | **Mass burn on agitating grates with excess air** |
| **Clinical** | **Ashing rotary kiln** <br> Pulsed hearth <br> Starved air |
| **Chemical** | **Slagging rotary kiln** <br> **Ashing rotary kiln** <br> Liquid injection <br> Multiple hearth furnace |
| **Sewage sludge** | **Fluidised bed furnace** <br> Multiple hearth furnace |

**Bold face** shows the system being used at present in new UK plants.
The systems are described in appendix A.

4.11    It is desirable to make incineration a continuous process wherever possible. Thermal stresses associated with startup and shutdown can result in premature failure of a plant. If there are shutdowns for maintenance or repair, wastes must either be disposed of elsewhere or stored until the plant is back in operation. In the past large municipal waste plants sometimes had a spare combustion chamber for use in such circumstances; but, with the 90% annual availability now achievable, it is no longer economic to provide reserve capacity.

**Types and amounts of pollutants**

4.12    The main pollutants associated with waste incineration are listed in box 4B. As explained above, the process of incineration itself produces wastes; box 4C shows how pollutants are typically distributed between the forms of waste produced by an incineration plant for municipal waste.

4.13    Some pollutants (acidic gases, vaporised metals, volatile organic compounds and particulate matter) originate directly from combustion of the waste. Organic compounds produce carbon dioxide and water if completely burnt, but in practice intermediate products are formed. In addition, nitrogen oxides are formed both by oxidation of nitrogen in the waste and by fixation of atmospheric nitrogen in high temperature flames. The latter mechanism predominates in the slagging kilns used for the incineration of chemical waste at temperatures of 1350°C and above. As the gases pass through the post-combustion stages, secondary reactions involving organic compounds, chlorine, fluorine and sulphur may occur. These reactions are catalysed by fine particles present in the gas stream or deposited on surfaces within the plant.

4.14    The great majority of the pollutants present in the exhaust gases are removed by the gas-cleaning system. The new HMIP standards for emissions to air from incineration plants (2.27 and tables 2.1 and 2.3) are expressed as the mass of pollutant per cubic metre of gases released from the stack. Table 4.1 allows comparisons to be drawn between those standards and concentrations of pollutants measured in

---

| BOX 4B | POLLUTANTS ASSOCIATED WITH WASTE INCINERATION |
|---|---|

**Acidic gases**
Hydrogen chloride, hydrogen fluoride, nitrogen oxides, sulphur dioxide.

**Carbon monoxide**

**Metals**
Regulatory limits are set for the following metals, either individually or in combination:
cadmium, mercury, arsenic, chromium, cobalt, copper, lead, manganese, nickel, thallium, tin.

Heavy metals can be in different chemical forms, including soluble salts such as chlorides and sulphates and less soluble oxides and silicates. Most of the mercury present is released as a vapour, as is some cadmium.

**Organic material**
Organic material occurs in volatile form, as well as bound to particulates. A large number of organic compounds can be present if combustion has not been complete or if compounds are allowed to form after incineration has taken place. An important class of such compounds is dioxins (see box 6A).

**Particulates**
Fine particles of inorganic materials such as silica have metals and organic material adhering to them. The size distribution, and thus surface area, of such particles can vary widely, as can their chemical composition and their ability to bind other materials.

- - - - - - - - - - - - - - - - - - - - - - - - - - - - - - - - - - - - - - - - - - - - - - - - - - - - - - - - -

**Carbon dioxide,** if adequately dispersed, is not conventionally regarded as a pollutant relevant to health or the local environment, and is thus not subject to direct regulatory control. It is however a contributor to the greenhouse effect.

---

**BOX 4C**                           **MAIN PRODUCTS OF AN INCINERATION PLANT**

**Grate ash**
Mainly inert slag and cinders, but also containing most of the metals.

**Fly ash**
The bulk of the fine particles from the exhaust gases, incorporating metals and organic material, including dioxins and other products of incomplete combustion.

**Liquid effluents**
Water from the scrubber containing used reagent and some particles. Waste water also comes, less heavily contaminated, from the quench tank used to cool hot ashes from the grate.

**Stack gases**
Contain the pollutants not removed by the gas-cleaning system. Nitrogen oxides are not readily removed by scrubbing, and proportions of the other acidic gases remain, as do some particulates, and proportions of the volatile organic compounds and volatile metals.

---

emissions to air from typical existing UK plants incinerating municipal waste, sewage sludge or clinical waste.

4.15 Although some columns in table 4.1 are based on data from only one or two plants, some broad conclusions can be drawn from this and other evidence about the present performance of existing plants in the UK:

**municipal waste**—none of a large number of plants studied meets all the HMIP standards. A few almost meet the limits for particulates and carbon monoxide and/or the combustion requirements[114]

**sewage sludge**—new plants easily meet HMIP's new standards for emissions, except in the case of cadmium[121]

**clinical waste**—most, if not all, existing plants fail to meet HMIP's new standards in a number of respects. They need improvements to gas-cleaning systems and operating procedures, and in some cases to combustion systems[122]

**chemical waste**—preliminary indications are that some plants at least come close to meeting HMIP's new standards. Others have more limited gas-cleaning systems and may require substantial modifications

**agricultural waste**—data are not available on emissions, except from demonstration or research projects. This type of incinerator has therefore been excluded from the tables in this chapter.

4.16 For many pollutants existing incineration plants produce only a small or negligible proportion of total UK emissions to air; the exceptions are cadmium, mercury and dioxins. Table 4.2 contains estimates of the total pollution load from UK incineration plants in 1991, both in absolute terms and as a percentage of total UK emissions of each pollutant. When the 1990 Act is fully implemented, the operators will be required to report to HMIP the total mass of each pollutant released annually under their authorisations. This information will be publicly available through the Chemical Release Inventory HMIP is establishing and will greatly improve the statistics available on this subject.

4.17 Material with a very low level of radioactivity (mainly carbon-14, sulphur-35 or tritium) may be present in clinical waste or waste from educational and research establishments handled in local incineration plants. Separate authorisation is required from HMIP under the Radioactive Substances Act 1960[123] before radioactive material can be sent to an incineration plant or discharged in emissions from it.

4.18 Other possible forms of hazard or nuisance which could arise at incineration sites are windblown litter or dust from municipal waste, leaks from drums of chemical waste, and *fugitive emissions* at points other than the stack.

**Table 4.2**

**Emissions to air: estimated 1991 emissions from UK incineration plants as proportion of total UK emissions of each pollutant**

| | Emissions to air from UK incineration plants in 1991 tonnes[120] | Percentage of total emissions to air % |
|---|---|---|
| Total particulate matter | 7,400 | a |
| Carbon monoxide | 5,000 | 0.1 |
| Volatile organic compounds (excluding particulates; expressed as total carbon) | 100 | Negligible |
| **Acidic gases:** | | |
| Sulphur dioxide | 5,140 | 0.1 |
| Hydrogen chloride | 10,500 | 3.0 |
| Hydrogen fluoride | 20 | a |
| Nitrogen oxides (as $NO_2$) | 875 | Negligible |
| **Heavy metals:** | | |
| Cadmium | 10 | 32 |
| Mercury | 4 | 11 |
| Lead | 161 | |
| Copper | 22 | |
| Chromium | 16 | 2 |
| Nickel | 10 | |
| Manganese | 6 | |
| Arsenic | 3 | |
| Dioxins | 668 (gTEQ) | b |
| Carbon dioxide[c] | 2,750,000 | 1 |

a   Percentage not known because no estimate of total UK emissions was available.
b   see para 6.3
c   Data for carbon dioxide refer only to the incineration of municipal waste.

To produce these estimates of total emissions to air from incineration plants WSL multiplied emission factors calculated from the measurements in table 4.1 by the estimated amount of each type of waste incinerated in the UK in 1991. In the case of chemical waste incinerators, as no measurements of emissions were available, it was assumed that the average concentrations of pollutants in emissions from such plants were at the same levels as the new HMIP standards.

## Techniques for controlling pollutants

4.19   Correct design and operation of the combustion system is one of the most important factors in limiting emissions from incineration plants, particularly of nitrogen oxides and dioxins. Achieving highly efficient combustion and minimising the formation of pollutants within the process (4.13) is preferable to removing pollutants from the exhaust gases subsequently. Features such as design of grate, size and shape of primary and secondary combustion chambers, scale and profile of air injection, and arrangements for using supplementary fuel must all suit the physical nature, calorific value and volume of the feedstock. For example, higher temperatures are more effective in breaking down organic compounds; but if waste with a high solid content, such as municipal waste, reaches a temperature of more than 1050°C, the fly ash melts and on cooling forms a slag which may clog up the plant.

4.20   Several processes are available for cleaning the exhaust gases:

*particulates* (which may contain heavy metals and dioxins) are removed by physical sifting. This may be done by fabric filters, electrostatic precipitators or high energy wet scrubbers

*acidic gases* are removed ("scrubbed") by mixing them with an alkaline reagent such as lime. The reagent may be in powder, slurry or liquid form. The process also removes a proportion of the heavy metals present

*nitrogen oxides* are significantly more difficult to control than the other acidic gases because of their lower solubility in water, and are removed chemically by reduction with ammonia, with or without a catalyst

*volatile substances* such as mercury and some organic compounds can be adsorbed onto activated carbon.

An incineration plant will not normally have all of these devices. The most common pattern is a combination of physical sifting and scrubbing.

4.21   To achieve effective control of pollution, each gas-cleaning stage must be carefully matched to the physical conditions of the exhaust gases: the concentration of the gases and their temperature, pressure and flow rate, as well as the nature, size and distribution of particles. Some processes can cope with a number of pollutants in one step. For example semi-dry scrubbing is able to remove acidic gases, particulates, mercury and dioxins.

4.22   According to HMIP's guidance notes, the stack of an incineration plant should not produce smoke except within five minutes after startup from cold (one minute in the case of a plant for clinical waste). However a white plume of water droplets will appear if wet scrubbing is being used and the cleaned gases are saturated with water vapour. In order to prevent such a plume appearing, the stack gases are sometimes heated to lower their relative humidity. A high stack is commonly used to loft gases away from the site and disperse them. Reheating the gases adds further buoyancy. Regulatory authorities have sometimes imposed conditions about the length or proportion of time for which a visible plume is permitted.

4.23   In order to produce a liquid effluent suitable for discharge to sewers or to a river or estuary, water from quench tanks or wet scrubbing must be treated to remove residual lime slurry and particulates, and to neutralise and precipitate dissolved salts. The volume of water requiring treatment can be reduced by installing a condensing scrubber, which recirculates coolant through an indirect heat exchanger.

4.24   Ash from the grates of incinerators generally has sufficiently low levels of leachable pollutants to be acceptable for landfill. A common practice in the UK is co-disposal of such ash with municipal waste or sewage sludge. Anaerobic decomposition of the municipal waste forms organic acids, which would promote leaching of heavy metals by forming soluble metal complexes, but also produces hydrogen sulphide which forms insoluble sulphides of the metals. Other European countries have favoured the use of separate sites for landfilling grate ash from incinerators. The European Parliament has recommended that the draft Directive on landfill[124] should be amended to curtail co-disposal and limit the organic carbon content of grate ash sent to landfill.

4.25   Disposal of fly ash and scrubbing residues presents a more difficult task than disposal of grate ash. Heavy metal and organic pollutants are bound to these residues in sufficiently high concentrations for the risk of groundwater contamination to be a significant consideration. Fly ash should be placed in sealed containers at the incineration plant, transported securely and landfilled in a separate, sealed site. The risk of leaching can be further reduced if the residues are vitrified or solidified before disposal.

4.26   There have been problems in the past with the co-incineration of clinical waste and other wastes on permeable grates because clinical sharps such as needles have fallen through into the grate ash. Sharps can be effectively destroyed by incineration in an ashing rotary kiln (see appendix A, A.1–A.3), which ensures a long retention time.

## Monitoring

4.27   Where HMIP gives an authorisation for an incineration plant, compliance with the performance standards for emissions to air must be demonstrated by monitoring results obtained over a representative period of normal operation. If the initial monitoring results do not show compliance, a further assessment may be made after modifications to process variables such as feed rate, waste composition or air supply.

4.28    Optimum performance of an incinerator is achieved through continuous online monitoring by the operator of several aspects of the process, including:

  oxygen levels in exhaust gases

  carbon monoxide levels in exhaust gases

  temperature in the gas-cleaning system.

Raised levels of carbon monoxide indicate poor combustion. The continuous monitors for process variables are commonly linked to an emergency cut-off which interrupts the waste feed if abnormal conditions develop.

4.29    Temperature at each stage of the process is an important determinant of emissions, but there is no regulatory requirement to monitor it outside the actual combustion chamber. The measurement of combustion temperature is open to great variation depending on the position of the probes and the technique employed. It is thus important that methods of measuring temperature should be precisely specified by the regulatory authority.

4.30    Techniques are not available for direct measurement of retention time and turbulence within the combustion chamber. Assessments must therefore be made at the design stage, sometimes using models. WSL is carrying out research into ways of characterising retention time, as this is one of the key variables in the control of dioxin formation.

4.31    Metals and organic compounds may be present in the stack gases either as vapours or in particulate matter, and monitoring needs to cover both forms. It is not yet technically possible to make continuous measurements. Present practice is to carry out a comprehensive analysis of stack gases, covering all significant pollutants, once or twice a year at large plants and less often at small plants. As well as providing data about those pollutants which are not monitored continuously, this analysis also allows checks to be made on the accuracy of continuous monitoring.

4.32    For liquid effluents and solid residues regulatory requirements are limited to periodic monitoring. HMIP's guidance notes say that each solid waste stream from an incineration plant must be analysed at least once a year for likely substances on a prescribed list. In practice analyses of liquid effluents and solid residues are usually carried out monthly. It is open to the waste disposal authority which licenses the disposal of solid wastes to landfill to prescribe leachability tests for heavy metals in incinerator ash.

4.33    Off-site monitoring for dioxins (typically once a year) may be required by HMIP as a condition of authorisation. It may also be undertaken voluntarily by the site operator, possibly in collaboration with the local authority.

4.34    The validity of results obtained from monitoring depends on standardisation of sampling and analytical methods coupled with strict quality control over the way in which those methods are implemented. Care must be taken to obtain samples which are representative of the stack gases. Analyses should be carried out to the standards set by the National Measurement Accreditation Service (NAMAS) provided by the National Physical Laboratory. If the operator is not accredited the work should be performed by an accredited independent laboratory, which should also be responsible for checking the calibration of continuous monitoring devices used by the operator. **We recommend that HMIP should ensure that:**

  i.    **satisfactory protocols for sampling and analysing for all significant substances present in releases from waste incineration, and for measuring the conditions in combustion chambers and gas-cleaning systems, are prepared, published and kept up to date, and any research necessary for this purpose is carried out**

  ii.   **analytical laboratories used by operators of incineration plants have NAMAS accreditation.**

4.35   Except for plants with a capacity of less than 1 tonne an hour the EC Directives on municipal waste incineration (2.30) require continuous monitoring of emissions of particulates and carbon monoxide, and at new plants of hydrogen chloride. The draft Directive on the Incineration of Hazardous Waste (2.33) requires in addition continuous monitoring of volatile organic compounds, sulphur dioxide and hydrogen fluoride: the figures given in table 2.3 for pollutants monitored continuously are the limits on daily average values. There may be technical difficulties in achieving continuous monitoring with the necessary accuracy at the low concentrations involved. Monthly measurements would be required for the other pollutants for which standards are set, including dioxins.

**Capability of available techniques to achieve present and proposed standards**

4.36   The annexes to the relevant HMIP guidance notes (box 2B), which are based on studies by consultants[125], set out the techniques which the Chief Inspector regards as complying with BATNEEC (box 2A) for the incineration of different types of waste. HMIP's view is that, if appropriately designed and operated, plant of a variety of configurations should be capable of meeting the performance standards in the guidance notes. While the studies carried out for the Commission by WSL confirm that this is broadly the case, they have also drawn attention to difficulties which might arise if certain of the configurations mentioned were to be used for certain types of waste and/or sizes of plant. There is also a shortage of published data about the performance of some types of plant. If on the other hand new techniques are developed which are capable of reducing emissions still further without excessive cost, the BATNEEC concept implies that operators should be expected to adopt them. **We recommend that the annexes to the guidance notes should be revised periodically to take account of further information about plant performance.**

4.37   Figure 4-II shows that achievement of the performance standards in the guidance notes will very considerably reduce the total emissions of most pollutants to air from existing UK plants for incinerating municipal waste. Emissions of cadmium will fall by over 80%, and emissions of other metals, dioxins, hydrogen chloride and particulates will fall by over 90%, on the assumption that the amounts of waste incinerated remain at 1991 levels. These reductions represent a substantial gain in environmental terms. The HMIP performance standard would in theory permit an increase in the pollution load from emissions of hydrogen fluoride because some plants at least are already within the standard for that pollutant (see table 4.1). Figure 4-II shows upper bounds rather than what will happen in practice.

4.38   Because figure 4-II is based on the 1991 position, it is also necessary to consider what could happen if the quantities of waste incinerated increase in the future. Figure 4-III shows the possible total pollution loads from emissions to air from UK incineration plants of all types if the quantities of waste incinerated were to increase as follows:

a.   an increase in the amount of municipal waste incinerated from 3 to 5 million tonnes a year
b.   a tenfold increase in the amount of sewage sludge incinerated, to about 1 million tonnes dry solids a year
c.   incineration of 0.2 million tonnes of clinical waste a year
d.   a fivefold increase in the amount of chemical waste incinerated, to about 0.5 million tonnes a year.

The results of these calculations should be treated with caution because, except in the case of plants for municipal waste, the data used to calculate the 1991 pollution load have been drawn from a small number of samples at a small number of plants (see footnotes to tables 4.1 and 4.2). However it is reasonable to conclude that, even with such large increases in amounts of waste incinerated, substantial percentage reductions would still be ensured for some pollutants. Figure 4-III shows reductions of over 90% for dioxins and hydrogen chloride, and over 80% for particulates and other metals. Emissions of other pollutants, especially sulphur dioxide, could rise significantly. Although it should be emphasised again that the figures show upper bounds rather than forecasts of actual emissions, the scope for increases in emissions suggests that the standards for the latter pollutants ought to be re-examined. This is done in chapter 8 (8.15–8.25).

4.39   The draft EC Directive on the Incineration of Hazardous Waste[126] has already proposed even more stringent standards for emissions to air (table 2.3). The definition of hazardous waste for this

**Figure 4-II**
**Pollution load to air permitted by new HMIP standards from UK plants incinerating municipal waste as percentage of 1991 pollution load: 1991 amounts of waste incinerated**

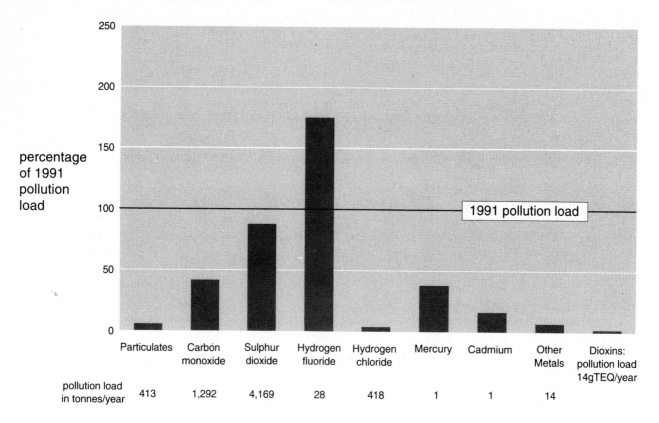

| pollution load in tonnes/year | Particulates | Carbon monoxide | Sulphur dioxide | Hydrogen fluoride | Hydrogen chloride | Mercury | Cadmium | Other Metals | Dioxins: pollution load 14gTEQ/year |
|---|---|---|---|---|---|---|---|---|---|
| | 413 | 1,292 | 4,169 | 28 | 418 | 1 | 1 | 14 | |

purpose may be sufficiently wide to bring the incineration of sewage sludge and clinical waste, as well as the incineration of special waste, within the scope of this Directive. It is also possible that the European Commission may take account of the provisions of this draft in its review of the existing Directives on incineration of municipal waste (2.32).

4.40   Proven techniques are available to meet some of the standards in the draft Directive on the Incineration of Hazardous Waste, considered in isolation. For example certain types of wet scrubbing can be combined with an electrostatic precipitator to give very effective control of particulates. However to meet the whole set of proposed standards a number of relatively expensive techniques would have to be employed.

4.41   The main difficulties would be over meeting the proposed standard of 0.05 mg/Nm$^3$ for mercury and the proposed guide value of 0.1 ngTEQ/Nm$^3$ for dioxins. Nevertheless there are good grounds for thinking that recent improvements in adsorption systems such as activated carbon injection have brought these figures within reach. The major uncertainty that remains is whether, using present techniques for sampling and analysis, concentrations of dioxins can be measured with sufficient confidence at these low levels to confirm compliance.

4.42   The draft Directive does not contain a limit for **nitrogen oxides**, but a limit of 200 mg/Nm$^3$ appears in the latest German legislation.[127] If this were to be adopted as an EC standard, it might not be achievable simply by modifying the design of the combustion chamber. One approach to the control of

**Figure 4-III**

**Pollution load to air permitted by new HMIP standards from UK incineration plants as percentage of 1991 pollution load: with large increases in amounts of wastes incinerated (see 4.38)**

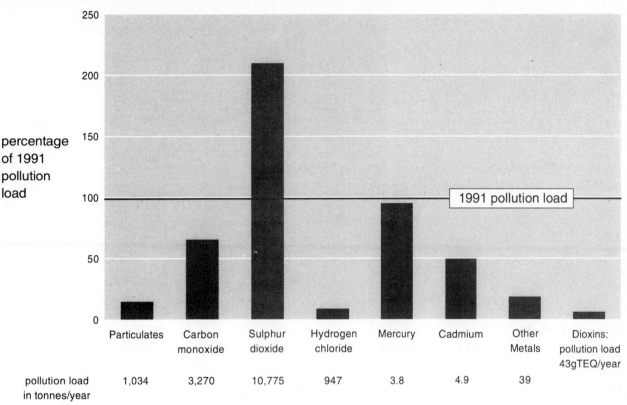

nitrogen oxides is to inject urea into the combustion chamber but this has not yet been thoroughly assessed. The same effect can be achieved by direct injection of ammonia (4.20); and, in conjunction with exhaust gas recirculation, this is said to be capable of meeting a 200 mg/Nm$^3$ limit.

4.43    Finally the draft Directive would prohibit **liquid discharges** to the aquatic environment from new incineration plants. Although wet, dry and semi-dry scrubbing systems are all in use at present, dry or semi-dry scrubbing systems would not be able to achieve the draft Directive's limit for particulates in emissions to air; and (because of the large quantities of chemicals required) would represent a more expensive method for achieving the proposed standards for hydrogen chloride and sulphur dioxide. Incineration plants also give rise to liquid wastes from quench tanks. The elimination of liquid discharges would have to be achieved through evaporation, by reinjecting the effluents back into the plant.

**Conclusion**

4.44    For most pollutants existing incineration plants produce a small or negligible proportion of total UK emissions (table 4.2). The exceptions are certain heavy metals, and also dioxins (which are discussed further in chapter 6). Achievement of the new HMIP standards will considerably reduce present emissions from plants for municipal waste (as figure 4-II shows). Even with very large increases in the amounts of waste incinerated (4.38) the total pollution load from modern plants meeting the new HMIP standards would not be a cause for concern (figure 4-III). There would be a considerable reduction in the 1991 pollution load for most pollutants, with a reduction of over 90% in emissions of dioxins. However mercury and cadmium are exceptions to this general rule: the reduction in emissions to air of mercury might be only marginal, and that of cadmium only 50%. Whether it is justifiable to aim for still more stringent limits (as proposed in the draft Directive on the Incineration of Hazardous Waste) depends on the health implications of the emissions and the feasibility of testing compliance at such low concentrations. Health issues are discussed in chapter 6. Chapter 8 considers the justification for the proposals in the draft Directive (8.15–8.25). Chapter 5 considers energy recovery from waste incineration, including some interactions between pollution abatement techniques and energy recovery which affect the production of dioxins (5.21–5.23).

# CHAPTER 5

# ENERGY RECOVERY

## Energy potential of waste incineration

5.1    The third stage in the four-stage decision procedure described at the beginning of this report (1.1) is to recover energy from waste if the waste cannot be recycled in the form of materials. For those kinds of waste which will burn readily, without the need for additional fuel, incineration is not only a method of treatment and disposal but can also result in the recovery and use for other purposes of a substantial proportion of the energy contained in the wastes. For the purpose of pollution control in the UK, incineration as a method of waste disposal has been distinguished from burning wastes with the primary purpose of providing energy (2.20–2.21 and box 2B); but that distinction is not necessarily a helpful one. The management of South East London Combined Heat and Power (SELCHP: 5.10), which is building a plant at Deptford (London) to incinerate municipal waste, says that it regards the sale of electricity generated by the plant as a method of reducing the cost of waste disposal, rather than an activity undertaken in its own right.[128] In contrast the Swedish Environment Protection Board told the Commission that it is "vital" that incinerators should be "resource recovery plants comparable with other energy producing units".[129] Sweden is one of a number of countries which make much more extensive use than the UK of energy recovery from municipal waste. A comprehensive environmental assessment of waste incineration must take full account of the energy aspects.

5.2    This chapter considers the energy potential of different kinds of waste (5.3–5.8), and the extent to which that potential is realised at present in the UK (5.9–5.12) and in other developed countries (5.13–5.16). It goes on to discuss the use of refuse-derived fuel (5.17–5.20); whether energy recovery impedes or facilitates the objective of minimising pollution from incineration plants (5.21–5.23); and the net impact of waste incineration on emissions of greenhouse gases (5.24–5.29).

5.3    The energy potentially available in a substance for release as heat is described as the *calorific value* of that substance, usually expressed as GigaJoules (GJth) per tonne. Typical calorific values for different kinds of waste are shown in figure 5-I, and compared to typical calorific values for coal.[130]

**Figure 5-I**
**Calorific values for different types of waste, in comparison with coal**

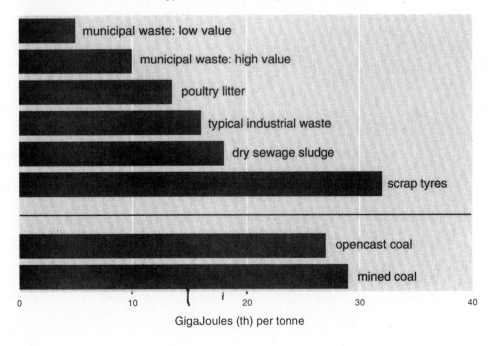

GigaJoules (th) per tonne

39

Most organic wastes hold significant stored energy. As will be seen, there is considerable variation in the calorific value of municipal waste. Clinical waste would show an even wider variation in calorific value, but has a higher value on average than municipal waste because of its plastics content. In general the higher the calorific value the greater the net benefit in energy terms, and the more attractive the case for investment to recover the energy. But other factors may also be important. Although scrap tyres, for example, have a high calorific value, there are problems in handling and shredding them. General industrial waste is more attractive than municipal waste as a source of energy, not only because of its higher calorific value (about 16GJth/tonne) but also because it has a lower moisture content (about 10%) and leaves less ash (6–10% of the original volume).[131]

5.4    There are a number of possible methods for utilising the energy in municipal waste, besides "mass burn" incineration. These include the gasification of the waste with or without combustion (although the techniques for this are not yet well established), the collection of the gas formed when municipal waste is landfilled (see box 5B) and the production of biogas as a by-product from composting the putrescible element of the waste (see box 5A). Another approach is to convert municipal waste into refuse-derived fuel (RDF), of which there are two main forms:

> Coarse refuse-derived fuel (cRDF) is typically produced by separating from municipal waste its bulky and noncombustible fractions (glass, tins, rubble) and chopping the rest to a consistent size. The moisture content is not substantially reduced.

> To produce densified refuse-derived fuel (dRDF), separation of bulky and non-combustible fractions is followed by substantial reduction of moisture content. The material is then formed into pellets.

Of the two types, dRDF has the virtue that it can be stored, whereas cRDF starts to rot immediately. From the technical point of view it is possible to sell dRDF to industrial users; in practice it has not been an attractive form of fuel, and has not overcome the cost penalty imposed by the dewatering part of the process.

5.5    Sewage sludge needs extra fuel for start-up, but will then burn without additional fuel provided that the organic solids content is about 28% or more. However over 90% of the energy recovered has to be used to remove sufficient water to reach this level; the remaining energy is usable only as low-grade heat on, or in the immediate vicinity of, the site.

5.6    The inherent limitations on the efficiency of combustion processes mean that only a proportion of the calorific value of a substance can be recovered in practice. The efficiency of coal-fired power generation will usually be in the range 30%–38%.[132] Because boilers fitted to incinerators must operate at lower steam temperatures to minimise corrosion, the overall efficiency of power generation fuelled by municipal waste rarely exceeds 25%, and is typically 20%. The thermal energy content of 90GJth in 10 tonnes of municipal waste is theoretically equivalent to about 25,000 kilowatt hours (kWh); but in practice can be assumed to generate only about 5000 kWh[133] of electricity. The efficiency of energy recovery can be roughly doubled however if, in addition to electricity generation, lower grade waste heat from combustion can be utilised in a combined heat and power (CHP) or district heating scheme.

5.7    It is convenient to measure the energy content of wastes in terms of tonnes of coal equivalent (tce), in other words the amount of coal that needs to be burned to produce an equivalent amount of energy. In approximate terms the total energy content of the UK's wastes is in the range 26 million tce to 30 million tce. Of this, perhaps half (about 15 million tce) is from industrial and commercial wastes, and one-fifth (about 6 million tce) from domestic wastes.[134] The total energy content represents about one-third[135] of the coal burned in UK power stations in 1991; but, because incineration typically recovers only about 20% of calorific value (as compared with 30%–38% recovery from coal), even burning the whole of the UK's burnable wastes to recover their energy content (which is not a likely prospect) would replace only about one fifth of the coal burned in UK power stations in 1991.

5.8    It would not in any case be desirable to burn all the UK's wastes. The four-stage decision procedure gives recycling priority over energy recovery. Recycling is environmentally preferable to incineration for a particular category of wastes if the energy saved by recycling exceeds the energy that can be recovered by incineration *plus* any energy that has to be used in separating out that category for recycling. To take a clear-cut example, a large amount of energy is saved by recycling aluminium (which

---

**BOX 5A**                                              **INCINERATION VERSUS COMPOSTING**

---

In order to compare incineration and composting, it has been assumed that vegetable and putrescible matter form about 29% of municipal waste. It is also assumed that removing putrescibles increases the theoretical calorific value of the waste from about 9 GJth/tonne to about 11 GJth/tonne; and that 70% of these calorific values can be recovered. Any requirement for energy in order to separate the waste streams has been disregarded. On that basis:

incineration of 1 tonne of unseparated municipal waste would produce **6.3 GJth**;

separating out the vegetable and putrescible matter for composting, and burning the remainder of the municipal waste, would produce 0.8 GJth of energy in the form of biogas from the composting process,[136] plus 5.4 GJth from incineration, giving a very similar total of **6.2 GJth**.

---

requires 20 times less energy than producing aluminium from bauxite); it is therefore environmentally preferable to recycle any aluminium contained in municipal or industrial waste. Composting of putrescibles is a less obvious case. Calculations were carried out for the Commission in order to draw a comparison in energy terms between burning putrescibles as part of municipal waste with energy recovery and separating them out in order to make compost, and are summarised in box 5A. Those calculations suggest that neither approach has a clear advantage: which is preferable in energy terms will depend on the circumstances of an individual case.

**Energy recovery from waste in the UK**

5.9    In the past the role of energy recovery from waste in the UK has been shaped by the withdrawal of local authorities from electricity supply (in the early years of this century there were over 70 incinerators using municipal waste to generate electricity) and by the rarity of district heating schemes. Of the 30 plants in the UK for incinerating municipal waste (table 3.4), only 4, plus another one in Jersey, recover energy.[137] Severe corrosion and fouling problems have often been experienced, but have been largely overcome by replacing the original smoke-tube boilers (as used in coal-fired plant) with water-tube boilers. The 5 plants which recover energy are:

Coventry        heat recovery at present, electricity generation proposed

Edmonton      turbo-alternators produce over 20MWe for the national grid

Jersey            a design that had given good service in continental Europe. Energy recovery has operated satisfactorily but the plant has not met the availability requirements: cleaning is needed every 1500–2000 hours instead of the planned 4000 hours

Nottingham    two incinerator streams and a coal-fired power station provide energy for the only citywide CHP scheme in the UK

Sheffield        now reliable and sells hot water to the city-centre district-heating scheme. Electricity generation is being considered.

The combined capacity of the mainland plants recovering energy is 800,000 tonnes of waste a year, about a third of the total UK capacity for incineration of municipal waste (3.19).

5.10    Under the Non-Fossil Fuel Obligation (NFFO), the regional electricity companies in England and Wales must buy electricity at a premium rate for a specified period from designated producers who are not using fossil fuels. At present[138] the companies must buy 261.48 MWe from producers who are generating the electricity from waste. Three projects to burn municipal waste were accepted for the second tranche of NFFO, covering the period to 1998:

the SELCHP plant under construction at Deptford (London) to take 420,000 tonnes a year of waste

the proposed Cory Environmental Ltd plant at Belvedere (Kent) to generate 126 MWe while burning 1.5 million tonnes a year of waste

a plant to take 600,000 tonnes a year proposed by National Power at Northfleet (Kent).

Their combined capacity of 2.5 million tonnes of municipal waste a year is more than 3 times the capacity of the 4 existing mainland plants. It is understood however that National Power do not intend to proceed with their scheme, and that the Cory plant has been reduced in size to 1.2 million tonnes a year of waste generating 106 MWe. The government is discussing with the European Commission the possibility of a further tranche of NFFO extending beyond 1998.

5.11    The RDF approach (5.4) has been the subject of substantial trials in the UK since the late 1970s, with the emphasis on dRDF. Of the 10 RDF production plants built in the UK, 5 have closed, 2 are for sale, and only 3 are working.[139] The largest is at Byker (Newcastle upon Tyne), where the pelleted product generates steam on site for combined heat and power.

5.12    Mention was made in chapter 3 of plants accepted for NFFO, and in operation or under construction, for generating electricity from scrap tyres (3.28) and poultry litter (3.34).

## Energy recovery from waste in other countries

5.13    A number of the countries which make more use of waste incineration than the UK (table 3.8) also place a greater emphasis on energy recovery.[140] Most often this is for electricity generation. In Denmark and Sweden, where every municipal waste incineration plant recovers energy, the primary purpose has been district heating. Sweden recovers about half the energy theoretically possible (about 5,000 GWh a year out of 9,000–11,000 GWh a year) and puts about 97% of that energy to beneficial use: 94% of the recovered energy is used for district heating, and this supplies about 13% of the country's total district heating requirement.

5.14    Of the 12 municipal waste plants in the Netherlands, 5 generate electricity and 2 supply hot water. In the near future all plants will be required to recover heat for the production of hot water, steam or electricity: electricity will predominate as only a few areas have infrastructure for district heating. It is estimated that, in 2000, municipal waste incineration plants will be able to supply about 5% of Dutch electricity production.[141] Some large German cities have incineration plants capable of meeting 5–10% of their total power demand.[142]

5.15    Some European countries now require the inclusion of energy recovery in all new incineration plants for municipal waste, and if possible in plants for other types of waste. The US National Energy Strategy, published in February 1991,[143] called for a sevenfold increase in electricity generation from municipal waste by 2010: plants planned or under construction are likely to increase capacity for this purpose to about a quarter of the arisings of municipal waste forecast for the year 2000.

5.16    Energy recovery from wastes is thus a significant and established element of waste management in countries whose awareness of pollution risks is at least as great as the UK's. The projects accepted under the second tranche of NFFO (5.10, 5.12) still leave very considerable scope for further expansion in the UK.

## The refuse-derived fuel option

5.17    The arguments for using cRDF (5.4) have been summarised[144] as follows:

   a. cRDF has a higher calorific value than raw municipal waste, and is more uniform in its combustion characteristics

   b. cRDF has a lower heavy metal content than raw municipal waste, so reducing the demands on the gas-cleaning equipment

   c. cRDF has a much lower proportion of non-combustible materials than raw municipal waste, so there is less ash to be handled

   d. efficiency is increased because the combustion conditions can be tailored more precisely to the feedstock specification.

5.18    Sweden and the USA have considerable experience of using cRDF. The USA has in the past tended to mix cRDF with coal (typically 1:4); but newer incinerators, integrated with the waste processing plant, run efficiently on 100% RDF. Sweden[145] has carried out trials of fluidised bed incinerators fuelled entirely with cRDF at Sundsvall and Lidkoping, and regards this technology as largely proven.

5.19   Even so, the UK experience with dRDF indicates that success with any form of RDF requires the continuous engagement of professional skills in both the procurement of the plant[146] and the management of the operation. The general lack of success of RDF plants in the UK has been attributed to "bad design, ... incorrect definition of the required plant performance, ... inadequate studies of the market, ... inadequate understanding of the nature and quality of the available feedstock, and ... poor plant reliability".[147]

5.20   In drawing up the national waste management strategy recommended later in this report, the possible advantages of using cRDF should be considered. In its Eleventh Report the Commission expressed concern about emissions from burning of RDF and recommended that, until more was known about them, it should be burnt only under closely controlled conditions: this would rule out on environmental grounds the sale of dRDF to outside users. In any case there has never been a sufficient number of outside buyers to justify the extra cost of producing this form of RDF (5.4).

### Relationship between energy recovery and pollution abatement

5.21   The inclusion of energy recovery has certain technical advantages for the design of incineration plants. The exhaust gases need to be cooled in any case before they enter the gas-cleaning system; cooling them by injecting air or water, rather than by directing them through a boiler or heat exchanger, can cause thermal shock or condensation, and in any event increases their volume and thus the dimensions of all the downstream sections of the plant. There are also certain specific advantages for gas-cleaning systems: lower temperatures greatly improve control of acidic gases and heavy metals in dry or semi-dry systems, and in wet or semi-dry scrubbing systems may reduce the amount of quench water needed by up to 85%.

5.22   There are also certain disadvantages. More precise control of combustion is needed, especially when starting up or shutting down, and this may require increased use of auxiliary fuel. Moreover, if fly ash containing metal chlorides is present, the temperature in the boiler used for energy recovery (200–400°C) and the availability of oxygen provide favourable conditions for the catalytic formation of dioxins. To counter that, the gases need to be cooled through this temperature band as quickly as possible and the surfaces of the boiler tubes need to be cleaned frequently to remove fly ash, particularly in plants for municipal waste. There may also need to be additional expenditure on removing dioxins from the exhaust gases.

5.23   For municipal waste it seems likely to become standard practice in the UK to design new plants with provision for energy recovery. This is already standard practice for sewage sludge, in order to obtain the large amount of energy needed to prepare the sludge for incineration (5.5). For clinical waste, energy recovery is common in existing plants, but not necessarily in a satisfactory form. Energy recovery has not generally been incorporated in plants incinerating special waste, except for the purpose of reheating stack gases (4.22). Although energy recovery may have disadvantages as well as advantages for pollution abatement, it seems most unlikely that it would prevent new incineration plants from achieving the new HMIP standards for emissions to air. If it increases the total cost of the gas-cleaning systems required to achieve those standards (and it is not clear that it would do so), the additional cost would have to be offset against the financial benefit from energy recovery.

### Waste disposal and the greenhouse effect

5.24   Waste incineration leads to the emission of large amounts of carbon dioxide, which contribute to the greenhouse effect. In the hypothetical situation in which all UK municipal waste is incinerated, it is estimated that 37 million tonnes of carbon dioxide, containing 10 million tonnes of carbon, would be emitted each year. This would be equivalent to about 4% of total UK emissions of gases contributing to the greenhouse effect. Carbon dioxide is also emitted as a result of burning other types of waste, but the weight of waste involved, and thus its carbon content, is at least an order of magnitude smaller.

5.25   In assessing the significance of such emissions several factors have to be taken into account. Most of the carbon emitted to air from waste incineration does not originate from fossil fuel sources. Much of it comes from renewable sources such as paper and food: in the long term these emissions are balanced by the take-up of carbon by trees and agricultural crops. Even for the remainder of the carbon,

| BOX 5B | GREENHOUSE GAS EMISSIONS FROM WASTE DISPOSAL |

*Key assumptions used in the calculations underlying figures 5-II and 5-III*

(1)   A million tonnes of unsorted **municipal waste** contains 300,000 tonnes of **carbon** in various forms.

(2)   When municipal waste is **incinerated**, all the carbon it contains is emitted to the atmosphere in the form of carbon dioxide [in practice about 2% of the carbon may be left in the ash].

(3)   When municipal waste is **landfilled** and decomposes, 200,000 tonnes of the 300,000 tonnes of carbon it contains is released in the form of landfill gas.

(4)   To simplify the comparison with incineration, the timing of the release of landfill gas has been disregarded.

(5)   **Landfill gas** contains (by volume) 47% carbon dioxide and 47% methane.

Anaerobic decomposition of the biodegradable element in municipal waste may take 10–50 years, with maximum gas production one-third to one-half the way through the cycle. The proportions of carbon dioxide and methane observed in practice in landfill gas vary considerably. Some of the methane produced by decomposition is converted to carbon dioxide by oxidation before it reaches the atmosphere. The usual range is from equal amounts (as in assumption (5)) to a ratio of 13 methane : 7 carbon dioxide. If methane predominates the benefit of incineration would be even greater than that shown in the calculations reported here.

(6)   Of the landfill gas released through decomposition of the waste, 40% is collected and **burned to recover energy** and the remainder leaks to the atmosphere.

As landfill gas is in practice produced in varying amounts over a long period, a 40% collection efficiency appears to be the practical maximum with present levels of investment in landfill engineering. The gas collected can be either burned to recover energy or flared off. In either case the methane is converted to carbon dioxide. With energy recovery the resulting emissions of carbon dioxide are offset by reductions in the carbon dioxide emissions from the burning of fossil fuels, as also happens if the waste is incinerated and energy recovered.

(7)   Municipal waste has a **calorific value** of 7.5 GJth/tonne, of which 20% can be recovered in incineration.

(8)   Energy recovery by either of these means is in substitution for the burning of **coal** which is 90% carbon and has a calorific value of 26 GJth/tonne in a power station which utilises 38% of the calorific value.

(9)   The recovery of energy by burning 1 tonne of carbon in the form of methane from landfill gas saves the emission of 1 tonne of carbon as carbon dioxide from coal-fired power stations.

which will have been derived from oil-based materials such as plastics, what is released as a result of waste incineration is not a net addition to carbon dioxide emissions if energy is recovered from the incineration process and used in substitution for fossil fuels.

5.26   Only a small proportion of the UK's municipal waste is at present incinerated; nearly all of it goes to landfill, where it produces both carbon dioxide and methane and contributes substantially to the greenhouse effect. Methane has a particularly strong effect: over 100 years this is about 7.5[148] times greater than the effect of the same weight of carbon as carbon dioxide. Numerous old landfill sites, no longer in use, have the potential to emit methane. A recent estimate is that total emissions of methane from UK landfill sites are about 2 million tonnes a year of carbon as methane[149], about half[150] the UK total, and about 6% of total UK emissions of greenhouse gases.

5.27   A comparison has been made between the net greenhouse effect from incinerating municipal

**Figure 5-II**
**Incineration versus landfill: emissions of greenhouse gases (see also box 5B)**

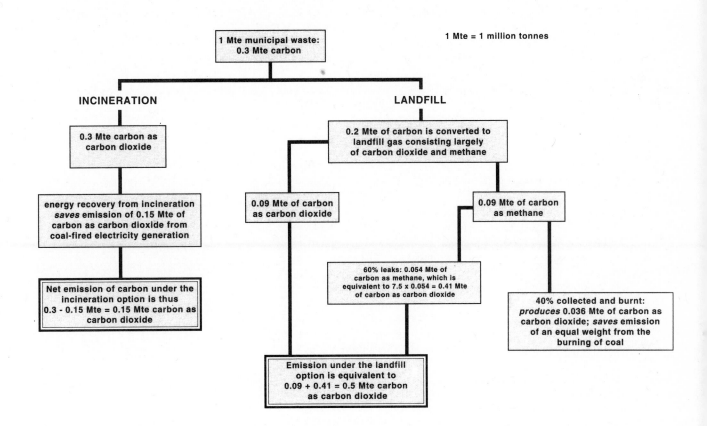

waste and the net greenhouse effect from landfilling it. A more detailed explanation of the relevant processes is given in box 5B, which also lists the key assumptions used in the calculations. Figure 5-II shows the comparison diagrammatically for 1 million tonnes of municipal waste. Incinerating the waste with energy recovery (left-hand side) produces net emissions of 0.15 million tonnes of carbon in the form of carbon dioxide. Landfilling it with energy recovery (right-hand side) produces emissions of greenhouse gases equivalent to 0.5 million tonnes of carbon as carbon dioxide. The incineration option therefore saves the equivalent of 0.35 million tonnes of carbon as carbon dioxide for every million tonnes of municipal waste incinerated.

5.28    The comparison is shown in a more general form in figure 5-III. The horizontal axis shows the percentage split between incineration and landfilling of UK municipal waste. The left-hand end of the axis represents total reliance on landfill and the right-hand end total reliance on incineration. Intermediate points represent combinations of the two methods of disposal; and a vertical line has been included to show the actual position in 1991. The vertical axis shows the combined global warming potential of the resulting emissions of carbon dioxide and methane: for this purpose the amounts of methane emitted have been converted to the weight of carbon as carbon dioxide that would have an equivalent effect. Figure 5-III takes into account that there are several other factors which determine the global warming potential of any given split between landfill and incineration. These are:

  i.    whether the incineration plants incorporate energy recovery, thus producing an offsetting reduction in the amount of carbon emitted from the burning of fossil fuels

  ii.   the proportion of the methane from landfill which is captured, rather than leaking to air

  iii.  whether the methane captured is flared off or burned to recover the energy in substitution for fossil fuels.

Six possible cases are shown.

**Figure 5-III**
**Incineration versus landfill: implications for the greenhouse effect**

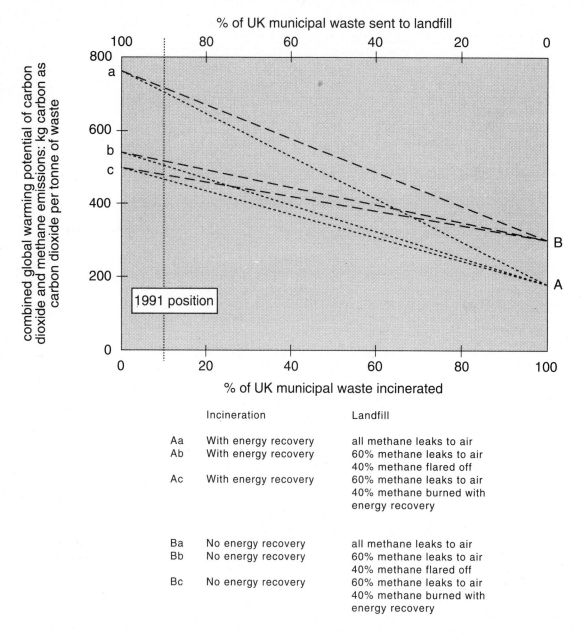

|  | Incineration | Landfill |
|---|---|---|
| Aa | With energy recovery | all methane leaks to air |
| Ab | With energy recovery | 60% methane leaks to air<br>40% methane flared off |
| Ac | With energy recovery | 60% methane leaks to air<br>40% methane burned with<br>energy recovery |
|  |  |  |
| Ba | No energy recovery | all methane leaks to air |
| Bb | No energy recovery | 60% methane leaks to air<br>40% methane flared off |
| Bc | No energy recovery | 60% methane leaks to air<br>40% methane burned with<br>energy recovery |

5.29   The conclusion from this comparison is that by incinerating municipal waste rather than landfilling it a significant and worthwhile contribution could be made to reducing emissions of greenhouse gases. If all UK municipal waste were incinerated rather than landfilled, the net annual reduction in emissions of greenhouse gases would be equivalent to about 12 million tonnes a year of carbon as carbon dioxide, or about 5% of the total UK emissions of greenhouse gases.

**Conclusion**

5.30   Energy recovery from waste incineration offers important advantages. It is likely that a substantial proportion of wastes will always require disposal, because recycling them is technically impossible or financially unrewarding. The coupling of energy recovery with disposal helps reduce emissions of greenhouse gases, not only in comparison to waste incineration without energy recovery but also in comparison to landfill with energy recovery (5.24–5.29). There can be a beneficial impact on the effectiveness of pollution abatement systems (5.21). Last but not least, income from the sale of electricity (and, where feasible, residual waste heat) helps close any gap between the cost of waste incineration and the cost of landfill, an aspect we discuss in chapter 9. We believe that these advantages can be obtained without breaching emission standards. For these reasons, **we recommend the government should give targets to waste disposal authorities for the recovery of energy from municipal waste.**

# CHAPTER 6

# HEALTH ISSUES

## Introduction

6.1    Chapter 4 reviewed the types and amounts of pollutants produced by incineration plants (4.12–4.18) and the techniques used to remove them from emissions (4.19–4.26). It considered the relative importance of emissions from incineration in comparison with other sources of the same pollutants (table 4.2); and highlighted the dramatic improvements in emission levels that are already being achieved in the newest plants, and will be required of all plants in future (figure 4-II). This chapter discusses the health implications of emissions from incineration. For that purpose it has been necessary to look at evidence about possible health effects which relates to plants not operating to the new HMIP standards.

6.2    The first part of the chapter looks at the possible health implications of particular classes of pollutant:

> dioxins (6.3–6.15)
>
> other organic compounds (6.16–6.17)
>
> heavy metals (6.18–6.21)
>
> acidic gases and particulates (6.22–6.23).

This is followed by a discussion of the findings from studies of older incineration plants in the UK (6.24–6.29) and cases in other countries (6.30–6.32). Finally it considers how risk analysis techniques can be used to evaluate in advance the possible health implications of a proposed new incineration plant (6.33–6.36).

## Dioxins in the environment and in food

6.3    Dioxins (see box 6A) can be detected in the environment in the UK as in other industrialised countries, with levels in urban areas four times higher than in rural areas.[151] Levels increased significantly between the late 1920s and the mid-1970s, but there is some evidence that they are now starting to fall.[152] It was estimated in 1989 that the municipal waste incinerators then operating in the UK contributed about a third of the dioxins emitted to air from combustion sources or about a fifth of total man-made releases to the environment.[153] Incinerators for chemical waste and clinical waste were estimated to contribute 0.06% and 0.4% respectively of total man-made releases to the environment.

6.4    Dioxins can reach man by inhalation or absorption through the skin. These pathways may be important where dioxins are emitted in close proximity to people, for example from vehicles or in cigarette smoke, especially where there is poor ventilation. The total quantity of dioxins in smoke from cigarettes in the UK however has been estimated as only a few grammes a year TEQ (see box 6A), less than 0.1% of total emissions.[155] Industrial plants are unlikely to produce sufficiently high concentrations of dioxins in air to make these pathways significant.

6.5    The background level of dioxins in humans is almost wholly attributable to intake from food.[156] Both volatile and particulate-bound dioxins can be deposited either on plants grazed by farm stock, from which they can enter meat or dairy products, or on fruit or vegetables for human consumption. If they are deposited on soil on the other hand, they bind tightly to soil particles and do not readily enter the food chain. Within the human body dioxins are fat-soluble and are retained for long periods, especially in the liver and fatty tissue.

6.6    The Ministry of Agriculture, Fisheries and Food (MAFF) carries out surveys of the levels of

---

**BOX 6A**                                                        **DIOXINS**

Dioxins are a group of compounds with the chemical name polychlorinated dibenzo-para-dioxins. The term is used widely, as in this report, to include polychlorinated dibenzofurans, otherwise known as furans. In total there are 210 dioxins and furans.

Dioxins have no industrial uses: they are formed as trace by-products in combustion and other high temperature processes involving chlorine and organic compounds, including waste incineration. They can be detected in emissions from motor vehicles, power stations, domestic and accidental fires, and the smelting of scrap metal. They are also formed during the manufacture of certain herbicides and wood preservatives. Dioxins are stable and appear to break down only slowly in the environment.

Dioxins differ in toxicity depending on the number of chlorine atoms in a particular compound and the positions these occupy in the molecule: 17 dioxins are considered important toxicologically. The most toxic is 2,3,7,8-TCDD.

Gathering information about exposure to dioxins is difficult because they occur as mixtures at very low concentrations. Systems have been devised to measure the overall toxicity of such mixtures. Biological and chemical data are used to generate a weighting factor which relates the toxicity of a particular dioxin to the toxicity of an identical amount of 2,3,7,8-TCDD. Multiplying the concentration of any such compound by this *toxic equivalent factor* produces a *2,3,7,8-TCDD toxic equivalent* (TEQ). The toxicity of a mixture of dioxins is expressed as the sum of the individual TEQs. All data for dioxins given in this report represent summed TEQs.[154]

---

dioxins in food.[157] The results indicate that dioxin levels in milk are higher at farms sited closer to urban and industrial areas than at farms in rural areas. A similar difference in levels of dioxins is found in other foods such as meat when samples from sources near towns are compared with farms in more rural locations. Milk is in practice bulked before retail sale, and higher concentrations of dioxins in milk from near-urban farms are reduced by dilution.

6.7    The typical dietary intake of dioxins by the UK population is estimated to be 125 pg TEQ a day for a 60 kg person. This figure is broadly comparable with other industrialised countries. It can be compared with the *tolerable daily intake* (TDI) for lifetime exposure to dioxins in food recommended by an expert group convened by the Regional Office for Europe of the World Health Organisation (WHO). The TDI is 10 pg TEQ/kg body weight a day, or, for example, 600 pg a day for a 60 kg person. From the TDI and data on milk consumption MAFF has calculated the *maximum tolerable concentration* (MTC) of dioxins in cows' milk, which is 0.7 ng/kg whole milk. The calculation was based on lifetime consumption by someone drinking an especially large quantity of milk.[158]

6.8    The level of dioxins is higher in breast milk than in cows' milk because they will have become concentrated in the mother's body fat; and it has been estimated that daily intake by a breast-fed infant is of the order of 100 pg/kg body weight. The government's medical advisory committee has endorsed WHO's view that any potential risks from exceeding the TDI for the short period involved are out-weighed by the considerable benefits of breast-feeding.[159]

6.9    Figure 6-I shows the levels of dioxins in various categories of cows' milk from the UK and the Netherlands in the period 1989–91. As levels varied widely even for a particular category, the maximum and minimum level recorded are shown in each case. For most categories of milk the maximum levels of dioxins recorded were well below the MTC. The Dutch case shown in figure 6-I involved dairy farms near a municipal waste incinerator in the Rotterdam area: dioxin levels were elevated (0.12–0.48 ng TEQ/kg, with a mean of 0.34 ng TEQ/kg compared to a national average of 0.03–0.1 ng TEQ/ kg) but did not reach the MTC.[160] A study of comparable dioxin levels in milk from the areas around two other Dutch municipal waste incinerators confirmed that they were caused by the incinerators: when these closed in 1990, the dioxin levels dropped within 6 months.[161] Levels significantly above the MTC were recorded in milk from two farms close to an industrial site in Derbyshire, and that case is described in box 6B.

**Figure 6-I**
**Dioxins in cows' milk**

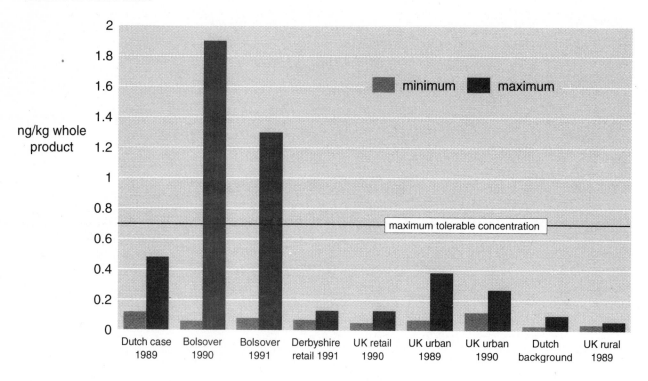

6.10   Dioxins have been found at above background levels in the soil in the vicinity of some waste incinerators, although it has not necessarily been possible to establish a direct link with emissions from the plants.[162] The new HMIP standards will produce a considerable reduction in emissions of dioxins from incinerators. If the amounts of waste incinerated remain broadly constant, emissions of dioxins from plants burning municipal waste would be reduced to not more than about 2% of the 1991 level (figure 4-II). Even if there are very substantial increases in amounts of waste incinerated, total UK emissions of dioxins would not exceed about 6% of the 1991 level (figure 4-III).

**Toxicity of dioxins**

6.11   Assessments of the toxicity of dioxins to humans are based on findings from studies of laboratory animals and records of accidental or occupational exposure: in accident situations there may have been high short-term exposures, whereas the occupational exposures studied were typically over several decades. For humans all the exposures recorded have been in contexts other than waste incineration. Interpretation of any effects observed is considerably complicated by the fact that exposure has been to mixtures containing other chemicals as well as dioxins. In animals the most widespread symptom of exposure to dioxins is weight loss, though a number of organs such as the liver, thymus, or skin are also affected. The only recognised effect in humans has been a severe skin condition, chloracne. This has also been observed in non-human primates that were experimentally exposed.

6.12   Dioxins are trace contaminants in pentachlorophenol, which forms the basis of some herbicides and wood preservatives. Studies of workers in plants manufacturing this chemical have provided

**BOX 6B** **THE BOLSOVER CASE**

In autumn 1990, as part of its general surveillance programme, MAFF collected samples of milk from farms in the Bolsover area of Derbyshire. Milk from nine farms contained concentrations of dioxins in the background range of 0.04 to 0.27 ng TEQ/kg. Milk from two farms however had dioxin levels of 1.8 to 1.9 ng TEQ/kg. This was about ten times higher than background and more than twice the maximum tolerable concentration (MTC) of 0.7 ng TEQ/kg.[163] Analyses of samples collected from these two farms in spring 1991 showed dioxin levels of 1.29 and 0.9 ng TEQ/kg, which still exceeded the MTC. Neither farm supplied milk direct to the public. In summer 1991 the Milk Marketing Board refused to accept their milk, which therefore could not be sold. The suckler herd on a third farm nearby was found to be contaminated with dioxins; sales of animals were suspended voluntarily in October 1991 and banned in March 1992. In December 1992 further analyses by MAFF showed that dioxin concentrations at all three farms had declined to levels which it regarded as acceptable. MAFF has now agreed that sales of milk and meat can be resumed.[164]

MAFF also analysed soil and herbage at the three farms. Soil samples were found to contain dioxin levels in the range 10 to 90 ng TEQ/kg, compared with the average UK background level of 6.2 ng TEQ/kg. Dioxins are quickly removed from herbage by natural processes but bind tightly to soil. The most recent analyses show that soil concentrations on the three farms have remained constant, whereas levels in herbage have declined since autumn 1991.[165]

An industrial site near the three farms contains a smokeless fuel plant and a chemical works with an in-house incinerator for chemical waste. In 1991 the maximum concentrations of dioxins inferred by HMIP from measurements of the stack gases were 1.2 ng TEQ/Nm$^3$ at the smokeless fuel plant and 18 ng TEQ/Nm$^3$ at the chemical waste incinerator.[166]

The operator shut down the chemical waste incinerator in November 1991 in order to carry out modifications.

The National Farmers' Union is seeking compensation from the operator of the chemical waste incinerator on behalf of the three farmers who were prevented from selling their milk and meat.[167]

NRA is considering legal action against the operator to recover the costs of removing river sediments in which there are high concentrations of dioxins. The sediments are downstream of the outlet for effluent from the scrubbers attached to the incinerator.[168]

Before the chemical waste incinerator can be used again it will require authorisation from HMIP. Because it will have been substantially altered its emissions will be expected to meet the new HMIP standards immediately.

suggestive evidence that exposure to dioxins is associated with the development of soft-tissue sarcomas.[169] Although such exposure may have extended back twenty years or more, it was possible to use some indirect measurements of it. The number of cases of soft-tissue sarcoma identified was small, but the fact that they were of a relatively rare type of cancer makes the finding arguably more significant. Interpretation of the results is confounded however by the likely presence in the plant of other potential carcinogens. A study which found an excess of soft-tissue sarcomas among workers exposed to herbicide sprays has attributed it to the effect of pentachlorophenol herbicides, and not specifically to those herbicides which were probably contaminated by dioxins.[170] In animals, dioxins are known carcinogens which modify cell growth and differentiation and appear to promote, rather than initiate, tumours. In summarising the evidence on dioxins the International Agency for Research on Cancer has classified the dioxin 2,3,7,8-TCDD as Group 2b (possibly carcinogenic in humans).[171]

6.13    There is evidence from experiments on laboratory animals, including primates, that dioxins can adversely affect reproduction and the immune system. Rodents receiving doses of 2,3,7,8-TCDD close to the lethal dose showed loss of fertility and deformed embryos.[172] In humans no effects on reproduction or the immune system have been clearly demonstrated, although there have been claims of such effects in people occupationally exposed.[173]

6.14   There is a wide variation between species in their susceptibility to dioxins. The dose at which 50% of laboratory animals do not survive (LD50) ranges from 1 μg/kg body weight a day for guinea pigs to 115 μg/kg body weight a day for rabbits and 5000 μg/kg body weight a day for hamsters. In the absence of reliable human epidemiological data the TDI (6.7) has been derived from the dosages at which no obvious effects are observed in the most sensitive species in terms of either the immune system or tumours.[174] A safety factor of 100 was applied to allow for interspecific variation and variation between individuals in a population (a safety factor of 1000 in the case of carcinogenesis).

6.15   The evidence from known cases of human exposure indicates that the toxicity of dioxins to humans is not as high as has sometimes been suggested. Certainly they have not been shown to be acutely or chronically toxic to humans in the concentrations likely to have been produced by emissions from incineration plants. The findings of relevant epidemiological studies are summarised below. Nevertheless the Committee on Toxicity of Chemicals in Food, Consumer Products and the Environment has recommended that appropriate measures should be taken to reduce inputs of dioxins to the environment, with the aim of reducing levels in food and in human tissues.[175] The reduction in emissions of dioxins to air from incineration plants that will come about as a result of the new HMIP standards (6.10) will make an important contribution. A major evaluation of the toxicity of dioxins is being carried out by the US EPA and the report is expected later this year. The report of a review carried out for the French Académie des Sciences is expected shortly. **We recommend that, as further evidence about the toxicity of dioxins becomes available, its implications should be kept under continuing surveillance by the Chief Medical Officers.**

## Other organic compounds

6.16   Apart from dioxins, there are no regulatory limits on emissions of individual organic compounds. Instead a limit is placed on the overall concentration of organic material in emissions, often as total organic carbon (TOC). The major component of TOC in stack gases (50–75%) is aliphatic compounds[176], which are unlikely to pose a threat to health. Concern has been expressed that several hundred aromatic compounds, which are potentially toxic, have also been identified.[177] The US EPA has approached the problem of dealing with a mixture of unknown compounds by estimating the carcinogenicity of a mixture of known compounds, including benzene and chloroform, which it considers a reasonable surrogate. Using this methodology in the risk analysis for a proposed incineration plant in the UK led to the conclusion that organic compounds other than dioxins accounted for only a very small part of the risk associated with that plant.[178] The possibility cannot be excluded that compounds more toxic than benzene could be present or that synergistic interactions might occur. At the very low concentrations of organic compounds present in the emissions from a new incineration plant however any under-estimation of this particular risk is unlikely to be large enough to alter the conclusion about the overall risk from such a plant.

6.17   Volatile organic compounds contribute to the formation of ground-level ozone (which can have health effects at high concentrations or in susceptible individuals). Incineration however is estimated to account for only a negligible proportion (less than 0.01%) of man-made UK emissions of these substances, about a tenth of the proportion contributed by landfill sites.[179]

## Heavy metals

6.18   Incineration releases metals present in the waste and (table 4.2) accounts for significant proportions of the total emissions to air of mercury (11% of UK total) and cadmium (32%). For lead other sources, such as petrol and metal smelters, are more significant. The combustion process makes some metals more biologically active. For example, it converts some cadmium to the soluble chloride and sulphate salts, and largely converts chromium to the hexavalent state, which is carcinogenic.[180] The new HMIP standards will reduce significantly the amounts of heavy metals emitted to air by incineration plants (figure 4-II), but produce a corresponding increase in the amounts present in solid residues sent to landfill, where the potential risk is the longer-term one that the metals will leach into groundwater. When possible future increases in the quantities of waste incinerated are taken into account, the estimated net reduction in emissions to air could be as small as 5% in the case of mercury and only 50% in the case of cadmium (figure 4-III).

6.19    The primary route for human exposure to heavy metals released by incineration is the food chain. Mercury is deposited on the surface of water and on soil; it bioaccumulates and fish and shellfish may be the dominant dietary sources. Emissions of cadmium to air are in particulate material: after deposition on soil it may pass into vegetables and crops.

6.20    There is a general government policy of reducing exposure to heavy metals on the ground that they interfere with human growth and metabolism. Health effects reported have occurred in situations involving either high or sustained exposure to a particular metal. The evidence that lower doses can have specific effects on health is much less clear. It proved impossible to identify any effects in the population of a Somerset village who are continuously exposed to fairly high levels of cadmium naturally present in the local soil.[181] A number of research projects have sought to test the hypothesis that children with even small increases in blood lead levels do less well in psychological tests, but the relatively small differences in test scores reported may have been confounded by social factors.[182] No effects on health have been linked to the release of heavy metals from incineration plants.

6.21    The total amounts of heavy metals released from an incineration plant (the combined total of the amounts present in emissions to air, solid residues and liquid effluents) are determined by the amounts of those metals present in the feedstock. A risk analysis at a chemical waste incinerator in the USA[183] found the risks from metals were higher than those from organic compounds. Nevertheless the overall risk was well below the EPA concern level. Despite the absence of direct evidence for health effects, the general policy of reducing exposures to heavy metals implies that further measures should be taken to reduce emissions of those metals to air and to reduce the likelihood that heavy metals remaining in solid residues from incineration will at some future date leach into groundwater. These further measures are discussed later in this report (8.21, 8.46, 8.50, 9.67–9.68).

## Acidic gases and particulates

6.22    The acidic gases that arise from the incineration of waste do not accumulate in the environment. Sulphur dioxide and nitrogen oxides persist in air and are important primarily for their contribution to acidification processes in the natural environment at some distance from the point of origin. However emissions from incineration plants are only a very small proportion of total UK emissions of these gases (table 4.2). Hydrogen chloride and hydrogen fluoride, which are more soluble and reactive, are rapidly removed from air. Particulates can have organic compounds or metals bound to them, but are also a pollutant in their own right.

6.23    In health terms the main significance of both acidic gases and particulates is that they can cause respiratory irritation, especially in susceptible groups like asthmatics. It is most unlikely that such symptoms would be induced at the concentrations emitted by an incineration plant designed and operated to present standards. To make sure that does not happen, a site-specific risk assessment, on the lines described later in this chapter, ought to be carried out before approval is given for the construction of a new incinerator. This is particularly important where other major combustion plants are already operating in the locality or where there is the possibility of an unfavourable microclimate which might tend to trap emissions and require an increase in the height of the stack.

## Epidemiological studies

6.24    Several epidemiological studies have been carried out in areas surrounding chemical waste incineration plants in the UK. They were undertaken in response to public concern that there had apparently been unusually high numbers of either cancers or birth abnormalities in the areas. The findings are of limited relevance as a basis for future policy because the plants were not required to comply with the emission standards now in force. The plants at Bonnybridge (West Lothian) and Charnock Richard (Lancashire) were closed some years ago, and the plant at Pontypool (Gwent) has had additional gas-cleaning equipment installed.

6.25    Solvent wastes were burned at the Charnock Richard plant between 1972 and 1980. Reports of a possible cluster of cases of cancer of the larynx led to a study by the Small Area Health Statistics Unit (SAHSU, see box 6C). Data from Charnock Richard were supplemented with data from

---

**BOX 6C**                                                   **SMALL AREA EPIDEMIOLOGY**

The Small Area Health Statistics Unit was set up in 1987 following a recommendation of the Black Committee, which had investigated the incidence of leukaemia near Sellafield. Its work is based on a comprehensive national database of cancer registrations and specific causes of death. Cases are located by the post code of the place where a person was living at the time of registration or death. In combination with census data this means that rates of cancer incidence or mortality in a given area can be compared with the expected rate in that area or any other area . This is the most suitable statistical approach for studying an apparent cluster of cases of a particular disease linked to a point source of pollution. In order to confirm or refute an apparent association, a systematic study must be made of whole regions without prior reference to the detailed spatial distribution of cases. Factors such as social deprivation, which has often been found to be related to disease, can confound epidemiological studies. However techniques are available for assessing, and to some extent adjusting for, the effect of socioeconomic status. Shortcomings in the data as a result of movements of population or inadequate recording are more difficult to eliminate.

---

areas surrounding nine other incinerators which burned solvent wastes: at Westbury, Wiltshire; Strood, Kent; Stafford; Ulverston, Cumbria; Newbie, Annan; Montrose, Tayside; Kirkby, Lancashire; West Bromwich; and Rye, East Sussex. The incidence of cancer of the larynx and the lung, at Charnock Richard and for all ten areas, was compared with the national incidence. The comparisons were made both with and without adjustment for the socioeconomic profile of the surrounding areas. No deviation from the expected incidence was detected and there was no decrease in incidence with increasing distance from the incinerator. The only qualification which must be attached to these findings is that solid tumours may take 20 years or more to develop, and any cancers caused by emissions from the plants may not therefore have become apparent by the time the study was carried out.[184]

6.26   The plant at Bonnybridge incinerated chemical waste (including PCBs) between 1974 and 1984, when it closed. The mortality of animals on two neighbouring farms was unusually high. There also appeared to be an unusually high incidence of twin births to both cattle and humans in the vicinity[185]; but it was not possible to tell whether this was a real effect without a further study with more systematic controls. Further attention was given to certain birth defects in cattle but no firm conclusion could be drawn from the available data; it was concluded that, if there was any effect related to the incinerator, it was small.[186] Because of the concern that existed a study was carried out into the health over a 3 year period (1980–82) of the population in a 5 km radius around the site[187]; but no significant effects could be detected, and it was suggested that the deaths of animals had been the result of poor nutrition.

6.27   The plant at Pontypool was opened in 1974 to incinerate chemical waste. Electrical components contaminated by PCBs have become an important element in the waste treated. As well as improvements to the gas-cleaning equipment, modifications have been made to prevent fugitive emissions and a new rotary kiln is being installed. The plant is situated on a valley floor near a number of other heavy and light industries, some of which have been suggested at one time or other as possible sources of PCB contamination in the area. Investigations into the health of the population in the areas around the incineration plant found that the incidence of cancer or of birth defects showed no detectable trend in an area within 5 miles of the site over a 10 year period when compared with Gwent as a whole or the rest of Wales.[188] A full investigation of the levels of PCBs and associated compounds in the area has been undertaken for the Welsh Office, and the report is expected shortly.

6.28   None of the studies described above, which involved in total 12 incineration plants, found any significant effects in the health of the population in the surrounding areas. It was not clear however that effects with long latency periods would all have become apparent by the time the studies were carried out. There are also some remaining uncertainties about the incidence of human twinning and the mortality of cattle in the Bonnybridge area. It must be emphasised however that the concentrations of pollutants in emissions from the Bonnybridge plant when it was operating were considerably higher than will be allowed in future from incineration plants.

6.29   SAHSU is at present carrying out epidemiological studies in areas surrounding existing municipal waste incineration plants. These plants have been in operation for periods broadly corresponding to the latency periods for delayed health effects and this research will enable us to benefit from any further evidence existing cases can provide. Epidemiological studies related to new incineration plants, with much lower concentrations of pollutants in their emissions, would be much less likely to reveal any health effects that have so far remained undetected.

**Studies in other countries**

6.30    A long-term retrospective study of incinerator workers has been carried out in Sweden.[189] There was evidence of an elevated level of ischaemic heart disease and a less certain link with lung cancer. Conditions in the plant, especially dust levels, were not representative of modern practice. Smoking was the most significant confounding factor although the behaviour of the subjects was reported to be representative of similar individuals in the population as a whole.

6.31    In a case in Ireland the Supreme Court decided that emissions from a poorly operated incinerator for chemical waste had probably caused the ill health suffered by a farmer and his herd of cattle.[190]

6.32    The limited amount of evidence available from other countries provides some support for the view that some poorly operated incineration plants in those countries may in the past have caused adverse health effects in workers or in people or animals living nearby. However they do not materially alter the general conclusion reached (6.28) from the studies in the UK.

**Risk-based analysis**

6.33    The potential impact of an incineration plant on health depends to some extent on site-specific factors. When a proposal for a major new plant is put forward therefore, it ought to be accompanied by a comprehensive risk assessment to demonstrate there will not be an unacceptable impact on the surrounding population. Although there is no specific regulatory requirement on applicants at present, either in the UK or the USA, to produce such an assessment, it is common practice to do so in the USA and some of the environmental statements recently produced in connection with planning applications in the UK (for example the industrial waste incinerator at Seal Sands, Billingham[191] or the sewage sludge incinerator at Knostrop, Leeds[192]) have included such an assessment.

6.34    Although the regulatory authorities have not issued formal guidance on the subject, there is a wide consensus about the broad form a risk-based health assessment should take. It has to proceed in a series of steps; and, at points where there is scientific uncertainty or lack of information, use the most cautious or worst case assumptions. The key stages are:

   i.    **estimating emissions**. Risk-based health analyses for incineration plants have normally covered only emissions to air, as these were regarded as overwhelmingly the most important route for the release of pollutants in practice. A cautious assumption is made about the mass of each pollutant likely to be emitted to air: the volume of stack gases specified in the design is multiplied by the permitted concentration of each pollutant. Parallel calculations are also made for potentially toxic substances which are not subject to a specific regulatory limit on concentrations: these may include, for example, metals such as beryllium and selenium. Risk assessments ought also to cover other pathways for pollutants, for example, the risk that heavy metals might leach from solid residues disposed of to landfill.

   ii.   **calculating exposures**. The estimated emissions of particular substances are fed into a dispersion model in order to produce estimates of their maximum ground-level concentrations. The model has to take into account the proposed height of the stack and the height by which the plume will rise above it. It also has to take into account the nature of the surrounding area, especially the slope and roughness of the ground, the probable weather conditions and any microclimates. After the areas of significant ground-level concentration have been identified, a further analysis must be carried out to characterise the population likely to be affected. For some pollutants, additional calculations will be necessary using a separate model, to estimate exposure through the food chain in the form of a maximum daily intake.

   iii.  **health impact assessment**. The final stage is to estimate the health impacts from particular pollutants, and then as far as possible sum those impacts to produce an indication of the overall impact. For non-carcinogenic effects the estimated maximum ground-level concentration (or maximum daily intake from food) may be compared with the appropriate regulatory standard (if there is one), or otherwise with the exposure generally regarded as having no effect. For carcinogenic effects, worst case assumptions are made in calculating the incremental risk of death to the individual who is subject to the greatest lifetime exposure. A cancer potency factor is applied for each compound that is calculated from toxicological data for the relevant form of exposure (for example, inhalation). The assessment of the health impact also has to take into account that different groups in the population are likely to vary in their sensitivity to a pollutant.

6.35    There is a consensus among regulatory authorities in the UK[193] and USA[194] that incremental risks of death greater than 1 in 10,000 ($10^{-4}$) are too high to be acceptable; and that a risk of 1 in 1,000,000 ($10^{-6}$) represents a reasonable upper bound beyond which measures to achieve a further reduction in the risk would not be justified in terms of the benefit gained.

6.36    The risk-based approach to health assessment is based on estimates of emissions which assume that operation is normal and complies with emission standards. However accidents and malfunctions may lead to emissions which exceed these standards. As a precaution against malfunction the plant itself ought to be subject to a risk assessment of the kind that is standard practice in the chemical industry. This assessment should be undertaken as part of the authorisation process. In some cases a special exercise may not be necessary because the plant design is familiar and a checklist or code of practice is available on the basis of analyses carried out elsewhere. Where a special exercise is needed it should start with qualitative assessments of likely hazards and move on to measure the risks involved. Several structured techniques for analysing engineering and human systems for this purpose have been developed within industry (for example HAZOP). When completed the plant risk assessment assists decisions on the introduction of safety measures. The assessment should also be made available to the public in some form: their concern is more often directed towards the perceived consequences of accidents than dangers in normal operations. Once operation of the incinerator has started the plant risk assessment should form the basis for regular reviews of the safety of the process.

**Conclusion**

6.37    The evidence is that the emissions from a well operated incineration plant complying with the new HMIP standards are most unlikely to cause any health effects (6.15, 6.16, 6.17, 6.21, 6.28, 6.32). This conclusion is taken into account in chapter 9 where we make an overall assessment of incineration as a method of waste treatment. Despite this conclusion, we believe there are some further measures which ought to be taken to reduce emissions from incineration and the risk that heavy metals from solid residues will leach into groundwater, and we discuss these in chapters 8 and 9. A site-specific risk assessment (6.33–6.36) provides a method for ensuring there will be no adverse impact in a particular case. Chapter 9 considers how assessments of this kind can be integrated with existing UK regulatory procedures.

# CHAPTER 7

# OTHER FORMS OF ENVIRONMENTAL IMPACT

## Introduction

7.1   Environmental assessment of incineration should cover all forms of environmental impact. It has been suggested to us that some issues, other than those discussed in earlier chapters, may have a significant bearing on the consideration of proposals for individual incinerators, and may thus bear on the overall acceptability of waste incineration. This chapter discusses some of these issues.

## Visual intrusion

7.2   The physical bulk of incineration plants is determined primarily by their capacity. An incinerator burning several hundred thousand tonnes of municipal waste a year, and incorporating storage areas for incoming waste and solid residues awaiting disposal, will clearly be of considerable size. Such a plant is more likely to be accepted if it is sensitively sited in an area where the landscape can accept a large new industrial building without serious damage to its existing qualities.

7.3   The visual impact of an incineration plant depends not only on its bulk but also on its design. The choice of processes; the massing of the individual elements and the extent to which they are exposed rather than hidden behind cladding; the resources devoted to landscaping including screening by earth sloping and tree planting; and the choice of surface materials and colours for buildings and structures all contribute to the overall visual impact. Aesthetic preferences vary and different people may prefer different solutions. Four recently built incineration plants are illustrated:

> the new plant for municipal waste at Stuttgart (plate I) is being constructed on a cramped site within the city alongside its predecessor, which must continue in operation until the new plant is commissioned. This location is the result of public opposition to alternative sites. Special design and construction solutions have been required to deal with a highway, a railway and a historical monument which adjoin the site, and have involved considerably increased cost

> a bold and striking approach has been adopted for a municipal waste plant within an urban area in Paris (plate II). The main parts of the plant are enclosed but the enclosing structures have been designed in a way that dramatises their technological origins and different functions

> the Cleanaway plant at Ellesmere Port (plate III), located within an extensive industrial area, shows clearly its nature as a chemical plant, as does Yorkshire Water's plant for sewage sludge from Sheffield (plate IV).

It is clearly prudent for any firm wishing to build an incineration plant to devote high priority to its architectural design, and to open discussions with the local planning authority at an early stage so that a common view can be reached on what approach to design and landscaping is likely to be acceptable.

7.4   Although incineration plants produce only a very small proportion of UK emissions of acidic gases (table 4.2), large incineration plants are required to incorporate high stacks (commonly 60–90 metres) in order to disperse gases and reduce local effects. Such stacks are bound to be visible over a wide area. The height required is determined with the aid of a mathematical model which takes into account local topography, the heights of nearby buildings and the quantity of the emissions. Local residents in Germany are said to press for very high stack heights.[195] In contrast, on at least one occasion in Britain local opinion has favoured a lower stack in order to limit visual impact, whereas the regulatory authority has pressed for a higher stack to achieve better dispersion of emissions.[196] Improved emission standards may help to resolve this tension.

**Nuisance**

*Smells*

7.5   One of the conditions for authorisation of processes under pollution control legislation is that they must not cause odours at the boundary of the site. As compounds that would cause offensive smells are destroyed in an efficient incineration plant, any risk of smells would be associated with fugitive emissions from the plant or with leaks from drums of waste awaiting incineration. In environmental assessments of proposed incineration plants the extent of the risk is assessed by applying numerical dispersion models to highly odorous compounds such as hydrogen sulphide or ethyl mercaptan.[197] Predicted concentrations can then be compared with standards such as the WHO guideline for nuisance (rather than health effects) from hydrogen sulphide.[198]

7.6   It is important that operators, particularly of plants for special waste, should take rigorous precautions, including regular inspections for leaks, to prevent the kind of incident which could produce odour problems and/or pose a health risk. They should also have the necessary procedures, equipment and materials in place to deal rapidly and effectively with any spills. **We recommend that HMIP should require the operators of incineration plants for special waste to carry out transfers of waste within buildings and that those buildings should be maintained under reduced air pressure.**

*Smuts and char*

7.7   Older plants for municipal waste have in the past drawn complaints from local residents because they released smuts and char.[199] Modern gas-cleaning equipment effectively prevents such gross emissions.

*Noise*

7.8   Incinerators, in common with all process plants using mechanical equipment, will create some noise, for example from fans in the gas cleaning and emission systems. This process noise can be reduced to unobtrusive levels by careful design and specification of equipment. Noise from vehicles manoeuvring on site can also be noticeable to people in the neighbourhood but covered reception areas, earth banks and trees can provide effective shields.

**Vehicle movements**

7.9   There will be a large number of vehicle movements at most incineration plants handling municipal waste. The impact will be felt primarily by people living in the neighbourhood of the plant, although traffic will also be generated over a wider area. Journeys to bring in raw waste will tend to be shorter and more frequent than journeys to carry the reduced volumes of solid residues for disposal to landfill. The effects of this traffic will be minimised if the plant is properly sited so that access to it is well away from residential areas, and if the fullest use is made of major roads. In some cases modifications to local roads to reduce the effects of increases in traffic will be called for. For some sites convenient water or rail access may be possible, as with the planned use of river transport to bring waste to the proposed Belvedere plant (5.10) and the rail facilities at the Seal Sands plant (3.33).

7.10   Plants for special and clinical waste are usually much smaller than municipal waste plants, and the traffic generated is correspondingly less. The trend towards regional clinical waste incinerators expected in the next few years however will involve much more extensive transport of wastes away from hospital sites. Special waste is often carried considerable distances to the limited number of suitable plants. Concern over the transport of clinical and special waste may be directed more towards the nature of the waste than the vehicle movements involved, and if public confidence is to be maintained, it is important that the relevant statutory controls applying to transportation should be strictly observed and enforced.[200] Relevant controls should apply to raw wastes of all types transported to all incinerators and to ash residues transported from them.

**Effects on wildlife**

7.11   An assessment of the risk that an incineration plant might harm wildlife or vegetation must take into account both the pollutants produced and any disturbance to habitats created by the construction of the plant. High body burdens of dioxins and heavy metals have been measured in some wildlife in other parts of the world, especially in some predators at the higher points of food chains.[201] It has been suggested that incineration of waste (which is more widely used in other countries) is partly responsible and that serious adverse effects have become apparent for predators.[202]

7.12   In the past incineration has made a significant contribution to total UK emissions of dioxins (6.3) and some heavy metals (table 4.2), and has therefore contributed to body burdens in wildlife. However emissions of these substances from UK incineration plants will be very considerably reduced in the next few years (figure 4-II); and it is recommended elsewhere in this report that measures should also now be taken to reduce emissions of cadmium and mercury still further (8.21, 8.46, 8.50). Emissions from new incineration plants are not expected to have unacceptable consequences for wildlife generally, even on very cautious assumptions about environmental pathways. The problem of environmental contamination from past releases of heavy metals and complex organic compounds from all sources will however take time to disappear.

7.13   The direct disturbance to wildlife caused by the presence of an incineration plant can be assessed only in the context of a specific site, but there is no reason why construction of an incineration plant should have more impact on wildlife than any other industrial development of a similar size and nature.

**Socioeconomic effects**

7.14   Another type of impact usually included in the environmental statements prepared in support of proposals for incineration plants is their socioeconomic effects. The argument has been put forward, particularly in regions with long-term high unemployment, that a plant will add to employment and economic activity in a particular area. The operation of a proposed plant in north-east England was described as providing employment for 60–70 people with an annual wage bill of £0.9–1.5 million and leading to other contracts worth £0.5 million a year.[203] In contrast opponents of similar proposals have argued that an incineration plant would have a blighting effect on property values and damage other local industries such as food processing; and that this harmful impact on the local economy would more than outweigh any benefits.[204]

7.15   A new incineration plant, designed and operated to the new HMIP standards and appropriately sited in an industrial area, should have little effect on the environmental quality of the locality or on property values, nor should it cause any contamination of food produced or processed in the locality. Any wider economic benefits from the construction and operation of an incineration plant are unlikely to be a material consideration in the decision whether to grant planning permission.

**Conclusion**

7.16   In this chapter a range of possible environmental impacts has been discussed. All of them should be taken into account in considering a planning application for an incineration plant, and subjected to wider scrutiny if a public inquiry is held. None of the aspects considered need give rise to unacceptable effects, provided an incineration plant is appropriately sited and carefully designed, operated and maintained.

7.17   Siting is of crucial importance. Public opposition to large incinerators will tend to be less if they are not in close proximity to residential areas or public buildings, but on sites which are appropriate in planning terms for major industrial uses. **We recommend that the siting of large incineration plants should reflect their character as major industrial enterprises, and that local planning authorities should ensure suitable areas are identified during the preparation of development plans.**

7.18   Careful attention ought to be paid to the way in which wastes will be brought to the plant. Usually this will be by road, and the adequacy of the roads affected will need to be carefully examined in the context of a particular proposal. Where there is the opportunity to use other methods of access, it should be taken. **We recommend that waste disposal facilities should wherever possible be on sites which allow wastes to be moved by rail or water transport rather than by road.**

# CHAPTER 8

# THE FUTURE OF THE TECHNOLOGY

## Introduction

8.1   This chapter assesses the prospects for improvements in technology or management which might significantly modify the impact of waste incineration plants, or alternatively remove the need for them. It reviews the present status of new technologies for waste destruction to see whether they might have the potential to supersede incineration (8.2–8.11). It considers whether techniques are available for reducing emissions from incineration plants to levels even below those set by the new HMIP standards, and whether it would be justifiable for the regulatory authorities to require the adoption of such techniques (8.12–8.26). It discusses the need for improvements in management and training (8.27–8.31) and for research and development (8.32–8.35). It then reviews the scope for modifying industrial processes and expanding recycling of household waste in order to reduce the amounts of waste requiring disposal (8.36–8.43). Finally it examines the scope for removing from waste streams those substances which are most likely to create pollution problems (8.44–8.50).

## New technologies for waste destruction

8.2   A number of alternative technologies for waste destruction have been suggested or researched. They can be divided into:

**other high-temperature methods:** plasma arc, high-temperature liquids (salt, glass, steel), pyrolysis, gasification, cement kilns

**other physical methods:** supercritical water, microwaves

**low-temperature chemical methods**

**biological methods**.

8.3   The **plasma arc torch** is already coming into use in North America and continental Europe for disposing of toxic and clinical wastes and treating contaminated soil.[205] This is an electrical device which uses the resistance of an ionised gas to convert electrical energy to heat and produce a very hot plume (see figure 8-I). A wide variety of gases can be used (including air), and the nature of the chemical reaction depends on whether the gas selected has an oxidising or a reducing effect. Waste can be heated to a temperature in the region of 2000°C although some versions of the process use lower temperatures than this in order to achieve a higher throughput.

8.4   The plasma arc appears to have definite environmental advantages. The use of very high temperatures not only ensures that all organic materials present in the waste are broken down into a mixture of hydrogen and carbon monoxide but also prevents subsequent formation of complex organic substances. The solid residues form a glass with low leachability. Energy can be recovered, and if necessary a simple scrubbing system can be used for gas cleaning.

8.5   The plasma arc process can accept liquid or solid wastes, including unshredded metal containers. Like many of the new technologies, it also has the advantage that it can be operated in batch mode.

8.6   The disadvantage is the high energy consumption of the plasma arc (1 MWe for 1 tonne an hour of clinical waste), although about 40% of that can be recovered, and a plant can be run in batch mode on cheap rate electricity. The problem of providing an adequate power supply is likely to place limits on the maximum size of plant: the largest size at present in use has a primary chamber 2.5m in diameter and uses 1 MWe.[206]

8.7   Cement kilns have been widely used in France as a high temperature method for destroying chemical wastes.[207] Such kilns work at flame temperatures of about 2000°C; have long retention times for both solids and gases, with a chemical environment which neutralises acidic gases; and accept a variety of by-products for recycling as fuel. In the UK, Blue Circle for some years operated a commercial

**Figure 8-I**
**A plasma arc furnace**

*Chapter 8*

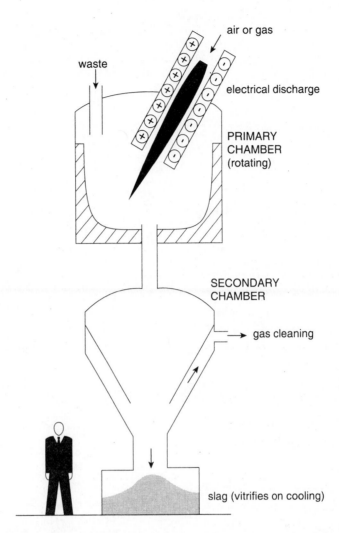

scheme at their Westbury (Wiltshire) works, adding municipal solid waste to the coal fuel. Blue Circle are not using the technique at present: the resources needed for the preparation of the feedstock are considerable, and municipal solid waste's adverse effect on kiln throughput is commercially disadvantageous when demand is high.[208] We have not looked in detail at the environmental implications of these methods.

8.8　　There are some organic wastes for which specific **chemical** methods of destruction are suitable. There are often limitations on the range of concentrations that can be handled and the process may be inhibited by the presence of particular substances. AEA Technology has patented an electrochemical process which is said to be capable of handling a wide range of chemical wastes, but a commercial-scale plant is several years away.[209] The pollution aspects of chemical methods will need evaluation case-by-case, the main issues being volatilisation, the extent to which trace amounts of hazardous substances may remain after treatment, and the final disposal of the sludges or residues.

8.9　　**Biological methods** have been quite widely used on sewage sludge and on the vegetable and putrescible matter in municipal waste. The simplest process is outdoor composting in windrows, although this causes smell problems. Wessex Water has opened a composting plant for sewage sludge at Avonmouth incorporating the Swiss Combi process which is already widely used in parts of continental Europe.[210] Anaerobic decomposition occurs when unsorted municipal waste is landfilled and can also be carried out as a chemical engineering process under controlled conditions. It produces methane from which energy can be recovered although, even on the favourable assumption that all the methane is used for this purpose, the overall outcome in energy terms for vegetable and putrescible matter separated from municipal waste is much the same as if energy was recovered from incineration of the original waste

(5.8 and box 5A). There is no technical reason why biological processes should not be used on a wider scale. However use of composting may be constrained by the limitations of the market for the product or the presence of contaminants (8.47). Composting can also be carried out by individual householders, using either traditional methods or digestion by worms.[211]

8.10   None of the alternative technologies so far identified seems to be suitable for the destruction of the large volumes of heterogeneous materials which make up municipal waste. However some of them can be expected to find specialised markets in the UK. Plasma arc may find an early commercial application by merchant operators handling clinical and/or special waste. An independent panel appointed to advise the Australian government about hazardous wastes has recently recommended disposal using mobile plasma arcs, in conjunction with cement kilns, molten salt and other technologies.[212]

8.11   **We recommend that the government should encourage research into alternative strategies for waste destruction and demonstrations of alternative methods.** We do not believe however that any method other than conventional incineration or landfill will be commercially available in the foreseeable future for unsorted municipal waste.

## Improvements at incineration plants

### *Further reductions in emissions*

8.12   Chapter 4 described the substantial reductions in emissions from incineration plants which will result from the new HMIP standards based on the BATNEEC concept (box 2A). The draft Directive on Incineration of Hazardous Waste[213] proposes even more stringent limits on emissions (2.33 and table 2.3); and the European Commission has explained that its aim is that hazardous waste incinerators should be "operated in such a way as to ensure as complete an incineration as possible to destroy organic, and in particular organohalogenated compounds". The draft Directive "is based on progressive Best Available Technology (BAT) only. Only in that way, we consider, can the environment be protected against pollution resulting from the incineration of hazardous waste." The European Commission claims that the proposed limits on emissions "are technically feasible".[214] The definition of hazardous waste for this purpose (see glossary) may be sufficiently wide to bring the incineration of sewage sludge and clinical waste, as well as special waste, within the scope of the Directive. It is also possible that the European Commission may take account of the provisions of this draft in its review of the existing Directives on incineration of municipal waste (2.32).

8.13   Techniques appear to be available (4.36) to meet the new HMIP standards. Proven techniques are also available to meet some of the standards proposed by the European Commission considered in isolation (4.40). Meeting all of the standards proposed in the draft Directive however could be expensive and problematic in other respects (4.41, 4.43). In the light of that, we have considered whether these even more stringent standards can be regarded as justified on environmental grounds.

8.14   Assessing the case for the proposed standards includes taking into account the additional energy and/or materials which would have to be used in gas-cleaning systems in order to achieve them. It also means considering their opportunity costs in more general terms: in other words, whether they would lead to investment in additional equipment for incineration plants which could have been better devoted to achieving another environmental purpose. The new HMIP standards for emissions to air from incineration plants are already more stringent, in some cases considerably so, than the standards applied to what are classified by HMIP as combustion processes (table 8.1). This suggests there is the danger of a misallocation of resources, which would be accentuated if the standards for incineration plants were tightened still further. As a higher priority than improving on HMIP's new standards for incineration plants, **we recommend that HMIP's standards for emissions to air from combustion processes, particularly those utilising wastes as fuel, should be re-examined to see whether they ought to be brought more closely into line with the new HMIP standards for incineration processes.**

8.15   A case has not been made for the ban on **liquid discharges** to the aquatic environment from new incineration plants which the European Commission has proposed. It might have the effect of ruling out the use of wet scrubbing, with consequences for the achievement of other standards in the draft Directive (4.43). Some pollutants no longer discharged in liquid effluents would appear instead in solid residues, which have to be landfilled. A ban of this kind would conflict with the aim of integrated

# Table 8.1
**UK standards for emissions to air: new HMIP standards for waste incineration compared with new HMIP standards for combustion processes**

Pollutant concentration (mg/Nm³)

| | Waste Incineration | Combustion processes | | | | |
|---|---|---|---|---|---|---|
| | Municipal waste (IPR 5/3) | Large boilers (IPR 1/1) 500MWth or more | Large boilers (IPR 1/1) 50MWth or more | Waste oil and recovered oil (IPR 1/4) | Waste derived fuel (IPR 1/5) or tyres (IPR 1/6)[e] | Wood waste, straw (IPR 1/8) or poultry litter (IPR 1/7) |
| Total particulate matter | 30 | 50[a] | 100[a] | 50/100[d] | 30 | 100 |
| Carbon monoxide[b] | 100 | - | - | - | 100 | 500 |
| Volatile organic compounds (excluding particulates; expressed as total carbon) | 20 | - | - | - | 20 | 20 |
| **Acidic gases:** | | | | | | |
| Sulphur dioxide | 300 | 400[af] | 2,000[af] | 2,250[a] | 300 | 300[g] |
| Hydrogen chloride | 30 | - | - | 100 | 50 | 100[h] |
| Hydrogen fluoride | 2 | - | - | 5 | 2[i] | - |
| Nitrogen oxides (as NO$_2$) | 350 | 650[a] | 650[a] | 650 | - | 600[g] |
| **Heavy metals:** | | | | | | |
| Cadmium | 0.1 | - | - | 0.5 | 0.2[j] | - |
| Mercury | 0.1 | - | - | - | 0.2[j] | - |
| Others[c] | 1 | - | - | 7.5[k] | 6[k] | - |
| | | | | | | (ngTEQ/Nm³) |
| Dioxins | 1[m] | - | - | - | 1[n] | - |

a  calendar month average
b  one hour average
c  arsenic, chromium, copper, lead, manganese, nickel and tin
d  for plant of 50 MWth or more, emissions should not exceed 50mg/Nm³ as a calender month average; for plant of up to 50 MWth emissions should not exceed 100 mg/Nm³
e  subject to an EC derogation for waste-derived fuel plants which expires on 1December 1994
f  standard for plants with capacity of 100-500 MWth is 2000 - 4x(MWth-100) mg/Nm³; less stringent standards may apply to plants of all sizes when indigenous solid fuel is burnt
g  no standard set for plants burning wood waste or straw
h  250 mg/Nm³ standard applies to plants burning wood waste or straw
i  no standard set for plants burning tyres

j  for waste-derived fuel plants 0.2 mg/Nm³ standard applies to the combined weight of mercury and cadmium
k  these figures represent the sum of separate limits for particular metals or groups of metals
m  HMIP's guidance note says that the emission of dioxins should be reduced as far as possible by progressive techniques with the aim of achieving a guide value of 0.1 ng/Nm³
n  this limit applies only to plants burning waste-derived fuel; there is in addition a guide value of 0.1ng/Nm³

Note: Limits are set additionally for:
formaldehyde and hydrogen cyanide in emissions from plants burning wood waste or straw
PCBs in waste/recovered oils.
For some pollutants less stringent standards apply to plants burning tyres and having a capacity of less than 3 tonnes/hour.

pollution control by pre-empting the choice of the best practicable environmental option for disposal of a given pollutant.

8.16    **Acidic gases** are produced by all large-scale combustion plants. Emissions of such gases from incineration plants are very small proportions of the UK totals (table 4.2), and would remain so even if incineration became the predominant disposal method for municipal waste. Moreover the decisions taken by HMIP inspectors on authorisations are plant-specific; and we recommend later (9.78) that a site-specific risk assessment should be carried out before approval is given for any new incineration plant. The HMIP standards for hydrogen chloride (10 mg/Nm$^3$ at chemical waste plants and 30 mg/Nm$^3$ at other incineration plants) are already stricter than the standards applied to the types of combustion plant at which any standard is set for this substance. There is not therefore a strong case for reducing them to the figure of 5mg/Nm$^3$ in the draft Directive. The new HMIP standards will reduce emissions from incineration plants to less than 10% of 1991 levels even if there is a large increase in the amount of wastes incinerated (figures 4-II and 4-III).

8.17    For hydrogen fluoride and sulphur dioxide there is a different position. The new HMIP standards (2 mg/Nm$^3$ for hydrogen fluoride, 50 mg/Nm$^3$ for sulphur dioxide at chemical waste plants, 300 mg/Nm$^3$ for sulphur dioxide at other incineration plants) would leave scope for large increases in the pollution load if there is a large increase in the amount of waste incinerated (figure 4-III); for hydrogen fluoride there would be scope for a large increase in emissions from plants for municipal waste even if the amount of waste incinerated remains at the 1991 level. There is therefore an argument based on the precautionary principle for the lower figure of 1 mg/Nm$^3$ for hydrogen fluoride which appears in the draft Directive if concentrations as low as that can be achieved without excessive cost; and for adopting a lower figure than 300 mg/Nm$^3$ for sulphur dioxide at plants incinerating municipal or clinical waste or sewage sludge.

8.18    The HMIP standards also cover nitrogen oxides, for which no limit is proposed in the draft Directive. The HMIP standard of 650 mg/Nm$^3$ at sewage sludge plants leaves scope for large increases in the present pollution load, even with no increase in the amount of sludge incinerated; and there is therefore an argument for bringing this standard into line with the HMIP standard of 350 mg/Nm$^3$ for other types of incineration plant, which can be met easily by newer sewage sludge plants (table 4.1). In fact at some new plants for sewage sludge it is planned to achieve the limit of 200 mg/Nm$^3$ in the latest German legislation (4.42). We emphasise however that emissions of all these acidic gases from incineration plants will continue to represent very small proportions of UK totals.

8.19    The draft Directive's figure of 0.1 ng/Nm$^3$ for **dioxins** is a guide value, and could therefore be regarded as consistent with the provision in the new HMIP standards that a concentration of 0.1 ngTEQ/Nm$^3$ should be achieved where possible. Germany, the Netherlands and Japan have adopted 0.1 ngTEQ/Nm$^3$ as a mandatory limit. It would be undesirable to reduce the limit from 1 ngTEQ/Nm$^3$ however because the technical difficulties of monitoring for dioxins at such low concentrations would make it difficult to confirm compliance. These difficulties arise not only at the stage of chemical analysis but even more over obtaining a representative sample of stack gases (as illustrated in plate VIII) and quantitatively extracting and concentrating the dioxins in a sample in preparation for analysis.

8.20    There has been general recognition of the importance of designing combustion and pollution control systems in such a way as to minimise at source the levels of dioxins and other products of incomplete combustion (4.3, 4.13, 5.22). Regulatory authorities have sometimes prescribed operating conditions (for example, retention time of not less than 2 seconds and temperature of not less than 850°C in the EC Directives on municipal waste incinerators[215]), but it is questionable whether there is sufficient technical knowledge at present to prescribe numbers which will be valid for all incinerators. The time and temperature needed will be affected by the amount of turbulence within the combustion chamber of a particular incinerator, which depends on its design. Moreover, if there are cool spots or eddy zones, it may be difficult to obtain measurements of temperature which are representative of the overall conditions (4.29). This approach to the control of dioxin emissions is sound in principle therefore, but further work is needed to ensure its satisfactory application in practice.

8.21    There is a stronger case for seeking further reductions in emissions of **cadmium** and **mercury** (6.21). Emissions from existing UK incineration plants represent a substantial proportion of man-made

UK emissions of these two metals to air (table 4.2). The new HMIP standards are 0.1 mg/Nm³ each for cadmium and mercury and 1mg/Nm³ for other metals; the draft Directive proposes 0.05 mg/Nm³ for mercury, 0.05 mg/Nm³ for cadmium and thallium combined, and 0.5 mg/Nm³ for other metals. Existing plants also release a large amount of lead into the air (table 4.2). **We recommend that, rather than continuing to include it with other metals, HMIP should set a separate standard for emissions of lead to air from incineration plants.**

8.22    Some processes which might have to be used to achieve large reductions in emissions of mercury, cadmium and dioxins, over and above those required by the new HMIP standards, would entail the use of considerable quantities of activated carbon in filters or beds. We question whether that could be regarded as representing the best practicable environmental option. The production of activated carbon requires significant amounts of energy. Regeneration of spent carbon is carried out by heating, which is likely to remobilise the original pollutants and thus replicate the original problems of controlling emissions. Indeed, in one proposed process most of the spent carbon is burned on the incineration plant's own grate.[216]

8.23    We are also concerned that, if all the standards in the draft Directive were to be applied to plants for sewage sludge and municipal waste (8.12), this could have an adverse environmental effect by significantly increasing the cost of incineration (which we discuss in chapter 9) and thereby increasing the financial incentive to use what we regard as less environmentally satisfactory methods of disposal.

8.24    The benefits of seeking further reductions in emissions must be weighed carefully against the likely disbenefits. We believe the emphasis for the future ought to be, not on further reductions in emissions achieved by installing additional and excessively costly equipment at the gas-cleaning stage, but on eliminating pollutants at an earlier stage, either through tighter control of the feedstock (in the case of cadmium, lead and mercury) or through improvements in the design and operation of combustion systems (in the case of dioxins). We develop these points below.

8.25    To summarise our views as they relate to the draft EC Directive on Incineration of Hazardous Waste[217]:

    i.    a scientific justification has not been provided for the proposed ban on liquid discharges (8.15)

    ii.   there is not a strong case for further tightening of the HMIP standards for hydrogen chloride (8.16)

    iii.  there is an argument based on the precautionary principle for a further tightening of the HMIP standards for hydrogen fluoride and sulphur dioxide, though not necessarily to the figure of 25 mg/Nm³ for sulphur dioxide which appears in the draft Directive (8.17)

    iv.  similarly there is a case for at least bringing the HMIP standard for nitrogen oxides at plants incinerating sewage sludge into line with the present standard for other types of incineration plant, and possibly for a more stringent standard for this pollutant at all types of incineration plant (8.18)

    v.   a guide value of 0.1 ngTEQ/Nm³ for dioxins is acceptable, and it would not be appropriate in the present state of technology to convert it into a mandatory limit (8.19)

    vi.  standards ought to be tightened further for emissions of heavy metals (8.21–8.24).

8.26    We emphasise the general desirability of basing proposals for EC environmental legislation on a scientific justification, which should be published at the same time as the proposed legislation. Adequate enforcement of any standards depends on proper monitoring, which in turn depends on the availability of validated techniques for sampling and analysis, implemented in a strictly controlled way (4.34). In the context of EC negotiations, **we recommend that the UK government should continue to place importance on ensuring that all EC legislation is drafted in such a way as to be enforceable; and includes provisions about monitoring, sampling and analysis which will enable satisfactory enforcement to take place on a comparable basis in all member states.**

*Management and training*

8.27  Effective pollution control also depends crucially on how well an incineration plant is managed. Even the best technology may perform badly if the staff operating it are not sufficiently skilled or management is poor. Our investigation has shown that standards of operation and management appear to vary widely. HMIP does not provide specific guidance at present about plant operation, and we believe it should do so in future. **We recommend that it should be one of the aims of the regulatory authorities to stimulate improvements in the overall management of incineration plants, and inspectors should seek to raise the standards of operation to match the best practice in the chemical industry.**

8.28  We also believe that quality management systems ought to be established at individual sites and action ought to be taken at national level to improve training. Quality management systems at incineration sites can best be achieved through the site operator seeking certification under the British Standard for quality management in industry generally (BS5750[218], which is equivalent to International Standard 9000). In order to achieve certification, an organisation has to define its management structure; allocate staff responsibilities for quality management; and demonstrate satisfactory organisation of processing, monitoring, training and safety. **We recommend that all firms operating incinerators should install systems of quality management which are approved under BS5750 (or any future development of that standard), and that the regulatory authorities should give them appropriate encouragement to do so.**

8.29  At large plants where there has been considerable capital investment, there is a strong incentive for the operator to give proper priority to training because of the damage that could be caused by unskilled staff. Smaller plants, especially those incinerating clinical waste, require comparable skills: plate VII shows the control room of a medium-size clinical waste plant. In the case of plants incinerating chemical wastes, a significant amount of technical knowledge is also required by ancillary workers such as drivers and those who receive, assess, store and retrieve the wastes. We have found there is systematic provision for workforce training in the USA, where commercial firms train operating staff to achieve qualifications awarded by the American Society of Mechanical Engineers under the supervision of the EPA.[219] A higher level of qualification is provided for supervisors, whose responsibilities include authorisation of repairs and emergency shutdowns. There is no corresponding provision in the UK at present. Although HMIP recognises the importance of the training and supervision of properly qualified staff, it is in effect left to the operators of incinerators to take their own decisions about what training is required and make arrangements for it, although in the case of new plant considerable assistance may be provided by the manufacturers. **We recommend that:**

i. **a recognised formal qualification should be developed without delay for staff operating incinerators**

ii. **it should be made a legal requirement, by not later than 31 December 1996, that all key workers must be so qualified**

iii. **there should also be appropriate qualifications for all workers involved in the collection, assessment and storage of chemical waste.**

8.30  The Commission recommended in its Eleventh Report that national standards for competence and qualifications should be established for all those involved in the management of waste.[220] Considerable progress has been made since then, but with the emphasis so far on landfill. The work of the Waste Management Industry Training and Advisory Board on developing standards of qualification[221] needs to be extended to cover incineration. The courses on waste management provided by the National Association of Waste Disposal Contractors (NAWDC)[222] and the Institute of Wastes Management[223] also provide a suitable vehicle for specific training about incineration.

8.31  The efficient recovery of energy in order to fulfil contracts for the sale of electricity or heat requires careful control of the combustion process. Such contracts therefore highlight the need for better training and management.

*Research and development*

8.32   Research and development should continue on new methods of pollution control. There have been encouraging results from at least pilot-scale trials of the following processes[224]:

    i.   inhibiting the catalytic formation of dioxins by injecting either triethanolamine and tri-ethylamine or ammonia into the exhaust gases

    ii.  decomposing dioxins by using a two-stage catalyst of mixed metal oxides

    iii. decomposing dioxins and reducing nitrogen oxides by injecting zeolites

    iv. heating solid residues in a nitrogen atmosphere for several hours to destroy dioxins.

The costs, effectiveness and possible side-effects of these processes would need thorough assessment before they could be regarded as available for general introduction.

8.33   The real need is to discover how to create the most effective total system for waste incineration, rather than devising more ingenious techniques for individual stages. We drew attention above to the limitations of present knowledge and understanding about conditions in the combustion chamber (8.20). We have been surprised there is so little research and development in the UK at present, not only on new waste destruction techniques but also on the scientific basis for waste incineration; and that research and development programmes seem to be poorly co-ordinated. **We recommend that DOE should review the present research programmes and determine priorities for future work. As well as work to facilitate the preparation of monitoring protocols (4.34), the priorities should include the development of optimisation techniques for the total waste incineration system.**

8.34   The only pilot-scale incinerator available for research which we have located in Europe is the TAMARA facility at Karlsruhe, which we visited (plate IX). It has the limitation of representing only one of the possible combustion systems. Because work at pilot scale is expensive, and the firms in the industry are of only moderate size, progress in research and development is likely to be much more rapid if there is international collaboration. **We recommend that research and development on incineration processes should be included in EC research programmes.**

8.35   Alongside formal research and development programmes, there is substantial scope for site operators to make incremental improvements in the existing techniques in the light of experience. **We recommend that industry and professional associations should collaborate with their counterparts in other member states of the EC so that knowledge and experience of efficient incinerator operation can be pooled to mutual benefit.**

**The scope for waste minimisation or recycling**

8.36   In terms of the four-stage decision procedure described at the beginning of this report (1.1), the first priority in waste management must always be to avoid creating wastes wherever possible. The view was expressed to us that waste minimisation, if pursued with sufficient determination, might remove the necessity for incinerating any wastes, other than the most intractable clinical wastes.[225] The reduction of waste arisings was discussed by the Commission in its Eleventh Report[226], which noted that "Avoiding waste can bring increased commercial benefit by altering a process, by changing from one process to another which might cost less in itself, or by decreasing disposal costs by generating less waste." We have tried to assess, within the limits of the information available to us, the progress made since 1985 in the development of low waste or clean technology; whether it has been on so large a scale as significantly to affect the quantities of waste requiring disposal; and what the future trend might be.

8.37   There have been some encouraging accounts of what has been achieved. The amount of chemical waste produced by Austrian industry is said to have halved between 1986 and 1991; in the USA there has been a reduction of almost one-third since 1987 in releases of substances recorded in the Toxic Release Inventory and in transfers of toxic substances.[227] ICI reduced its tonnage of hazardous waste by almost 50% between 1990 and 1992, and its tonnage of other waste by almost 10%.[228] In all these cases however there are still very large quantities of waste requiring disposal.

8.38    Various studies have examined the potential for waste minimisation in industrial production in a more detailed way. Some of them have emphasised that environmental benefits from cleaner technology are likely to be accompanied by reductions in cost.[229] However there is a disappointing lack of hard evidence that the environmental potential of waste minimisation has so far been realised in practice, still less that the claimed cost reductions have been achieved.

8.39    The second priority in terms of the four-stage decision procedure is the recycling of materials. In 1991 the Advisory Committee on Business and the Environment recommended various measures to encourage the spread of recycling, and these are being pursued.[230] Even if these initiatives meet with success however, there are insufficient grounds as yet for the waste disposal industry to expect process waste as a whole to decrease substantially in volume or change markedly in content, bearing in mind the long lead-times for the redesign and modification of industrial processes.

8.40    The Commission's Eleventh Report also advocated measures to promote recycling of household wastes. In 1985 a number of local authorities were already providing separate containers for recyclable wastes at their civic amenity sites; by 1992 the number of recycling collection points had grown considerably, to over 7500 for glass and over 3700 for paper.[231] The government has undertaken to secure the recycling of 50% of recyclable household waste by 2000.[232] Achievement of this target would reduce household waste by at least 12.5% as at least 25% of household waste is estimated to be recyclable. But such a reduction could be balanced by increases in the total of household waste from other causes (3.5).

8.41    Energetic and enthusiastic local authorities such as Adur (West Sussex) and Richmond-upon-Thames, in conjunction with the private sector, have been able to achieve high rates of recycling for various types of household waste. In the USA the city of Seattle is reported to have recycled 40% of its waste in 1991 (45% in the residential sector).[233]

8.42    There are limits however to what can be achieved. Separate collections of a number of waste streams can be costly in financial and energy terms; and the sorting of wastes by households will always be imperfect. Sorting of large quantities of waste at a central point will require a certain amount of capital investment, as well as possibly the redesign of the entire system operated by the waste collection authority and the waste disposal authority. The most important factor however is likely to be the limitations of the markets for recycled materials. It was suggested above that success in achieving the government's recycling target for 2000 would reduce household waste by about 12.5%. Even if it proves possible in the longer term to achieve twice that target rate of recycling as a national average, some 75% of municipal waste will still require disposal.

8.43    We believe it is sensible to plan future waste management on that basis. We also believe that the municipal waste still requiring disposal will not be so different in composition to present municipal waste as to prevent successful use of incineration or create a requirement to use auxiliary fuel. Other European countries and the USA are combining a strong emphasis on recycling of materials with a strong emphasis on energy recovery from incineration (3.37, 3.40, 3.43–4, 3.50, appendix C). Contractual security of supply will however be needed, because the unexpected loss of a high calorific value fraction could severely affect the profitability of an incineration plant for municipal waste.

**Segregation of waste streams**

8.44    Quite apart from the general arguments for waste minimisation and recycling, the previous sections of this chapter have demonstrated that there is a strong case for minimising the amounts of heavy metals in waste streams (8.21). For waste that is incinerated, removal of heavy metals from the feedstock will make an important contribution to reducing emissions of such metals from incineration plants (8.22, 8.24). It will also reduce levels of heavy metals in the solid residues left after incineration, and thus the extent of the precautions needed to ensure that such metals do not leach into groundwater after the residues have been disposed of to landfill (4.24–4.25). Equally, reducing levels of heavy metal contamination in sewage sludge will remove some of the obstacles to the alternative disposal methods of spreading on land and composting (8.9).

8.45    Almost half the sewage sludge in the UK is already spread on farmland (table 3.7). Due to the present heavy metals content, this practice is not necessarily a sustainable one in the sense that such land can continue to be used in the long term for food production. Limiting the heavy metal content of sewage sludge will be crucial to maintaining even the present level of disposal to farmland[234], let alone to possibly increasing that level to accommodate the increased quantities of sludge requiring disposal and compensate for the ban on disposal at sea after 1998. The heavy metals content of sludge was one of the key arguments advanced in favour of that ban.

8.46    Analyses of sludge disposed of at sea show there has been a decline in the heavy metals content (table 8.2). However there is still a considerable way to go before typical sewage sludges will be acceptable for general use as manure. The reductions in heavy metal content between 1985 and 1990, which continue a downward trend already apparent in 1985, may largely reflect the cessation or improvement of unsatisfactory trade effluent discharges to sewers and the effect on surface water runoff from increased use of unleaded petrol. DOE and the water industry are conducting a joint research project to discover where the remaining significant inputs of heavy metals to the sewerage system arise. **We recommend that substantial further reductions should be sought through a policy of controlling trade effluent discharges to sewers more stringently and modifying the associated charging system in such a way as to give industrial dischargers more incentive to undertake pretreatment of their effluents.**

8.47    Problems also arise over the heavy metals content if sewage sludge is made into compost. Compost made from municipal waste also tends to contain a certain amount of broken glass and other contaminants. Buyers are unlikely to accept such a product unless they can be offered a precise specification of acceptable quality and assurance about an effective system of quality control. For the moment the markets appear to be limited. The compost Wessex Water is producing from sewage sludge (8.9) is being used in landscaping or land reclamation, rather than for agriculture or horticulture.[235] There is also some scope for using unprocessed sewage sludge in situations of that kind where the heavy metals content is less critical, including forestry schemes.

8.48    Even if the problem of heavy metals content is overcome, there will be a number of other factors limiting the scope for spreading sewage sludge on land. There is a risk that harmful organisms in the sludge may infect grazing animals, or enter drinking water supplies or streams and rivers. While the disinfection methods used for public water supplies render most harmful organisms ineffective, viruses and parasites may survive. Satisfactory methods have not yet been developed to eliminate these risks, or to sterilise sewage sludges at economic cost. There can also be serious logistic problems in transferring sludge to farmland, especially from large cities. We are confident therefore that, in view of the international ban on disposal at sea, incineration will play a more important role in the disposal of sewage sludge in future.

8.49    It would also be desirable to eliminate heavy metals from clinical waste sent for incineration. The case for seeking a more general segregation of clinical waste streams is less clear-cut. Limiting the volumes of clinical waste sent to specialist incineration plants, and the volumes of residues subsequently

**Table 8.2**
**Heavy metal concentrations in sewage sludge disposed of at sea**[236]

| Heavy metal concentration (g/tonne dry solids) | 1985 | 1990 |
|---|---|---|
| Zinc | 1,380 | 1,050 |
| Lead | 710 | 470 |
| Copper | 630 | 535 |
| Chromium | 405 | 380 |
| Nickel | 100 | 75 |
| Cadmium | 15 | 10 |
| Mercury | 5 | 5 |

sent to specialist landfill facilities, would have the advantage of keeping the costs of disposal to a level which NHS bodies can more easily absorb. On the other hand maintaining segregated waste streams may well be operationally difficult, as well as involving some additional financial costs. If more hazardous clinical waste were incorrectly sorted and ended up in the wrong stream, this would create a significant health risk. **We recommend that these issues should be investigated in the course of preparing the national waste management strategy which we advocate in the next chapter.**

8.50    The incineration of municipal waste is also at present an important source of heavy metals in emissions to air (tables 4.1 and 4.2). Reducing the amounts of these metals in municipal waste may involve changing the composition of domestic products or introducing special schemes for the recycling of products containing heavy metals. The latter approach could involve legislation requiring manufac-turers or distributors to take back such products, and possibly pay a residual value for them. Although there has been EC legislation to reduce the levels of mercury and cadmium in household batteries, they will remain the most readily identifiable sources of those metals in municipal waste.[237] **We recommend that schemes should be introduced for the recycling of batteries containing mercury or cadmium.** However batteries are not by any means the only products containing heavy metals which appear in municipal waste sent for incineration. **We recommend that studies should be carried out to identify other ways of substantially reducing, and as far as possible eliminating these metals from munic-ipal waste.** Regulations are already being prepared to restrict the supply and use of cadmium and its compounds as a pigment, stabiliser and plating agent.[238]

**Conclusion**

8.51    Even with the highest priority given to avoiding the creation of wastes wherever possible and increasing recycling of materials, there will continue to be large quantities of waste requiring disposal year by year (8.42–8.43), more particularly of municipal waste and sewage sludge. Greatly increased quantities of sewage sludge for disposal will result from tighter controls now being imposed on marine, coastal and freshwater pollution. Incineration using broadly the present technology will remain an important disposal method for the foreseeable future. The plasma arc torch is a promising new technol-ogy for the destruction of chemical and clinical wastes; but there is no alternative technology suitable for the destruction of municipal waste (8.11).

8.52    As was shown in chapter 4 , the new HMIP standards will bring about large reductions in the emissions of pollutants to air from UK incineration plants. We have examined carefully the case for a further tightening of standards, in the light of the draft EC Directive on Incineration of Hazardous Waste. Further reductions should be sought in emissions of heavy metals. This is likely to require the introduc-tion of recycling schemes for electric batteries and other measures to remove heavy metals from waste streams as far as possible (8.46–8.50). There is also a case on the basis of the precautionary principle for a further tightening of the HMIP standards for hydrogen fluoride, sulphur dioxide and nitrogen oxides, although incineration plants produce only a small proportion of UK emissions of these gases (8.17–8.18).

8.53    Important contributions to minimising environmental impact can be made if the regulatory authorities place a strong emphasis on the quality of plant operation (8.27), quality management systems are established by operators (8.28) and formal training is introduced for all key workers at incineration plants (8.29). Research and development should continue on combustion technology and pollution control techniques (8.32–8.35).

8.54    Having clarified the technological context for waste incineration in the foreseeable future, we consider in chapter 9 the place it should occupy within a national strategy for waste management.

(a)

**Plate I    Municipal waste plant at Stuttgart, Germany**

A new incinerator is under construction (a) behind the existing plant, on a site restricted by river, railway and road.

**Plate II    Municipal waste plant at St Ouen, Paris**

Ramps give access to the tipping hall. The combustion chamber, energy recovery and gas-cleaning systems are enclosed in the main building. Processing of solid residues takes place in a separate building to the right.

**Plate III   Chemical waste plant at Ellesmere Port, Cheshire**

A scrubbing tower (a) removes acidic gases and an electrostatic precipitator (b) removes particulates. Cleaned gases are released from the stack (c).

**Plate IV   Sewage sludge plant at Blackburn Meadows, Sheffield**

Energy is recovered from exhaust gases by a heat exchanger (a). An electrostatic precipitator (b) removes particulates and a scrubbing tower (c) removes acidic gases. Cleaned gases are released from the stack (d).

**Plate V   Feeding in municipal waste, St Ouen, Paris**

The crane operators select waste for transfer to the hopper shown on the TV screens. (See also Plate II).

**Plate VI   Feeding in chemical waste, Ellesmere Port, Cheshire**

Drums are selected according to the waste's calorific value and chemical composition, placed on a conveyor and transferred to a lift on the right. (See also Plate III).

**Plate VII    Control room at a clinical waste plant**

A TV shows loading and combustion of the waste to supplement instrument readings on a computer display.


**Plate VIII    Sampling stack gases for dioxins**

A probe linked to a pump is used to obtain a representative sample of gases and particulates from the stack (on the left) of a municipal waste plant. Dioxins retained in the filters and traps (on the right) are subsequently analysed.

**Plate IX    TAMARA research incinerator at Karlsruhe, Germany**

This pilot plant has a capacity of 200 kg/h of municipal waste. The effectiveness of different combustion conditions can be measured. The exhaust gases and solid residues are also used for research on pollution control systems.

# CHAPTER 9

# THE PLACE OF INCINERATION IN A WASTE MANAGEMENT STRATEGY

## A national waste management strategy

9.1   We see an increasing need for a national strategy for waste management based on the four-stage decision procedure described at the beginning of this report (1.1). Among other things, this should cover the selection of best practicable environmental option for particular waste streams and guidance in broad terms about the resulting requirements for waste treatment and disposal facilities. Underlying this strategic approach ought to be a commitment by the regulatory authorities to ensure that, where there is clearly a best practicable environmental option, it is adopted even if it is more expensive: the cost of waste disposal remains a small percentage of the cost of the product from which the waste arises. A national strategy would provide the framework within which to assess proposals for new waste disposal facilities.

9.2   The government has proposed that the present arrangements, under which waste disposal plans are drawn up by waste regulation authorities, should be replaced by a national statement of waste policies and priorities prepared by the Secretary of State with the advice of the newly created Environment Agency (2.46). This would be supplemented by regional guidance given by the Secretary of State under planning legislation (2.47). We are concerned at both the lack of information about the intended content of these documents and the timetable for their preparation. The government envisages the national statement would not be produced until a year or two after the Environment Agency takes up its functions, which means it is unlikely to be produced before 1997. The regional guidance, which will provide the basis for considering individual proposals, would not appear until some time after that. **We recommend that DOE should give high priority to completing a national strategy for waste management based on the four-stage decision procedure; and that this task should not wait until the Environment Agency is in operation.** The Environment Agency will then be free to review this strategy and provide its own advice to government at a later date. The government has recognised the need for interim arrangements at the local level until the Environment Agency is in full operation, based on the preparation of waste disposal plans by the existing waste regulation authorities (2.41), but we believe there must also be a strong lead from the national level. We have been impressed by the systematic approach which the Dutch government has adopted to waste management in its National Environmental Policy Plan and in the Ten-Year Programme on Waste Management produced by the Waste Management Council (from which we have printed an extract in appendix C). Although not all features of this approach are necessarily transferable to a UK context, it could serve as a useful model.

9.3   **We recommend that, as part of preparing the national waste management strategy, DOE should press forward with the studies already in hand to establish the best practicable environmental option for particular waste streams.** The kind of study required was outlined in the Commission's Twelfth Report.[239] DOE is already carrying out studies of individual waste streams in order to provide advice to the regulatory authorities through Waste Management Papers; and participating in European projects to consider priority waste streams. These studies will need to take into account whatever potential may exist for avoiding the creation of the relevant wastes or for recycling them.

9.4   In our view incineration will have an important place in the national waste management strategy. In this chapter we discuss what we regard as the key policy issues involved:

    i.   the overall impact of waste incineration plants (9.5–9.15)

    ii.  the costs of waste disposal (9.16–9.28)

    iii. the use of economic instruments to promote waste minimisation and encourage incineration (9.29–9.45)

iv.   the likelihood that sufficient incineration plants operating to the necessary standards will be constructed and brought into operation (9.46–9.55)

v.    the relative advantages of centralised plants and local plants (9.56–9.63)

vi.   how the present regulatory mechanisms can be rationalised and improved (9.64–9.80)

vii.  the appropriate response to public concern about waste incineration plants (9.81–9.86).

**Overall impact of waste incineration plants**

9.5   The acceptability of waste incineration has to be considered from several aspects. Some site-specific impacts would be immediately noticeable to the public, for example vehicle movements, litter, noise, or the visual intrusion of stacks and buildings. These are primarily aesthetic or amenity factors which are important in the planning authority's consideration of the application for planning permission for a new incineration plant. We have stressed the need for discussions with the local planning authority well before an application is submitted. For noise or other forms of nuisance, control could also be exercised over an existing plant under appropriate legislation.

9.6   Factors like visual intrusion (7.2–7.3) or traffic generation (7.9–7.10, 7.18) can be assessed only in the context of a specific site. We concluded in chapter 7 that other impacts such as noise (7.8) and smell (7.5–7.6) can be eliminated or reduced to an acceptable level in incineration plants of up-to-date design which are being properly operated. In some cases care will have to be taken to strike the right balance between limiting visual intrusion and using a tall stack to disperse emissions (7.4). There is no reason, however, why modern incineration plants should be regarded as environmentally unacceptable on any of the grounds mentioned above, provided they are on sites which are appropriate for industrial use on the relevant scale (7.16–7.17).

9.7   Assessing the acceptability of waste incineration in terms of pollution means considering primarily the emissions to air, although the risk of pollution from liquid effluent and the disposal of solid residues also has to be taken into account. The public relies on the regulatory authorities to prevent emissions and disposals from affecting health or causing harm to wildlife, vegetation or environmental processes. Acceptability depends on whether there are satisfactory criteria for determining upper limits for both local concentrations of a particular pollutant and the total load of that pollutant released, together with efficient techniques and procedures for ensuring that such limits are not exceeded.

9.8   We have discussed the relevant health issues in chapter 6. The new HMIP standards for emissions (2.27) implement, and in some respects go further than, the requirements of the existing EC Directives covering incineration plants for municipal waste.[240] Because they are expressed in terms of emissions rather than environmental quality, and because some limits cover more than one substance (for example, a group of heavy metals), it is impossible to relate the new HMIP standards directly to World Health Organisation guideline values for specific substances or to other accepted criteria for human exposure. The exposures likely to result from a particular plant on a particular site have to be assessed through a site-specific risk assessment (6.33–6.36).

9.9   Studies of the health of people living in the vicinity of incineration plants were analysed in chapter 6 (6.24–6.29). None of the studies found any significant effects on human health. We emphasise again that the plants studied were not operating to the new HMIP standards. Given that new plants will have much lower levels of emissions than the plants studied, it is reasonable to conclude that any impact on health of an incineration plant working to the new HMIP standards would be negligible. We nevertheless welcome SAHSU's intention to carry out further epidemiological studies related to older incinerators for municipal waste. The general safeguards for public health against unforeseen effects from any source of pollution are also relevant, including the surveillance system operated by the Royal College of General Practitioners and the role of Directors of Public Health.

9.10   In view of the considerable improvement the new HMIP standards represent on the previous situation, the aim should be to achieve their full application, to existing plants as well as to new plants, as soon as possible. **We recommend that all existing incineration plants be required to meet the new HMIP standards at the earliest opportunity, and in any event by not later than the date of 1 December 1996 given in HMIP's Guidance Notes.**

9.11    The emissions from an incineration plant may contain minute quantities of large numbers of organic substances. The approach adopted by the regulatory authorities has been to set an overall limit for volatile organic compounds and a limit for dioxins; and supplement these by requiring a specified temperature and retention time in the combustion chamber in order to minimise formation of dioxins and other products of incomplete combustion (8.20). In view of the low concentrations involved, it is a very difficult task to monitor individual organic micropollutants either in emissions (8.19) or in the environment. For dioxins the new HMIP standard of 1 ngTEQ/Nm$^3$ represents the limit of reliable detection under operational conditions using present analytical methods, and is supplemented by a guide value of 0.1 ngTEQ/Nm$^3$. We regard the approach to dioxins adopted in the new HMIP standards as an acceptable one.

9.12    In chapter 8 we noted the case for seeking further reductions in emissions of heavy metals from incineration plants (8.21), and the argument for a further tightening of standards for emissions of hydrogen fluoride, nitrogen oxides and sulphur dioxide (8.17, 8.18). Our views on these points are not based on any health effects observed in the vicinity of previous or existing incineration plants, still less on health effects expected from plants which comply with the new HMIP standards. Rather, we are applying the precautionary principle, in the light of possible large increases in the amounts of waste incinerated in the UK in future.

9.13    Although emissions to air are the main form of pollution from incineration plants, the integrated system of control operated by HMIP also covers liquid effluent and solid residues. Removing pollutants from stack gases may entail an increase in the amounts of those pollutants in liquid effluent and/or in solid residues. The objective in designing and operating pollution abatement systems must be to achieve the best overall solution in environmental terms. A scientific justification has not been provided for the complete ban on liquid discharges proposed in the draft EC Directive on Incineration of Hazardous Waste[241] (8.15). On the other hand, we recommend certain measures to reduce the risk that heavy metals might leach into groundwater after solid residues from incineration plants have been landfilled (9.67–9.68 below).

9.14    We have also considered the contribution incineration plants make to the total amounts of particular pollutants in the environment. We have indicated in chapters 6 (for dioxins), 5 (for greenhouse gases) and 4 (for other pollutants) how emissions from existing incineration plants compare with total UK emissions to air of certain substances. For heavy metals, dioxins and carbon dioxide, waste incineration makes a significant contribution to the national totals, although there are not as yet the data and scientific understanding that would be needed to construct a complete national budget for dioxins.[242] Emissions to air of a number of pollutants from incineration plants, including dioxins and to a lesser extent heavy metals, will fall substantially over the next few years, as the new HMIP standards are applied (figures 4-II and 4-III). In the case of greenhouse gases, incineration has to be assessed against the option of landfilling the same wastes: for municipal waste (the largest category) incineration makes a significantly smaller contribution to the greenhouse effect (5.26–5.29).

9.15    Our view about the impact of waste incineration in environmental and health terms can be summarised as follows. The acceptability of this method of waste management has to be assessed, not against some ideal standard of proof, but in relation to the environmental impact and longer-term uncertainties associated with alternative methods, in particular landfill. We consider the new HMIP standards provide an appropriate basis for the building and operation of new incineration plants. We also believe that those standards can be achieved by new plants: they are already at least close to being achieved at some of the newer existing plants (4.15 and table 4.1). Despite the reassuring nature of the evidence, we believe it is right to continue to maintain a cautious and questioning attitude towards the possibility of health effects from incineration plants, and to ensure that site-specific risk assessments are carried out for proposed plants. No new incineration plant should be authorised unless it can be demonstrated by this method that its design and siting are satisfactory. We discuss later in this chapter whether the present regulatory mechanisms need to be extended in that and other respects.

## Costs of waste disposal

9.16    Many existing UK incineration plants for municipal and clinical waste are likely to close, because they will be unable to meet the new HMIP standards for emissions (3.26, 3.32). It is not certain that sufficient new plants will be built to increase present incineration capacity, or even maintain it. With too few new plants there would be serious problems in achieving satisfactory disposal of clinical waste, and more municipal waste would have to be sent to landfill. We have therefore tried to assess the likelihood that the private sector will construct and operate new incineration plants for municipal waste, in addition to those for which planning permission is being sought (3.27). We then consider more briefly the provision of new plants for clinical waste (9.48–9.50) and other types of waste (9.51–9.53).

9.17    Waste disposal authorities are not required by law to accept the lowest tender for disposal, and must take into account the environmental effects of their decisions. Any additional cost would be likely to fall upon local householders and firms through higher council tax payments and waste collection charges. In practice however their choice of method for disposal is likely to depend primarily on the facilities available and the charges made by the operators of those facilities. In deciding on investment and setting charges for disposal, the operators of facilities will take into account the costs they incur on acquiring land, investing in plant, operating, interest charges on loans, and paying dividends. These private costs to operators are affected by the need to comply with regulatory requirements designed to minimise undesirable environmental effects.

9.18    The alternatives open to waste disposal authorities are landfill and incineration. We accordingly asked Aspinwall & Co to analyse the capital and operating costs of new landfill and incineration facilities capable of meeting all existing and pending regulatory requirements, and convert these into costs per tonne. They were not asked to cost the environmental disbenefits of these methods of disposal. The main analysis was based on facilities dealing with 200,000 tonnes of municipal waste a year, a capacity sufficient for a city the size of Bristol or Sheffield. As there are significant economies of scale for incineration, the costs per tonne at facilities with capacities up to 400,000 tonnes a year were also estimated. Aspinwall & Co's analysis forms appendix B to this report.

9.19    An additional objective was to assess the effects of two major factors on the overall cost of disposal. The first of these is the potential for recovering energy from the waste. For each disposal method the costs of incorporating on-site electricity generation and the revenue from the sale of the electricity were included in the calculations.

9.20    The other major factor is transport costs. Landfill and incineration require sites with different characteristics, and sites with the relevant characteristics will not usually be equidistant from the area in which the waste is collected. Estimates were therefore made of the extra cost of transporting waste to more distant sites. Landfill sites will often involve higher transport costs than incineration plants. For incineration, an estimate was also made of the extra cost of transporting the solid residues of incinerated waste to a landfill site for disposal.

9.21    The main findings are illustrated in figure 9-I, together with estimates of the unit costs at landfill sites and incineration plants with annual capacities up to 1.6 million tonnes. Commercial disposal charges for landfill and incineration facilities equidistant from the source of the waste are shown in pounds per tonne for different capacities. With both methods of disposal, unit costs decline with increasing capacity, the effect being more marked for incineration. A third curve shows a combined transport and disposal charge for a landfill site a further 25 miles away. At such a distance it becomes more cost-effective to use a transfer station near the source of the waste to compact it and transfer it to larger vehicles, rather than carry the uncompacted waste direct to the disposal site in the vehicles which collected it.

9.22    The commercial size for an incineration plant will be affected by the availability of wastes, as well as technical economies of scale. On present patterns of waste generation (3.4–3.5), an incineration plant with a capacity of 200,000 tonnes a year could take all the municipal waste from a medium-size city; and if waste had to be brought in from elsewhere to match a larger capacity, transport costs would be higher. The optimal size for a particular plant will therefore vary in practice with circumstances and opportunities.

9.23    We have tried to assess the impact on the economics of waste incineration of a substantial growth in waste minimisation and recycling. The view of the waste management industry is that the overall effect of such a trend would be to leave the average calorific value of municipal waste essentially

**Figure 9-I**
**Incineration versus landfill: unit costs, in relation to capacity and distance**

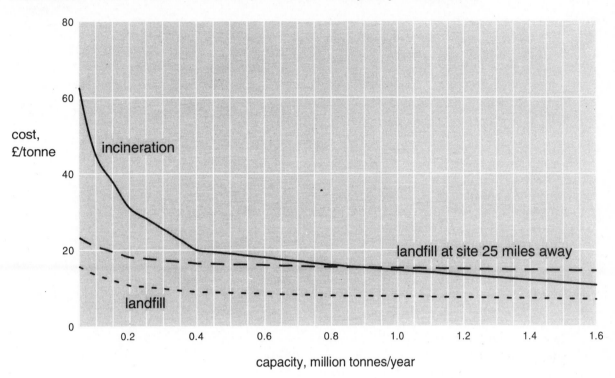

unaltered, or even perhaps increase it. Because of the reduced quantity of municipal waste available for incineration however, plants would have to gather wastes from a larger area in order to maintain throughput and fulfil contracts for energy supply, and local shortages could develop. There are also other factors which affect decisions on the sizes of incineration plants, and we discuss these at 9.56–9.63.

9.24    A recent study by Coopers & Lybrand for DOE also deals with the present and likely future costs of waste disposal.[243] They considered the overall cost of waste disposal to local authorities, including transport; and included all disposal facilities, irrespective of their ability to meet new regulatory requirements. They found that total costs at present incurred by waste disposal authorities vary substantially with method and location; landfill costs ranged from £5 to £30 per tonne including transport, and incineration costs from £15 to £30 per tonne. Landfill costs were forecast to increase between now and 2000, mainly because of tighter regulatory requirements. By then combined transport and disposal costs for landfill were expected to range from £10 to £45 per tonne at 1992 prices, while incineration costs would be £30 to £35 per tonne without the subsidy from NFFO (5.10).

9.25    While not directly comparable with the work of Aspinwall & Co, these findings are broadly consistent about relative costs. Coopers & Lybrand suggest that the cost advantage of landfill will decline over time as regulatory requirements become more stringent, and that this will increase the proportions of municipal and commercial waste incinerated. Even if that is the case, there will be a substantial variation in costs between individual incineration plants or landfill sites, particularly if transport costs are included. An overall conclusion which can be drawn from the Aspinwall report is that landfill is likely to cost substantially less than incineration at the moment in most situations, the exceptions being where wastes have to be transported some distance to landfill sites or where incineration plants have high capacity and consequently lower costs.

9.26    Some incineration plants now being constructed will benefit from the subsidy to non-conven-

**Figure 9-II**
**Incineration versus landfill: effect of electricity subsidy on unit costs**

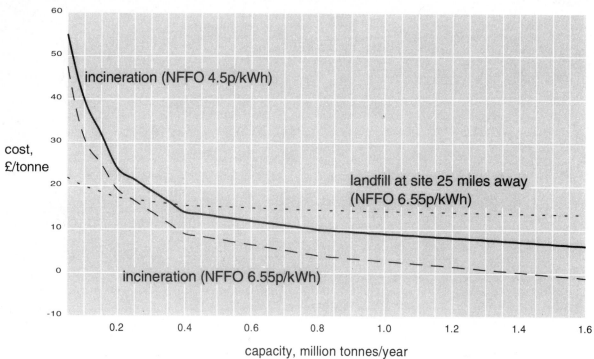

tional energy sources provided by NFFO. Aspinwall & Co considered the implications for incineration charges if such a subsidy were to continue to be available, on the assumption that it would also be available for electricity generated from the methane gas produced by landfill sites. Such a subsidy strongly favours incineration over landfill because energy recovery from incineration is much more efficient. (An increase for any other reason in the price at which the electricity could be sold would have an effect on relative costs similar to that of a subsidy.)

9.27    Figure 9-II shows the effects of an electricity subsidy in two alternative forms:

**NFFO 6.55p/kWh:** an income from electricity sales of 6.55p/kWh over the first 7 years of operation rather than the base case electricity pool price of 2.5p/kWh. (6.55p/kWh was the price guaranteed under the second tranche of NFFO in 1991)

**NFFO 4.5p/kWh:** a hypothetical scheme in which electricity could be sold for 4.5p/kWh over the first 10 years of operation.

It can be seen that a subsidy for electricity generated from waste has a considerable effect on the relative costs of incineration and landfill. With the first and higher subsidy the costs of incineration equate to the costs of using a landfill site a further 25 miles away even for an incineration plant with a capacity of 200,000 to 250,000 tonnes of municipal waste a year. With a less generous subsidy an incineration plant with a capacity of 350,000 to 400,000 tonnes a year would be needed to achieve equality in costs.

9.28    Aspinwall & Co also compared disposal costs for sewage sludge and hazardous wastes. Given the more stringent requirements that now exist for municipal waste, the additional costs of handling more difficult wastes at a landfill site would in their view be small; and transport costs and any potential for energy recovery would be relatively less important. They concluded that landfill will remain considerably cheaper than incineration for these categories of wastes. It must be emphasised however that these are wastes for which landfill may not represent the best practicable environmental option.

**Use of economic instruments**

9.29    The analysis by Aspinwall & Co specifically excluded the costs of environmental disbenefits associated with incineration or landfill. They also appear to have been excluded from Coopers & Lybrand's analysis. The disposal costs calculated by Aspinwall & Co do not therefore reflect the full economic costs to the community. Even the low levels of releases of pollutants permitted under the new HMIP standards will have some environmental impact, and the residual possibility of leaching from landfill represents a potential threat to groundwater, both locally and further afield. There are also environmental costs to the neighbouring population from the visual or other amenity impact of a disposal facility and from the disruption caused by vehicle movements.

9.30    These environmental costs do not have to be met by the operators of a waste disposal facility, and in consequence are unlikely to be taken into account in their investment and operational decisions. In other words, the private costs to the operator are not likely to reflect fully the overall cost of waste disposal to the community. If disposal charges are as a result set lower than the full economic costs of disposal (including the environmental costs), the quantities of waste sent for disposal may be larger, and the proportion recycled smaller, than would be the case if the charges reflected the full economic costs. Moreover the methods of disposal chosen may not correspond with the best practicable environmental option.

9.31    Regulatory requirements for the construction and operation of disposal facilities have an important role to play in reducing environmental costs but may not be sufficient on their own. A suitable economic instrument such as a tax or a subsidy, designed to influence commercial decisions through an impact on operators' costs and charges, may be an effective additional means of regulation. Moreover economic instruments may often be more efficient than other forms of regulation in reallocating resources. We believe that a combination of operational regulation and economic instruments is the most cost-effective means of meeting environmental objectives.

9.32    Decisions about the introduction of economic instruments should take account of the priorities expressed in the four-stage decision procedure (1.1). It is therefore important, for example, not to introduce a subsidy which would reduce the incentive to recycle materials.

9.33    The Advisory Committee on Business and the Environment (ACBE) has proposed that a landfill levy should be introduced.[244] It appears that ACBE's objective in proposing a levy was to create an additional incentive for the recycling and re-use of waste, and provide revenue to help finance the provision of infrastructure for recycling. There is already a system of recycling credits, introduced in April 1992[245]: local authorities make payments to those who collect material for recycling to reflect the money the authority has saved through not having to collect or dispose of the material as waste.

9.34    We are convinced that a levy on waste disposal is justifiable in order to reflect the cost to the community of the environmental effects of waste disposal and the benefit from the reduced use of raw materials and energy made possible by recycling. We would expect the cost of a levy to be passed on in charges to waste disposal authorities, and in turn passed on by them to households through higher council tax payments and to firms through charges for disposal of commercial waste. Both households and (more directly) firms would then have an incentive to produce less waste and recycle waste materials, so reducing levels of pollution.

9.35    A waste disposal levy should in principle apply to all forms of disposal, insofar as they give rise to environmental disbenefits. However, an economic instrument can also be used to encourage environmentally preferable methods of disposal. There are some forms of waste for which the best practicable environmental option is probably sufficiently obvious to be enforced by operational regulation. Those forms of waste for which it is clear that incineration is likely to be particularly suitable are:

  a.    industrial chemical wastes that are not suitable for recycling

  b.    clinical waste

  c.    used tyres after the scope for recycling is exhausted

  d.    animal carcasses and offal where a dangerous infection or pathogen is present or suspected.

For other forms of waste it may be appropriate to place more emphasis on the use of economic instruments to achieve the environmentally preferable result.

9.36    From an environmental point of view the pretreatment of municipal waste by incineration prior to landfill disposal is desirable, in order to reduce the long-term risks of pollution from landfill sites. Because incinerated waste in the form of slag and ash is biologically inactive by comparison with raw municipal waste, the risk of leaching can be greatly reduced. Moreover incineration reduces the volume of municipal waste by up to 90% (4.7), so significantly reducing the area of land needed for landfill. Although both incineration and landfill give rise to emissions of greenhouse gases, we have calculated that the environmental damage potential of municipal waste is substantially reduced by incineration before landfill disposal (5.24–5.29).

9.37    **We therefore recommend that a levy be applied to all waste deposited in landfill sites.** Incinerated waste sent to landfill in the form of slag and ash should be subject to the same levy as untreated waste. Because of its reduced quantity, such waste would even so attract a smaller levy payment than if it had not been incinerated first. This difference in levy payment can be regarded as reflecting the smaller overall potential for environmental damage if waste is incinerated.

9.38    The question of how to use the revenue raised by such a levy lies outside the scope of this study, but the promotion of recycling schemes would be an appropriate use, and would contribute further to reducing the volume of waste requiring disposal.

9.39    A report by Environmental Resources Ltd for DOE and DTI[246] has reviewed the scope for using economic instruments in relation to waste management and the study by Coopers & Lybrand has considered the possible form of a landfill levy.[247] Coopers & Lybrand recommended that any levy should be based on the weight of waste landfilled rather than on volume or on type and source of waste. They suggested that either (preferably) the waste regulation authorities or Customs and Excise might administer the levy. Alternative rates of levy were considered up to £20 per tonne; a levy of £10 per tonne was calculated to increase the proportion of domestic waste recycled from 2% to 3% by 2000 and the proportion incinerated from 15% to 28%. With a £20 per tonne levy, the proportion recycled was calculated to increase to 12% and the proportion incinerated to 38%. The speed of any switch to incineration would be constrained by the availability of incinerator capacity. Coopers & Lybrand estimated that a £10 per tonne levy would have increased the community charge by nearly £5 a head if it was funded wholly from local authorities' own revenues; and that this would eventually have dropped to £3 a head as local authorities switched to alternative disposal methods.

9.40    Another possible form of economic instrument which would reflect the environmental superiority of incineration over landfill is a subsidy for incineration. In Japan the central government provides a grant of 25–50% of the capital cost of incineration plant. In our view any form of subsidy, such as capital allowances, would be inherently inferior to a landfill levy, at least in the UK. To promote efficient resource allocation the full economic costs of waste disposal including environmental costs should be reflected in charges; and a subsidy for waste disposal would work against the objective of waste minimisation.

9.41    However we believe there is a strong justification for a continuing subsidy for energy recovery from waste. Recovering energy from wastes which cannot be recycled as materials contributes to sustainable resource use and achieves a net reduction in carbon dioxide emissions from power generation. These environmental benefits should be reflected in a subsidy for such energy recovery. NFFO (5.10) was introduced primarily to support the nuclear industry as an alternative power source, but has also provided a financial incentive for the exploitation of renewable sources. This has provided electricity generation from waste with the sort of subsidy we consider appropriate. Its implications were taken into account in the analysis by Aspinwall & Co described above (9.26–9.27).

9.42    The Renewable Energy Advisory Group, set up to review national strategy for renewable energy, has recommended that NFFO should be continued for renewables after 1998 under the title of the Renewable Energy Obligation; and believed that this would be accepted by the

European Commission.[248] We believe a REO which included energy from waste would be justified on environmental grounds, and we accordingly endorse the Advisory Group's views. **We recommend that a financial incentive should continue to be available for electricity generated from waste; and this incentive should be available not only in England and Wales, as is the case with the present NFFO, but throughout the UK.**

9.43   The subsidy provided by NFFO is confined to electricity generation. The energy recovered from incineration can be substantially increased by recovering low-grade waste heat for local heating, but this typically requires heavy investment in a distribution system. Aspinwall & Co excluded this element from their analysis as they considered that it would seldom be economic. However, in view of the use made of such heat in Scandinavia, **we recommend that the potential for low-grade waste heat recovery should be reviewed, including the circumstances in which it might be economic in the UK without any specific subsidy.**

9.44   To summarise, we support the use of appropriate economic instruments, alongside other forms of regulation, to reduce the environmental impact of waste disposal and encourage waste minimisation and recycling. We have recommended a levy on landfill as an incentive to recycling, and a continuing subsidy for energy recovery from waste. Both will also provide an incentive for the incineration of municipal waste.

9.45   If, as we hope, recycling is assigned greater importance in future, or if new technological developments offer new opportunities for waste disposal, we believe that further use of suitable economic instruments to regulate disposal would be appropriate, and that their introduction should be guided by the "polluter pays" principle.

## Availability of incineration plants

9.46   An important factor which the analysis by Aspinwall & Co identifies is the high capital cost of incineration. To provide enough capacity to incinerate all municipal waste in the UK would require 100 plants each with a capacity of 200,000 tonnes a year, or the equivalent. The development costs for a plant of that size are estimated to be in the range £40–50 million for a typical greenfield site, compared with only £5 million for a landfill site of similar capacity. The present structure of the waste disposal industry has been shaped by a situation in which firms have competed, primarily on price, in providing landfill facilities which have not required heavy capital expenditure.

9.47   Even if the economic instruments we have recommended tilt the balance towards incineration, the private sector will not have the confidence to build a sufficient number of incineration plants of the size indicated unless it faces stable conditions from both a regulatory and a contractual point of view. We strongly support the present tightening of standards for emissions. But it is important that, when there are further changes in standards, adequate time should be given for compliance, particularly if new standards are designed to achieve technology-forcing. In order to provide a stable regulatory framework, **we recommend that the government should work within the EC to achieve reasonable stability in legislative requirements and oppose any proposals for changes at short notice. We also recommend that the government should encourage waste disposal authorities to enter into long-term contracts with the operators of incineration plants, extending over 10 years or more.**

9.48   The availability of sufficient incineration plants for **clinical waste** will also depend on the scale of investment by the private sector. Hitherto the usual practice has been that such wastes are disposed of in incinerators owned by the NHS (3.22). Many of these are operated in an unsatisfactory way by part-time and/or unskilled staff. Most of them will be unable to meet the required standards for emissions (4.15 and table 4.1) by the specified dates (2.22) and will therefore have to close.

9.49   In searching for satisfactory alternative disposal facilities, the NHS will have to operate within the government's general policy that services must be put out to tender. Several private firms have entered or are planning to enter this market, including a subsidiary of Yorkshire Water plc. One firm which has constructed a new plant for clinical waste has experienced poor demand for its services which it attributes to competition from low-cost facilities still operating within the NHS. However this factor should decline in importance as 1995 approaches. There is a need for district health authorities and hospital trusts to make provision in their financial planning for the cost (which they have not hitherto had to meet) of disposing of their waste in an environmentally acceptable way, and to carry out an early review of their waste management arrangements in order to achieve a smooth transition.

9.50    DOE, in conjunction with the Department of Health, will need to assess whether the new plants being built for clinical waste (3.32) will be able to deal with the quantities of waste involved; and if not take action to ensure that the shortfall is remedied. If clinical waste incinerators become subject to the standards in the draft EC Directive on the Incineration of Hazardous Waste (8.12), significant additional expenditure will be necessary on gas-cleaning equipment.

9.51    Additional incineration plants for **sewage sludge** will be provided by water companies in England and Wales to meet their sewage disposal obligations (3.29–3.31). Arrangements need to be found which will give a similar assurance that funding will be available for this purpose in Scotland and Northern Ireland.

9.52    There have been suggestions that the amount of **chemical waste** incinerated will increase considerably. It was assumed in discussing future trends in emissions from incineration plants that a fivefold increase might take place over the next 10–15 years (4.38). With this category of waste, the cost of incineration is likely to be a secondary consideration in decisions about disposal. Any new incineration plants required will be owned and operated by the private sector. It is not clear what will be the respective roles played in future by merchant operators and by in-house plants operated by chemical companies (3.23), but both will be subject in the same way to the new HMIP standards.

9.53    Apart from the large plants now being built to recover energy from poultry litter, incineration of **agricultural wastes** is usually a small-scale operation. The problematic area is animal carcasses. Against the background of a depressed world market for the products from the rendering of animal carcasses (3.12), renderers have introduced various charges for removing wastes from firms of knackers. This, and the depressed prices for hides and skins, have obliged knackers to charge for the removal of fallen stock from farms. That in turn has made some farmers explore other options for disposal. Apart from knackers, which still retain an important role in most areas, the options available to farmers include hunt kennels, careful burial in a location where there is no risk of causing water pollution, burning on the farm and burning in an incinerator. There have been some reports of carcasses left lying on farms, creating possible risks to water supplies. The provision of specialist incineration facilities is expensive, leading to levels of charges which farmers are unlikely to be able to afford. Moreover in small plants it may be necessary to cut up carcasses before placing them in the incinerator in order to achieve their effective destruction. If there were a more widespread availability of incineration plants for municipal waste, these might also be able to handle animal carcasses when necessary. Government action is justified to achieve the best practicable environmental option in cases where a dangerous pathogen is either present or suspected. **We recommend that MAFF and other Agriculture Departments take the initiative in ensuring that suitable incineration facilities are available for animal carcasses and offal.**

9.54    Although we have examined the prospects for the introduction of new technologies (8.2–8.11), the only ones apart from composting which are likely to have practical application in the near future are suitable for chemical or clinical wastes. We are less concerned at the moment about future capacity for the incineration of chemical waste. New capacity for clinical waste is likely to be provided partly by new plants using established technology but operating to the new HMIP standards and partly by the new technology of the plasma arc. **We recommend that the possible future introduction of alternative technologies for waste disposal should not be regarded as a reason for rejecting proposals for new incineration plants for either municipal waste and sewage sludge or clinical waste, provided these are in themselves environmentally acceptable.**

9.55    The future availability of incineration plants will depend, not only on the technical merits of the process and the availability of finance, but also on planning permission for a sufficient number of suitable sites. The rest of this chapter discusses key factors which will influence public attitudes towards proposals for incineration plants.

**The proximity principle**

9.56   One aspect of controversy about waste incineration has been the closely related issues of the scale of incineration plants and the sizes of the areas from which wastes are brought for incineration. Present UK government policy recognises the "proximity principle" (which is also incorporated in EC and US legislation) that wastes should be disposed of as close as possible to the point where they arise. The primary justification for this principle is to minimise the transport and storage of wastes, particularly where toxic or otherwise hazardous substances are involved. However support for the proximity principle also reflects a view that each country, or region within a country, ought to be self-sufficient in terms of waste disposal. It is a frequent ground of objection to proposals for incinerators that wastes from elsewhere will be brought into the area in which the incinerator will be located, and that the other areas involved ought to take responsibility for dealing with the wastes created by their population or by their industries.

9.57   The proximity principle is clearly observed where an industrial firm, or a hospital, operates an incinerator to dispose of its own wastes at the site where they are produced. This may be acceptable if the incineration plant has the necessary pollution abatement equipment and is operated by staff with the required expertise. In all other cases some movement of wastes between sites will be involved. And there are a number of other factors that have to be taken into account besides the proximity principle.

9.58   Other things being equal, the smaller an incineration plant, the smaller the pollution load it will impose on the immediately surrounding area. Any potential advantage in this respect is reduced however if a small plant is not required to achieve as stringent limits on the concentrations of pollutants emitted as would be required for a larger plant.

9.59   From other points of view larger plants have advantages. With larger plants it is economic to have the expert full-time staff with appropriate engineering skills and knowledge of chemistry needed to achieve sophisticated management of the process and feedstock and high standards of operation and monitoring. There are also major economies of scale in pollution abatement and monitoring equipment; and some gas-cleaning techniques, such as semi-dry scrubbing, do not work well on a small scale.[249] Larger plants should therefore be able to achieve lower concentrations of pollutants in their emissions. Moreover the economics of energy recovery are normally more favourable for large plants.

9.60   Certain types of chemical waste, such as PCBs, may have to be transported over long distances because stringent regulatory requirements and the specialised nature of the demand mean that there are few incineration plants capable of dealing with them. There may also be cases in which a plant is not being fully used to incinerate wastes generated in its immediate area, and its operator therefore seeks business further afield in order to cover his costs. This has happened in the UK in the last few years with merchant incinerators of clinical wastes. Equally organisations producing wastes may send their wastes some distance for incineration if there is a price advantage which more than compensates for additional transport costs.

9.61   The availability of suitable sites may affect the number and size of new incinerators built. The difficulties of obtaining planning permission may encourage those seeking approval for an incinerator to propose a large plant capable of handling waste from a wide area, although this might in itself make the proposal more controversial. It is often attractive in land use planning terms to locate a new incineration plant on the site of a previous plant. On the other hand such sites may be of limited size, and provide space for what is only a relatively small plant by modern standards.

9.62   We have concluded that the proximity principle should be regarded as a broad aim rather than an overriding criterion for the siting, design and size of incinerators. It must be weighed carefully against other factors in the context of specific sites and specific waste streams. However we have reached certain general conclusions. A major reason for the unsatisfactory way in which incineration of clinical waste is carried out at present is that most existing plants are too small. Incinerators serving individual hospitals or groups of hospitals ought to be replaced by centralised plants designed and operated to the new HMIP standards, whether these are provided by the private or the public sector. **We recommend that, in drawing up the national strategy for waste management, DOE should have regard to the following considerations:**

    i.   **the present proliferation of small and inadequately staffed plants for clinical waste should be replaced by a smaller number of large plants with expert staff**

    ii.   **on-site incineration of industrial wastes should continue to be regarded as a satisfactory solution where the quantity involved is substantial and the firm producing the wastes can also provide the necessary expert management for their incineration in a way that complies with the new HMIP standards**

    iii.   **for incinerators disposing of municipal waste, the minimum optimal scale in technical terms should be regarded as 200,000 tonnes a year.**

9.63   Municipal waste plants with a capacity larger than 200,000 tonnes a year give substantial further economies of scale and the advantages of a larger plant should therefore be carefully assessed. Plants with capacities of as much as 1.5 million tonnes a year have been proposed. The potential benefit from increased size will have to be weighed against the prospects of obtaining an assured supply of wastes on a sufficient scale in a particular case, and against the costs and environmental impact of transporting those wastes over the distances involved.

**Improvements in regulatory mechanisms**

9.64   The regulatory framework within which incineration plants are constructed and operated at present, together with certain modifications already planned for the future, were described in chapter 2. We have concluded that there are ways in which the present regulatory mechanisms ought to be rationalised and extended. Although considerable improvements have recently been made, particularly through the introduction of integrated pollution control, the relationships between the different codes of regulation are still not always defined in a clear and satisfactory way (2.49). There are also certain gaps in the legislation which need to be remedied. We examine below the interfaces between:

    the waste regulation authority and HMIP (9.65–9.69)

    HMIP and the environmental health functions of district councils (9.70–9.72)

    HMIP and HSE (9.73–9.75)

    HMIP and the local planning authority (9.76–9.80).

9.65   We have already made recommendations about the preparation of a national strategy for waste management, which among other things should identify the best practicable environmental option for particular waste streams (9.2–9.3). It is essential that there should also be adequate powers available to implement such a strategy. The present waste regulation authorities are required to prepare waste disposal plans covering, among other things, priorities for different methods of waste disposal and treatment; but there is no explicit obligation on a waste regulation authority to work to a plan it has prepared (2.41). The authority is obliged to grant a waste management licence, except in certain specified circumstances (2.16–2.17). The availability of an alternative disposal route which would represent the best practicable environmental option does not seem to represent a sufficient legal ground for refusal. **We recommend that the new Environment Agency should have power to prevent the disposal of particular wastes if the method proposed does not represent the best practicable environmental option.**

9.66   There also needs to be unified regulation of the operations on an incineration site. Processes authorised under integrated pollution control are exempt from the requirement to obtain a licence from the waste regulation authority; but in practice such a licence is likely to be required at present for the associated storage of wastes. This element of dual control appears to be contrary to the intention of the legislation and should be brought to an end.

9.67   Incineration of municipal waste gives rise to substantial quantities of solid residues. It should be possible to market some of them as construction materials, for example as fill for road foundations, in preference to landfilling them. **We recommend that DOE, in conjunction with the Department of Transport and DTI, should explore the potential for recycling solid residues from waste incineration as materials for road and other construction.** For the longer term, **we recommend that research should be carried out into the feasibility of processes for reclaiming metals from such residues at an economic cost.**

9.68    Even if these alternative approaches are successful, there will remain a substantial quantity of incineration residues requiring disposal to landfill. It is desirable that these should be produced in the form of a solid slag with low leachability; or, if they are produced initially in the form of ash, the operator should install the necessary plant on site for consolidating this ash before it is sent for disposal. At present control of such residues is divided between HMIP and the waste regulation authority. **We recommend that HMIP should use its existing powers (2.25) to ensure that solid residues are sent for disposal from incineration plants in a form which minimises the risk that toxic substances in the residues will contaminate groundwater.** The precise form that satisfies this criterion will depend on the concentrations of pollutants in the residues and the detailed characteristics of the disposal method adopted. The regulation of the actual disposal is the responsibility of the waste regulation authority which licenses the relevant landfill site. Because of their relatively high concentrations, **we recommend that solid residues from fly ash and scrubbers should not be landfilled with unprocessed municipal waste**.

9.69    **Although the functions of HMIP and waste regulation authorities are both due to pass to the new Environment Agency, we recommend that the substance of the legislation should be reviewed and amended at the same time to make it more coherent and deal with specific points identified in this report.** The legislation applying to pollution from industry generally may require some adaptation to cover the special case of waste management, in view of its particular environmental importance.

9.70    When a major incineration plant is brought into operation, there should be periodic monitoring of air, soil and water, and possibly also of wildlife, in the surrounding area. This ought to begin before the plant comes into operation in order to establish a baseline. As well as being a direct check on environmental impact, this monitoring would also show whether the assumptions made in selecting the best practicable environmental option for releases from the plant and the dispersion models used in carrying out the risk assessment were valid, and would contribute to a progressive improvement in methodology.

9.71    At present there is no clearly defined responsibility for environmental monitoring around an incineration site. The operator may carry out some environmental monitoring voluntarily, but there needs to be oversight by the regulatory authorities. The regulatory responsibility does not fall clearly either to HMIP or to the district council. Although the authorisation issued by HMIP is likely to contain requirements about environmental monitoring, these often do not extend beyond the site boundary. The district council's environmental health officer (who has many other statutory responsibilities) may well carry out investigations only if faced with a specific incident or complaint. In those circumstances HMIP may also carry out check monitoring involving off-site investigations and measurements. Although the monitoring programme required will vary from plant to plant, we believe a more systematic approach ought to be adopted for the future, and that more environmental monitoring ought to be carried out. **We recommend that HMIP, and subsequently the new Environment Agency, should specify which pollutants ought to be monitored, and how often, in the area surrounding each incineration plant, new or existing; and should ensure that the necessary monitoring is carried out.**

9.72    District councils are responsible at present for regulating emissions to air from plants incinerating less than 1 tonne an hour of waste, with the exception of chemical waste plants. These smaller plants are not subject to integrated pollution control, and do not have to meet such high standards for their emissions (2.28 and table 2.2). This difference in standards reflects both the smaller pollution load small plants produce and the difficulty of fitting gas-cleaning equipment to them at a reasonable cost. Plants of this kind are likely to continue to play a part in waste management. Although the full mechanism of integrated pollution control may not be necessary for smaller plants burning more straightforward types of waste, their emissions to air should be controlled in such a way as to achieve a level of environmental protection which is comparable to that achieved at larger plants. We regard the present division of responsibility for controlling pollution from incinerators burning 1 tonne an hour or more of waste and those burning less as unsatisfactory. **We recommend that the new Environment Agency should regulate, for both waste management and pollution control, all plants which incinerate wastes as, or as part of, a commercial operation, or incinerate clinical waste**, as will be the case with the proposed Scottish Environment Protection Agency.

9.73    It is desirable that the requirements placed on incineration plants in order to protect the environment and the surrounding population should be co-ordinated with those needed to preserve occupational health and safety. Although a few incineration sites handling toxic wastes may in future be subject to the top-tier requirements of the Control of Industrial Major Accident Hazards Regulations, this will be the result of the quantities of specified substances stored on the site rather than hazards of the incineration process (2.35–2.36). There is no significant overlap in practice between HMIP's responsibilities and the responsibilities of HSE for major accident hazards.

9.74    Variations in the composition of feedstocks have a considerable effect on the operating conditions in incinerators. Waste composition may stray outside the range within which the performance of incineration plant is guaranteed by the manufacturer. That does not necessarily mean that the capacity of the pollution abatement equipment will be overwhelmed, provided the plant has adequate capacity in relation to the volume of waste being incinerated, and provided it is skilfully operated. The evidence received from plant operators claimed that it is rare for abnormal conditions of this nature to lead to breaches of the limits on emissions.

9.75    HMIP needs to pay careful attention to the possibility of abnormal conditions, whether resulting from variations in waste composition, exceeding the rated capacity of the plant, or equipment failure. **We recommend that records of plant operation should be regularly audited to determine how often abnormal conditions have occurred, under what circumstances, and what remedial action has been taken.**

9.76    The dividing line between HMIP's functions and those of local planning authorities (2.10–2.12) is one that DOE aims to clarify in Planning Policy Guidance on planning and pollution control at present in draft.[250] It would not be practicable, or even desirable, to think in terms of merging two forms of regulation which have such different purposes. For example, authorisation by HMIP is given to a named person, whereas planning permission is given for a defined site. Improvements must rather be sought through improved co-ordination. **We recommend that there should be close liaison between HMIP and the local planning authority from the earliest stages of proposals for new incinerators.**

9.77    Where separate statutory responsibilities are involved, it is all the more important that decisions should be taken on the basis of a common core of scientific and technical analysis. There is already a requirement in specified circumstances that an environmental statement should be submitted with the planning application for an incinerator (2.37–2.39). However statements produced in recent cases have differed considerably in scope, depth and detail, apparently at the discretion of the applicants. That is not a satisfactory position in the case of such controversial developments as major incineration plants. Environmental statements in their present statutory form do not therefore always represent the kind of comprehensive assessment covering all aspects of an incineration plant's design, operation and impact, and making a rigorous assessment of risks, that we believe to be necessary.

9.78    One fundamental issue which is covered in some environmental statements[251] at present but not in others is the selection of the most appropriate disposal method. **We recommend that it should be a statutory requirement for all environmental statements for incineration plants to contain:**

   i.    **a demonstration that the proposed form of treatment represents the best practicable environmental option for the wastes in question**

   ii.   **a risk-based health assessment of the kind we described in an earlier chapter (6.33–6.36), and**

   iii.  **a demonstration that the proposed size of facility is appropriate, taking into account the size and nature of the area from which wastes will be drawn; the possible pollution load on the area surrounding the plant; and economies of scale in construction and operation.**

**We recommend that the same requirement should apply to environmental statements for landfill sites.**

9.79    A comprehensive assessment of the kind advocated above needs to take full account, not only of the emissions from a proposed incineration plant, but also of the effect these will have on air quality in the relevant area, which may already be affected by emissions from other industrial plants (whether or not these include incinerators). Cases have also arisen in which more than one incineration plant, or other form of large-scale combustion plant, is being proposed simultaneously within the same area. Consideration of such proposals by the regulatory authorities must take full account of their cumulative impact. In order to make that possible, their promoters should be required to produce a joint assessment. **We also recommend that planning authorities should take account of prevailing air pollution levels when considering what would be suitable locations for incinerators, and HMIP should arrange to provide them with the information about air pollution levels needed for this purpose.**

9.80    Both the Environment Agency and the planning authority will have to scrutinise carefully the environmental statement assessing the impact of a proposed waste treatment facility. If a proposal for a major incineration plant is controversial enough to lead to a public inquiry under planning legislation, it is likely that those appearing at the inquiry will raise issues about pollution. The Secretary of State has recognised this by appointing a technical assessor to provide advice to the inspector at such public inquiries on technical issues that are relevant to the planning decision. This practice should continue.

### Public concern about incineration plants

9.81    One of the matters on which we invited evidence was public concern about the incineration of wastes, and how this should be addressed. Many of the factors which have prompted concern, such as levels of emissions, or the appropriateness of the site, have been fully discussed earlier in this report. We have found that the relations between the plant operator and the community are also important in explaining differences in the level of concern. Before the public will accept a large incineration plant, whether existing or proposed, the site operator will have to earn their trust and establish his credibility as a source of accurate and reliable information about the functioning of the plant. The mechanisms for establishing trust and credibility are regular meetings with representatives of the community and the fullest possible disclosure of information, not only to those attending liaison meetings but also to other members of the public who may have anxieties. We were impressed by the apparent success achieved by one site operator through a policy of regular liaison and disclosure of information to the public (see box 9A). **We recommend that the waste management industry should adopt a policy of openness in providing information to the public, identify the best practices in that respect, and take care to apply these generally.**

9.82    **We recommend that there should be a requirement on the operator of a plant to disclose information about the chemical composition of wastes incinerated, except where there is a genuine issue of security or commercial confidentiality affecting the customers sending waste for disposal.** Disclosure should in any event cover all the information available to the operator on emissions and on levels of contamination in the environment, irrespective of whether this is information held by the regulatory authority to which the public would have access under the existing statutory provisions.

9.83    Raw statistical data however are difficult to interpret, and there is a danger they may be misinterpreted. To counter that danger, the operators of major incineration plants will need to provide supporting factual information to make the data meaningful. This will obviously need to cover previous levels of emissions and contamination from the same plant, in order to provide a basis for comparison. It should cover other sources of the same pollutants which are relevant to that particular locality, and, where appropriate, natural background levels. It will also need to relate present observations to legal standards such as the limits on emissions in EC Directives and expert scientific guidance such as WHO guideline values. NAWDC, and if necessary DOE, should provide assistance to plant operators in collating and verifying such supporting factual information, perhaps in a common format.

9.84    Full information should also be given to liaison committees about the progress being made in various directions that we have indicated in earlier chapters, including improved training of the workforce, certification of quality management under BS5750, and more rigorous procedures for chemical sampling and analysis.

9.85 If public concern in the areas surrounding major existing incinerators can be allayed, there is likely to be an indirect effect in removing some of the opposition to proposals for new plants elsewhere. We accept that some level of opposition by local residents will always be present, both to proposals for incineration plants and to proposals for landfill sites, and indeed to other comparable industrial plants.

9.86 A number of the improvements we believe ought to be made should give reassurance to people living in areas in which a new incineration plant is proposed. These include the measures advocated above for coordinating the activities of the various regulatory authorities and ensuring that they take account of all the proposals affecting a given area at a given time, and the improvements in environmental monitoring and the auditing of plant operation. The establishment by the government of a strategic approach to waste management will also increase public confidence. Finally the comprehensive environmental statements which we consider should be a mandatory requirement both for incineration plants and for landfill sites ought to reassure the public that other options have been adequately investigated and that incineration is being adopted only for wastes for which it represents the best practicable environmental option.

---

**BOX 9A**                                    **LIAISON WITH A LOCAL COMMUNITY**

The Local Liaison and Monitoring Group at Ellesmere Port has been in existence since March 1989, before the present Cleanaway plant for incineration of chemical waste came into operation. It numbers about 20 people. Attendance at the two meetings analysed for the Commission was over 80%.

The largest set of participants represents local government, county and district, officials as well as elected members. A county councillor chairs the Group. Among the local government responsibilities represented are environmental health (district) and waste regulation and environmental planning (county).

The next largest set of participants, from Cleanaway, is led by the Technical Director and Incineration Division Director.

HMIP was represented at one of the two meetings.

Two associations of local residents are represented on the Group. A considerable part of the discussion at both meetings started from the complaints and concerns of the residents' representatives. At the June 1991 meeting it was decided that Cleanaway should bring its complaints and incident book to future meetings, and that complaints aired at meetings must be fully detailed.

All the complaints received responses. Where a failure or incident was the result of shortcomings in system design or operation, Cleanaway explained what was being done to introduce improvements.

The Group also considered other topics, including local epidemiology and the results of Cleanaway's monitoring of emissions.

Some of the data produced by Cleanaway at Group meetings will also appear in the public register. But the range of information conveyed at Group meetings is wider, and there are opportunities for comments, questions and interpretation.

# CHAPTER 10

# CONCLUSIONS AND RECOMMENDATIONS

### Incineration in relation to other forms of waste management

10.1    The purpose of this study has been to establish the environmental acceptability, and appropriate role, of one form of waste treatment, incineration. This
does not represent a comprehensive study of all aspects of waste management, in
the manner of the Commission's Eleventh Report published in 1985. The Commission's general approach to waste management can be presented as a four-stage
decision procedure:

**1st:** wherever possible avoid creating wastes

**2nd:** where wastes are unavoidable recycle them if possible

**3rd:** where wastes cannot be recycled in the form of materials, recover
energy from them

**4th:** when the foregoing options have been exhausted, utilise the best practicable environmental option to dispose of wastes.

10.2    We believe there needs to be a clear framework of national policy along
those lines. **We recommend that the Department of the Environment (DOE)**
**should give high priority to completing a national strategy for waste manage-**
**ment based on the four-stage decision procedure; and that this task should**
**not wait until the Environment Agency is in operation (9.2).**

Recommendation 1

10.3    Wholehearted adoption of this approach, through careful control of waste
creation at the point of production and vigorous promotion of the recycling of
unavoidable wastes, will eliminate some wastes, but not all. We conclude that
there will still remain, for the foreseeable future, substantial quantities of wastes
for disposal (8.36–8.43).

10.4    Disposal of UK municipal waste is now predominantly by landfill, supplemented by a small number of aging incineration plants designed to standards
which are now outdated. Other developed countries make much more extensive
use of incineration.

10.5    Landfill sites for municipal waste generate methane, which is a very powerful contributor to the greenhouse effect. A substantial proportion of that methane
is inevitably released into air. Use of incineration rather than landfill for municipal
waste will therefore bring a significant and worthwhile benefit in terms of reducing
emissions of greenhouse gases (5.29).

10.6    Although a detailed discussion of the environmental impact of landfill is
outside the scope of this report we drew attention to the potential for pollution of
ground and surface waters in our Sixteenth Report.[252] The Commission made a
number of recommendations in its Eleventh Report with the aim of improving the
management of landfill sites and the regulatory requirements are now being considerably tightened. Because a proportion of UK municipal waste will continue to
go to landfill for the foreseeable future the integrity of site containment and the
quality of surveillance for a long period after filling has ceased will remain crucial
concerns.

10.7   The impact of incineration plants on air quality will be considerably reduced because, as part of the introduction of integrated pollution control, Her Majesty's Inspectorate of Pollution (HMIP) has imposed stringent new standards for emissions to air. This immediately affects new plants, and will extend progressively to existing plants. We are satisfied that the incineration of waste in suitably located plants designed to meet these new HMIP standards represents an environmentally acceptable form of waste disposal. By contrast, the performance of the older generation of plants for municipal waste is likely to result in their closure, although retrofitting of additional pollution abatement equipment might enable a few of them to remain in use. Older plants for clinical waste are also likely to be closed for the same reason.

10.8   From an environmental perspective it is preferable that conversion of heterogeneous and unstable wastes to a stable state takes place under controlled conditions rather than over a lengthy period in conditions over which it is impracticable to exercise complete control. For unsorted municipal waste incineration is the only available process which provides such an assurance.

10.9   Although incineration of municipal waste reduces its volume by up to 90% and removes the potential for methane generation, a significant amount of solid residues remain. It will be necessary to dispose of these by landfill under appropriate conditions which take into account the pollutants in the fly ash from gas-cleaning systems. We make recommendations below (10.25, 10.26) about the technology and regulatory approach required in order to achieve a satisfactory level of protection for the environment in this respect.

10.10   Incineration, followed by landfilling of the solid residues, will in our view prove to be the best practicable environmental option for municipal waste.

**Recommendation 2**   10.11   Establishing the best practicable environmental option for particular waste streams may sometimes require detailed studies of the kind described in the Commission's Twelfth Report. **We recommend that, as part of preparing the national waste management strategy, DOE should press forward with the studies already in hand to establish the best practicable environmental option for particular waste streams (9.3).** For some categories of waste it is already clear that controlled incineration is particularly suitable. These are:

 a.   chemical wastes from industry which are not suitable for recycling
 b.   clinical waste, although in this case the plasma arc (8.3–8.6) may prove to be equally suitable
 c.   used tyres after the scope for recycling has been exhausted
 d.   animal carcasses and offal where a dangerous infection or pathogen is either present or suspected.

10.12   Disposal of sewage sludge presents a considerable problem, which will be accentuated by the ban on disposal at sea which will come into effect at the beginning of 1999. Sewage sludge is rich in nutrients but the ability of the agricultural and horticultural industry to use it beneficially is limited by several factors. It is likely to be logistically easier to meet much of the demand for nutrients of this kind from the very large quantities of waste the agricultural industry itself generates. The availability of land to receive sludge is seasonal, and sewage sludge can contain unacceptable levels of pathogens and heavy metals. The presence of heavy metals is also a barrier to converting sewage sludge into compost. Until these issues can be resolved, we conclude that incineration will play an important role in the disposal of sewage sludge (8.44–8.48).

10.13   The continued availability of incineration as a form of treatment for municipal and clinical wastes will depend on the construction of a substantial number of new plants (3.27, 3.32). Investment in new plant will be dependent on commercial judgements about the relative costs of providing and operating alternative disposal facilities.

10.14   We have looked at the relative capital and operating costs of a landfill and an incineration plant to handle the same amount of municipal waste. The comparison was based on new facilities which comply fully with the latest regulatory requirements. Landfill is still generally a less expensive method of waste disposal; but large incineration plants may be competitive (figure 9-I). In practice the options facing waste disposal authorities involve facilities of different capacities; and differences in the distances over which wastes would have to be transported can significantly affect relative costs. Incineration is therefore sometimes the less expensive option. It is also possible that costs will move in favour of incineration in future (9.25).

10.15   Decisions ought to take account of the environmental costs from waste disposal, such as emissions and other pollution and the impact on local amenity. We believe there is a good case for using economic instruments to reflect in operators' costs the environmental costs of alternative disposal methods. This would also encourage waste producers to adopt the four-stage decision procedure (10.1), and so reduce the amounts of waste going to disposal. **We recommend that a levy be applied to all waste deposited in landfill sites (9.37).** A landfill levy would bear less heavily on incineration than on landfill, thus matching the difference in their environmental impact. In conjunction with the subsidy for energy from waste we recommend below (10.17), such a levy would reduce whatever advantage landfill has over incineration at present in terms of commercial costs for disposal of municipal waste.

Recommendation 3

*Energy recovery*
10.16   Waste heat recovered from combustion gases can be used to produce steam: and if steam is available on a sufficient scale it can be used industrially, for district heating, for electricity generation, or a combination of these. Few of the existing incineration plants for municipal waste in the UK recover and sell energy (5.9). In some other European countries, however, this is the normal practice (5.13–5.15); and, as a form of recycling, contributes to the sustainable use of resources. Energy recovery is also desirable to maximise the contribution incineration can make to reducing emissions of greenhouse gases (5.24–5.29). **We recommend the government should give targets to waste disposal authorities for the recovery of energy from municipal waste (5.30). We also recommend that the potential for low-grade waste heat recovery should be reviewed, including the circumstances in which it might be economic in the UK without any specific subsidy (9.43).**

Recommendation 4

Recommendation 5

10.17   There is a good case for a financial incentive in the form of a subsidised price for electricity designed to encourage the generation of electricity from waste. A subsidy of this kind favours incineration because, although energy can also be recovered from landfill sites, it can be done more efficiently at incineration plants.

**Recommendation 6**  **We recommend that a financial incentive should continue to be available for electricity generated from waste; and that this incentive should be available not only in England and Wales, as is the case with the present Non-Fossil Fuel Obligation, but throughout the UK (9.42).**

### *Pollutants from waste incineration*

10.18   A particular cause of public concern has been reports of effects on the health of humans or animals in the areas around certain UK incineration plants for chemical waste. We have looked carefully at a number of studies carried out in those areas. None of them found any significant effects on human health (6.28). The plants were not subject to the new HMIP standards; and have either closed or been modified. We believe it is right nevertheless to continue to maintain a cautious and questioning attitude towards the possibility of health effects from incineration plants (9.15).

10.19   Compliance with the new HMIP standards will very considerably reduce emissions to air from incineration plants. An important consideration is how

**Recommendation 7**  rapidly existing plants will be required to meet the new standards. **We recommend that all existing incineration plants be required to meet the new HMIP standards at the earliest opportunity, and in any event by not later than the date of 1 December 1996 given in HMIP's Guidance Notes (9.10).**

10.20   There are techniques available for meeting the new performance standards for emissions, and these are set out in the annexes to HMIP's guidance notes. If new techniques are developed which are capable of reducing emissions still further without excessive cost, the concept of best available techniques not entailing excessive cost (BATNEEC, see box 2A) implies that HMIP's standards should be

**Recommendation 8**  revised accordingly. **We recommend that HMIP's Guidance Notes should be revised periodically to take account of further information about plant performance (4.36).**

10.21   Another particular cause of public concern has been the possibility of effects on health from dioxins. Dioxins detected in the environment come from a variety of sources. There are now for the first time in the UK standards for the release of dioxins. The new HMIP standards imply a 98% reduction in emissions of these substances from plants incinerating municipal waste, and almost as large reductions in emissions from plants incinerating other wastes. Separate legislation controls any risks that might be associated with accumulation of dioxins in the food chain.[253] Certain dioxins are highly toxic. However there are also large differences in susceptibility between species. These substances have not been shown to be acutely or chronically toxic to humans in the concentrations likely to have been produced by the emissions from incinerators. Work is continuing to increase our understanding of their physiological effects. A standard of 1 ngTEQ/$Nm^3$, with a guide value of 0.1 ngTEQ/$Nm^3$, appears appropriate in the present

**Recommendation 9**  state of knowledge (8.19). **We recommend that, as further evidence about the toxicity of dioxins becomes available, its implications should be kept under continuing surveillance by the Chief Medical Officers (6.15).**

10.22   Emissions of cadmium and mercury from incineration plants represent a substantial proportion of total UK emissions of these substances to air (table 4.2). More stringent limits are being placed on the concentrations of these substances in emissions to air but, because the total amount of wastes incinerated may increase substantially, we consider there is a case for a further tightening of standards. Similar considerations apply to lead, for which a specific standard has not so far been set. **We recommend that, rather than continuing to include it with other metals, HMIP should set a separate standard for emissions of lead to air from incineration plants (8.21).**

10.23   There is not a strong case for further tightening of the HMIP standards for hydrogen chloride (8.16). There is an argument based on the precautionary principle for a further tightening of the HMIP standards for hydrogen fluoride, nitrogen oxides and sulphur dioxide, though not necessarily to the figure of 25 mg/Nm$^3$ for sulphur dioxide which appears in the draft European Community (EC) Directive on Incineration of Hazardous Waste (8.17, 8.18); but incineration plants produce only a small proportion of UK emissions of these gases (table 4.2).

10.24   There is a danger of a serious misallocation of resources if widely differing standards for emissions to air are applied to waste incineration plants and other types of industrial activity, including combustion plants using wastes as fuel. **We recommend that HMIP's standards for emissions to air from combustion processes (table 8.1), particularly those utilising wastes as fuel, should be re-examined to see whether they ought to be brought more closely into line with the new HMIP standards for incineration processes (8.14).** HMIP's Chemical Release Inventory should facilitate comparisons between the pollution burdens from different forms of large-scale combustion.

10.25   Removal of pollutants from stack gases increases the amounts of those pollutants in solid residues and/or in liquid effluents. The system of integrated pollution control, now being applied to waste incineration along with other industrial processes, should ensure that the benefit from a reduction in releases to one medium is not outweighed by an increase in another form of pollution. Solid residues have to be disposed of to landfill, and there is therefore a risk that heavy metals could be leached out of them by prolonged contact with water. Action should be taken to reduce the amounts of those metals in waste streams sent for disposal, including those sent to landfill without prior processing. Electric batteries remain an important source of cadmium and mercury in municipal waste, even though there have been reductions in amounts of those metals used for this purpose. **We recommend that:**

    i.  **schemes should be introduced for the recycling of batteries containing mercury or cadmium (8.50)**

    ii.  **studies should be carried out to identify other ways of substantially reducing, and as far as possible eliminating these metals from municipal waste (8.50)**

    iii.  **the case for and against maintaining segregated streams of clinical waste (which may contain heavy metals as well as infectious material) should be investigated in the course of preparing the national waste management strategy (8.49).**

10.26   Specific measures should also be taken to reduce the risk that heavy metals will leach from solid residues from incineration plants. **We recommend that:**

    i.  **HMIP should use its existing powers to ensure that solid residues are sent for disposal from incineration plants in a form which minimises the risk that toxic substances in the residues will contaminate groundwater (9.68)**

    ii.  **solid residues from fly ash and scrubbers should not be landfilled with unprocessed municipal waste (9.68)**

    iii.  **DOE, in conjunction with the Department of Transport and the Department of Trade and Industry, should explore the potential** for recycling solid residues from waste incineration as materials for road and other construction (9.67).

**Recommendation 14**

**For the longer term we recommend that research should be carried out into the feasibility of processes for reclaiming metals from such residues at an economic cost (9.67).**

**Recommendation 15**

10.27  It is also desirable that heavy metal levels in sewage sludge should be reduced, with the dual objective of removing obstacles to its use on land and limiting emissions of heavy metals from incineration plants. **We repeat the recommendation in earlier Commission reports that substantial further reductions in the amounts of heavy metals in sewage sludge should be sought through a policy of controlling trade effluent discharges to sewers more stringently and modifying the associated charging system in such a way as to give industrial dischargers more incentive to undertake pretreatment of their effluents (8.46).**

10.28  Liquid effluents come primarily from quenching and gas cleaning. They must be treated to whatever standard is necessary to make them acceptable for discharge to sewers or to the environment. No scientific justification has been provided for the ban on liquid discharges proposed in the draft EC Directive on Incineration of Hazardous Waste (8.15).

### Management of incineration plants

**Recommendation 16**

10.29  Our investigation has shown that standards of operation and management appear to vary widely. It is important that managers should be thoroughly committed to a high quality of operation, and that the practices followed at all incineration sites should be brought up to the levels already being achieved at the best sites. **We recommend that:**

    i.   **it should be one of the aims of the regulatory authorities to stimulate improvements in the overall management of incineration plants, and inspectors should seek to raise the standards of operation to match the best practice in the chemical industry (8.27)**

    ii.   **all firms operating incinerators should install systems of quality management which are approved under British Standard (BS) 5750 (or any future development of that standard), and the regulatory authorities should give them appropriate encouragement to do so (8.28)**

    iii.  **industry and professional associations should collaborate with their counterparts in other member states of the EC so that knowledge and experience of efficient incinerator operation can be pooled to mutual benefit (8.35).**

**Recommendation 17**

10.30  The operation of an incineration plant is a skilled task. Even a small plant requires technician-level skills. Proper management of the feedstock is important. Many existing incinerators for clinical wastes are small and likely to have been operated inefficiently. **We recommend (8.29) that:**

    i.   **a recognised formal qualification should be developed without delay for staff operating incinerators**

    ii.   **it should be made a legal requirement, by not later than 31 December 1996, that all key workers must be so qualified**

    iii.  **there should also be appropriate qualifications for all workers involved in the collection, assessment and storage of chemical waste.**

10.31   Accident hazards at incineration sites are subject to inspection by the Health and Safety Executive (HSE). There has been no suggestion made to us that the relevant legislation and procedures do not work satisfactorily, but we think there ought to be more systematic checks on the functioning and management of plants. HMIP needs to pay careful attention to the occurrence of abnormal conditions. **We recommend that records of plant operation should be regularly audited to determine how often abnormal conditions have occurred, under what circumstances, and what remedial action has been taken (9.75).** We know of no occasion, in the UK or elsewhere, where physical damage beyond the site boundary has resulted from combustion processes in an incinerator. However, depending on the amounts of specified materials stored on them, the sites of a few incinerators for chemical waste may have to comply with statutory procedures in future as major accident hazards (2.35–2.36).

**Recommendation 18**

10.32   There is also a risk that pollution or nuisance could occur as a result of accidental leakage of wastes during storage or handling, and additional precautions are desirable. **We recommend that HMIP should require the operators of incineration plants for special waste to carry out transfers of waste within buildings and that those buildings should be maintained under reduced air pressure (7.6).**

**Recommendation 19**

10.33   An essential part of effective regulation is adequate monitoring. Monitoring cannot be carried out adequately without validated techniques for sampling and analysis implemented to strictly controlled standards. HMIP already places emphasis on quality assurance in monitoring. **We recommend (4.34) that HMIP should ensure that:**

**Recommendation 20**

   i.   **satisfactory protocols for sampling and analysing for all significant substances present in releases from waste incineration, and for measuring the conditions in combustion chambers and gas-cleaning systems, are prepared, published and kept up to date, and any research necessary for this purpose is carried out**

   ii.   **analytical laboratories used by operators of incineration plants have accreditation from the National Measurement Accreditation Service provided by the National Physical Laboratory.**

**We recommend that HMIP, and subsequently the new Environment Agency, should specify which pollutants ought to be monitored, and how often, in the area surrounding each incineration plant, new or existing; and should ensure that the necessary monitoring is carried out (9.71). We also recommend that the UK government should continue to place importance on ensuring that all EC legislation is drafted in such a way as to be enforceable; and includes provisions about monitoring, sampling and analysis which will enable satisfactory enforcement to take place on a comparable basis in all member states (8.26).**

**Recommendation 21**

**Recommendation 22**

### *Technological developments*

10.34   Improvements in combustion kinetics and in monitoring techniques will facilitate compliance with stringent standards for releases to the environment from incineration plants. There is a strong case for international collaboration in research and development, especially in the construction and operation of pilot plants. **We recommend that DOE should review the present research programmes and determine priorities for future work. As well as work to facilitate the preparation of monitoring protocols (recommendation 20 above), the priorities should include the development of optimisation techniques for the total waste incineration system (8.33). We recommend that**

**Recommendation 23**

**Recommendation 24**

**research and development on incineration processes should be included in EC research programmes (8.34).**

10.35   We have assessed the likelihood that incineration will be superseded as a method of disposal by new technologies. No alternative disposal method is in prospect at present for unsorted municipal waste. It would take at least 10 years to develop any new technology to the point where it could be successfully used in a large commercial plant. The plasma arc process (8.3–8.6) is already coming into use in North America and continental Europe for toxic and clinical wastes and the treatment of contaminated soil; and may therefore have commercial applications within the next 5 years in the UK. **We recommend that the government should encourage research into alternative strategies for waste destruction and demonstrations of alternative methods (8.11). However we also recommend that the possible future introduction of alternative technologies for waste disposal should not be regarded as a reason for rejecting proposals for new incineration plants for either municipal waste and sewage sludge or clinical waste, provided these are in themselves environmentally acceptable (9.54).**

Recommendation 25

Recommendation 26

### *The future availability of waste disposal facilities*

10.36   One point which emerges clearly from comparing the costs of incineration and landfill (10.14) is that incineration requires a large initial capital expenditure. Under government rules investment in new facilities for municipal waste must be funded by the private sector. The private sector will not be prepared to make such expenditures unless it is confident there will be a reliable long-term demand for incineration and a stable regulatory framework. **To ensure that these conditions are met, we recommend (9.47) that the government should:**

Recommendation 27

   i.   **work within the EC to achieve reasonable stability in legislative requirements, and oppose any proposals for changes in standards at short notice**

   ii.   **encourage waste disposal authorities to enter into long-term contracts with the operators of incineration plants, extending over 10 years or more.**

10.37   Individual proposals for incineration plants need to be related to a clear published strategy for waste disposal. At the moment waste regulation authorities are required to produce a waste management plan for their areas, setting out among other things the proposed balance between incineration and landfill. There is also co-operation between regional groupings of waste regulation authorities. But we believe there also needs to be a clear framework of national policy, and we have recommended above that priority be placed on preparation of a national strategy for waste management. A strategic approach is all the more important because it is likely to take at least 5 years to design, obtain approval for, and construct a major incinerator. A large part of this time is likely to be occupied with obtaining planning permission.

10.38   The national strategy for waste management needs to take into account the availability of suitable sites for landfill. The evidence we have received is that there is an adequate supply at present, but this will not necessarily remain the case if present disposal methods continue. As we have noted, incineration of municipal waste produces a significant amount of waste requiring disposal by landfill. The large reduction in the volume of the original wastes is a valuable contribution to making best use of the landfill capacity available.

10.39   There appears to be a shortage of appropriate facilities for animal carcasses and offal, which may require disposal in small numbers at widely separated points. We do not consider the government has given sufficient priority to this issue. **We recommend that the Ministry of Agriculture, Fisheries and Food (MAFF) and other Agriculture Departments take the initiative in ensuring that suitable incineration facilities are available for animal carcasses and offal (9.53).**

Recommendation 28

10.40 An important issue in waste management is the catchment area that should be served by an individual incineration plant. There appear to be considerable economies of scale in waste incineration. Moreover, below a certain size it may be difficult, or impossible, to provide the skilled staffing and management required. On the other hand larger plants will require wastes to be transported over longer distances; and may arouse more public opposition, because waste is being brought together from a wide area. The "proximity principle" should be regarded as a general aim, but not as a specific criterion for the siting and design of incinerators. **We recommend (9.62) that, in drawing up the national strategy for waste management, DOE should have regard to the following considerations:**

Recommendation 29

i. **the present proliferation of small and inadequately staffed plants for clinical waste should be replaced by a smaller number of large plants with expert staff**

ii. **on-site incineration of industrial wastes should continue to be regarded as a satisfactory solution where the quantity involved is substantial and the firm producing the wastes can also provide the necessary expert management for their incineration in a way that complies with the new HMIP standards**

iii. **for incinerators disposing of municipal waste, the minimum optimal scale in technical terms should be regarded as 200,000 tonnes a year.**

10.41 It is also desirable to minimise the transport of wastes by road. **We recommend that waste disposal facilities should wherever possible be on sites which allow wastes to be moved by rail or water transport rather than by road (7.18).**

Recommendation 30

### *Need for improved regulation and greater openness*

10.42 We do not consider there is a satisfactory relationship at present between the three major forms of regulation applying to incineration plants (planning permission, licensing by the waste regulation authority, and authorisation by HMIP). The result could be duplication of effort, or alternatively that some aspects of environmental impact might not be properly taken into account. **We recommend that:**

Recommendation 31

i. **planning authorities should take account of prevailing air pollution levels when considering what would be suitable locations for incinerators, and HMIP should arrange to provide them with the information about air pollution levels needed for this purpose (9.79)**

ii. **there should be close liaison between HMIP and the local planning authority from the earliest stages of proposals for new incinerators (9.76)**

iii. **the new Environment Agency should have power to prevent the disposal of particular wastes if the method proposed does not represent the best practicable environmental option (9.65)**

iv. **although the functions of HMIP and waste regulation authorities are both due to pass to the new Environment Agency, the substance**

**of the legislation should be reviewed and amended at the same time to make it more coherent and deal with specific points identified in this report (9.69).**

10.43   Improvements are also needed in the provisions governing the preparation of environmental statements in support of planning applications for waste disposal facilities. **We recommend (9.78) that it should be a statutory requirement for all environmental statements for incineration plants and landfill sites to contain:**

**Recommendation 32**

   i. **a demonstration that the proposed form of treatment represents the best practicable environmental option for the wastes in question**

   ii. **a risk-based health assessment of the kind described at 6.33–6.36**

   iii. **a demonstration that the proposed size of facility is appropriate.**

10.44   We regard the present division of responsibility for controlling pollution from incinerators burning 1 tonne an hour or more of waste and those burning less as unsatisfactory. The proposed Scottish Environment Protection Agency will regulate all incinerators. **We recommend that the new Environment Agency should regulate, for both waste management and pollution control, all plants which incinerate wastes as, or as part of, a commercial operation, or incinerate clinical waste (9.72).**

**Recommendation 33**

10.45   However high the standards achieved for emissions to air, other factors such as additional traffic and visual intrusion can have a substantial impact locally. But there is no reason in principle why modern incineration plants should be regarded as environmentally unacceptable on such grounds, provided a plant is appropriately sited and carefully designed, maintained and operated. **We recommend that the siting of large incineration plants should reflect their character as major industrial enterprises, and that local planning authorities should ensure suitable areas are identified during the preparation of development plans (7.17).**

**Recommendation 34**

10.46   No proposal for a waste disposal facility, or any other comparable industrial plant, is likely to be popular with local residents. Before they will willingly accept a large incineration plant (existing or proposed), the site operator will have to earn their trust. We have been impressed by the success achieved in one case through a policy of regular liaison and disclosure of information to the public (9.81–9.84 and box 9A). **We recommend that:**

**Recommendation 35**

   i. **the waste management industry should adopt a policy of openness in providing information to the public, identify the best practices in that respect, and take care to apply these generally (9.81)**

   ii. **there should be a requirement on the operator of a plant to disclose information about the chemical composition of wastes incinerated, except where there is a genuine issue of security or commercial confidentiality affecting the customers sending waste for disposal (9.82).**

### *The way forward*

10.47   We have investigated in particular those aspects of waste incineration which have given rise to public concern. The introduction of integrated pollution control for all larger incineration plants and for smaller plants incinerating chemical wastes has been an important advance in terms of ensuring protection for health and for the environment. It has led to the setting of stringent new standards for emissions to air. We have recommended certain other improvements. It is important that all incineration plants meet the new HMIP standards by 1996, and are closed if they cannot do so. This combination of measures, if clearly explained and made widely known, will remove basic factors that have caused concern in the past and go some way to reassure the general public. For the reasons set out in this report we conclude that incineration of waste at plants constructed and operated to the new standards ought to have an important and growing role in the national strategy the government should now prepare as soon as possible to cover all aspects of waste management.

ALL OF WHICH WE HUMBLY SUBMIT FOR
YOUR MAJESTY'S GRACIOUS CONSIDERATION.

John Houghton (Chairman)
Geoffrey Allen
Barbara Clayton
Henry Charnock
Henry Fell
Peter Jacques
John Lawton
Richard Macrory
J Gareth Morris
Donald Reeve
Emma Rothschild
Aubrey Silberston

David Lewis        Secretary

R B Adams        Assistant Secretary

# GLOSSARY

The different designs of incinerator are described in Appendix A. The various elements that make up an incinerator are explained in 4.8 and figure 4-I (pages 28 and 29). For the main units of measurement see box 2C (page 10).

Terms printed *in bold italics* have a separate entry in the glossary.

| | |
|---|---|
| Acidic gases | A general term used to cover sulphur dioxide, hydrogen chloride, hydrogen fluoride and nitrogen oxides. |
| Agricultural waste | A general term used to cover animal excreta, litter, straw waste, carcasses and silage liquors. |
| Anaerobic decomposition | The microbial breakdown of waste in the absence of air. The decay process produces methane, carbon dioxide and hydrogen sulphide. |
| BATNEEC | Best Available Techniques Not Entailing Excessive Cost. See Box 2A (page 8). |
| Best Practicable Environmental Option (BPEO) | The option that provides the most benefit or least damage to the environment as a whole, at acceptable cost, and in the long term as well as in the short term. See Royal Commission on Environmental Pollution (1988) *Best practicable environmental option* (Twelfth Report). |
| Calorific value | The heat liberated when a unit mass of a substance is burned as fuel under standard conditions. Calorific value is measured in Giga-Joules (GJ) per tonne. |
| Chemical waste | Liquid and solid waste materials resulting from industrial chemical processes. See also *hazardous waste, special waste*. |
| Clinical waste | Waste arising from medical and related practice, (including human or animal tissue, dressings and sharp instruments) which may cause infections or be a hazard. |
| Co-disposal | The disposal of more than one category of waste in the same landfill site. For example municipal waste and *solid residues* from incinerators. |
| Co-incineration | The incineration of more than one category of waste in the same plant. For example chemical waste with clinical waste. |
| Combustion fumes | Gases and *particulates* produced by the combustion of solid or liquid waste which subsequently burn in the gas phase at a higher temperature. |
| Controlled waste | Household, industrial and commercial waste. It is defined by section 75 of the Environmental Protection Act 1990. |

| | |
|---|---|
| Dioxins | See box 6A, page 49. |
| Dispersion model | A computer program that simulates the spread and dilution of pollutants in order to predict where the maximal deposition rate of a pollutant will occur. |
| Dry solids | Material left after the removal of water from sewage sludge. |
| Energy recovery | The removal of heat from the *exhaust gases* so as to provide heat and/or electricity for use either in the plant or elsewhere. |
| Environmental statement | Information about the likely effects of a proposed development submitted by an applicant for planning permission so that the planning authority is able to make an environmental assessment. |
| Exhaust gases | The gases that emerge from the combustion chamber of an incinerator, before they have passed through all the stages of the gas-cleaning system. |
| Feedstock | The waste loaded into an incinerator. |
| Fly ash | A fine ash collected from the *exhaust gases*. |
| Fugitive emissions | Releases of pollutants from an incinerator to the atmosphere at points other than the stack, including leaks from chemical waste during storage and handling. |
| Greenhouse effect | The warming of the Earth's surface and the lower atmosphere due to gases such as carbon dioxide and methane ("greenhouse gases") which form a barrier to infra-red radiation from the Earth. |
| Hazardous waste | Waste that meets the criteria in the Hazardous Waste Directive (91/689/EEC) by coming from a specified waste stream (annex I) and having one or more hazardous properties (annex III), and taking into account whether it contains any of some 50 hazardous substances (annex II). |
| Heavy metals | A general term used to cover the metals for which standards are set for emissions to air from incinerators: arsenic, cadmium, chromium, cobalt, copper, lead, manganese, mercury, nickel, thallium and tin. |
| Integrated Pollution Control | The regulatory system introduced in England and Wales by the Environmental Protection Act 1990 under which Her Majesty's Inspectorate of Pollution exercises control over releases of waste to air, water and land with the aim of achieving the *best practicable environmental option* (see 2.23–2.26). |
| Landfill | The shallow burial of wastes subject to conditions imposed by the *waste regulation authority* in the site licence. |
| Leaching | The movement of water through the ground especially at a landfill site, in the course of which substances present may dissolve and contaminate the water. |
| Municipal waste | Domestic waste together with similar wastes from commercial or |

trade sources. The term "municipal solid waste" is sometimes used to distinguish waste in this sense from sewage.

**Non-Fossil Fuel Obligation**

A requirement on regional electricity companies in England and Wales to purchase from specified producers, at a premium price, for a fixed period, specified amounts of electricity generated by methods other than burning fossil fuels.

**Particulates**

Defined for regulatory purposes as solid and liquid material trapped on a filter under specified conditions. The solid component may range in size from sub-micron particles to visible dust grains.

**Polychlorinated biphenyls (PCBs) and polychlorinated terphenyls (PCTs)**

Chlorinated aromatic hydrocarbons which have been banned from industrial use but still exist in large quantities in wastes, especially in old electrical equipment. PCBs and PCTs are persistent in the environment and are concentrated by living organisms.

**Pool price**

The normal price paid by regional electricity companies for marginal supplies of electricity.

**Precautionary principle**

The avoidance or the reduction of risks to the environment by prudent action taken before any serious problem is encountered. See Royal Commission on Environmental Pollution (1985). *Managing waste: the duty of care* (Eleventh Report).

**Putrescibles**

Wastes such as food which decay readily through **anaerobic decomposition**.

**Retention time**

The period of time during liquid/solid or gas phase combustion respectively, for which wastes or **combustion fumes** are maintained at a given temperature.

**Sewage sludge**

The residue produced at a sewage treatment works that is not discharged with the treated effluent (see 3.6).

**Slag**

**Solid residues** from incinerators that have melted and fused on cooling. At sufficiently high temperatures a glass may form.

**Solid residues**

A general term used to cover **fly ash**, **slag**, ash and clinker from the grate, and the sludge from the treatment of liquid effluents.

**Special waste**

In UK legislation wastes that consist of, or contain, any of 31 specified groups of substances and are dangerous to life as a result of their corrosivity, flammability or toxicity, or because they have a flashpoint of 21°C or less, or which are medicines available only on prescription.

**Stack gases**

The gases that are released to the atmosphere from the stack of an incinerator.

**Trade effluent**

Waste water from an industrial process discharged to sewer under an agreement with the statutory undertaker providing the sewer.

**Transfer station**

A depot where waste from local collection vehicles is loaded into larger vehicles, rail wagons or barges for carriage in bulk to a treatment or disposal site.

**Waste regulation authority**

A local authority which licences disposal facilities for **controlled wastes** (see 2.14–2.17 and 2.41–2.42).

# REFERENCES

1. (a) Gore, A. (1992). *Earth in the balance: forging a new common purpose.* Earthscan Publications Limited, London.

   (b) Greenpeace (1991). *Burning questions: incineration in the UK.* Greenpeace, London.

2. Royal Commission on Environmental Pollution (1985). *Managing waste: the duty of care.* Eleventh Report. Cmnd 9675. HMSO, London.

3. Environmental Resources Limited (1986). *Resource recovery.* A report for the Royal Commission on Environmental Pollution. HMSO, London.

4. Royal Commission on Environmental Pollution (1985). See reference 2 (paragraphs 7.35–7.39).

5. London Convention on the Prevention of Marine Pollution by Dumping of Wastes and Other Matter (1972). Cmnd 5169. HMSO, London.

6 & 7. Department of the Environment (1992). *Planning policy guidance: planning and pollution control.* A consultation paper. DOE, London.

8. European Communities (1975). Council Directive on waste, 75/442/EEC. *Official Journal of the European Communities* **L194**, 39–41.

9. European Communities (1991). Council Directive amending Directive 75/442/EEC on waste, 91/156/EEC. *Official Journal of the European Communities* **L78**, 32–37.

10. (a) European Communities (1975). Council Directive on the disposal of waste oils, 75/439/EEC. *Official Journal of the European Communities* **L194**, 23–24.

    (b) European Communities (1987). Council Directive amending Directive 75/439/EEC on the disposal of waste oils, 87/101/EEC. *Official Journal of the European Communities* **L42**, 43–47.

11. European Communities (1976). Council Directive on the disposal of polychlorinated biphenyls and polychlorinated terphenyls, 76/403/EEC. *Official Journal of the European Communities* **L108**, 41–42.

12. (a) European Communities (1978). Council Directive on toxic and hazardous waste, 78/319/EEC. *Official Journal of the European Communities* **L84**, 43–47.

    (b) European Communities (1984). Council Directive on the supervision and control within the European Community of the transfrontier shipment of hazardous waste, 84/631/EEC. *Official Journal of the European Communities* **L326**, 31–36.

    (c) European Communities (1986). Council Directive amending Directive 84/631/EEC on the supervision and control within the European Community of the transfrontier shipment of hazardous waste, 86/279/EEC. *Official Journal of the European Communities* **L181**, 13–15.

    (d) European Communities (1991). Council Directive on hazardous waste, 91/689/EEC. *Official Journal of the European Communities* **L377**, 20–27.

13. European Communities (1990). Council Directive laying down the veterinary rules for the disposal and processing of animal waste, for its placing on the market and for the prevention of pathogens in feedstuffs of animal or fish origin and amending Directive 90/425/EEC, 90/667/EEC. *Official Journal of the European Communities* **L363**, 51–60.

14. Great Britain (1990). *Environmental Protection Act.* HMSO, London.

15. Great Britain (1991). *Disposal of Controlled Waste (Exceptions) Regulations.* Statutory Instrument No. 508. HMSO, London.

16. Royal Commission on Environmental Pollution (1985). See reference 2 (paragraph 13.78).

17. European Communities (1984). See reference 12b.

18. European Communities (1993). Council Regulation on the supervision and control of shipments of waste within, into, and out of the European Community, 259/93/EEC. *Official Journal of the European Communities* **L30**, 1–27.

19. Great Britain (1991). *The Environmental Protection (Prescribed Processes and Substances) Regulations 1991*. Statutory Instrument No.472. HMSO, London.

20. Royal Commission on Environmental Pollution (1988). *Best practicable environmental option*. Twelfth report. Cm 310. HMSO, London.

21. Department of the Environment (1992). *Government response to the twelfth report of the Royal Commission on Environmental Pollution: best practicable environmental option*. DOE, London. (See paragraph 17).

22. (a) Department of the Environment (1992). See reference 21.

    (b) Johnston, M. (1987). *Municipal waste combustion study: costs of flue gas cleaning technologies*. EPA/530-SW-87-012e. US Environmental Protection Agency, Research Triangle Park.

23. (a) Her Majesty's Inspectorate of Pollution (1991–1992). *Chief Inspector's Guidance to Inspectors (Environmental Protection Act 1990): Waste Disposal and Recycling: Process Guidance Notes*. HMSO, London.

*Fuel and power combustion:*

| | |
|---|---|
| *Large boilers and furnaces 50MWth and over* | IPR 1/1 |
| *Waste oil and recovered oil* | IPR 1/4 |
| *Solid fuel from municipal waste* | IPR 1/5 |
| *Tyres, tyre rubber or similar rubber* | IPR 1/6 |
| *Poultry litter* | IPR 1/7 |
| *Wood waste or straw* | IPR 1/8 |

*Incineration:*

| | |
|---|---|
| *Merchant and in house chemical waste* | IPR 5/1 |
| *Clinical waste* | IPR 5/2 |
| *Municipal waste* | IPR 5/3 |
| *Animal carcass* | IPR 5/4 |
| *Sewage sludge* | IPR 5/11 |

(b) Department of the Environment; Scottish Office; Welsh Office (1991). *Secretary of State's Guidance: Processes Prescribed for Air Pollution by Local Authorities (Environmental Protection Act 1990, Part I)*. HMSO, London.

*Combustion processes less than 3MW net rated thermal input:*

| | |
|---|---|
| *Waste oil and recovered oil burners* | PG1/1 |

*Combustion processes between 0.4 and 3MW net rated thermal input:*

| | |
|---|---|
| *Waste oil and recovered oil burners* | PG1/2 |
| *Tyre and rubber combustion* | PG1/6 |
| *Straw* | PG1/7 |
| *Wood* | PG1/8 |
| *Poultry litter* | PG1/9 |
| *Waste derived fuel* | PG1/10 |

*Incineration:*

| | |
|---|---|
| *Clinical waste* | PG5/1 |
| *Animal carcase* | PG5/3 |
| *General waste* | PG5/4 |
| *Sewage sludge* | PG5/5 |

24. Germany (1990). *Siebzehnte Verordnung zur Durchführung des Bundes-Immissionsschutzgesetzes—Verordnung über Verbrennungsanlagen für Abfälle oder ähnliche brennbare Stoffe—17. BImSchV)* {Seventeenth regulation implementing the Federal immission protection law—regulation on incineration plants for waste or similar combustible materials} *23.11.1990. (BGB1. I, S. 2545)*

25. Commission of the European Communities (1992). Proposal for a Council Directive on

the incineration of hazardous waste, 92/C130/01. COM(92) 9 final—SYN 406. *Official Journal of the European Communities* **C130**, 1–20.

26. Royal Commission on Environmental Pollution (1985). See reference 2 (paragraph 13.79).

27. Great Britain (1990). *National Health and Community Care Act (Commencement No.1) Order 1990.* Statutory Instrument No.1329. HMSO, London.

28. European Communities (1984). Council Directive on combatting of air pollution from industrial plants, 84/360/EEC. *Official Journal of the European Communities* **L188**, 20–25.

29. European Communities (1989). Council Directive on the prevention of air pollution from new municipal waste incineration plants, 89/369/EEC. *Official Journal of the European Communities* **L163**, 32–36.

30. European Communities (1989). Council Directive on the reduction of air pollution from existing municipal waste incineration plants, 89/429/EEC. *Official Journal of the European Communities* **L203**, 50–54.

31. Commission of the European Communities, Directorate General XI (Environment). Evidence to the Royal Commission.

32. Commission of the European Communities (1992). See reference 25.

33. Germany (1990). See reference 24.

34. European Communities (1990). *Technical note on best available technologies not entailing excessive cost for hazardous waste incineration.* EUR 13007. CEC-DGXI, Brussels.

35. (a) Great Britain (1984). *The Control of Industrial Major Accident Hazards Regulations.* Statutory Instrument No.1902. HMSO, London.
    (b) Northern Ireland (1985). *The Control of Industrial Major Accident Hazards Regulations.* Statutory Instrument No.175. HMSO, London.

36. European Communities (1982). Council Directive on the major accident hazards of certain industrial activities, 82/501/EEC. *Official Journal of the European Communities* **L 230**, 1–18 and **L 289**, 35.

37. Great Britain (1974). *Health and Safety at Work etc. Act.* HMSO, London.

38. European Communities (1985). Council Directive on the assessment of the effects of certain public and private projects on the environment, 85/337/EEC. *Official Journal of the European Communities* **L175**, 40–48.

39. (a) England & Wales (1988). *Town and Country Planning (Assessment of Environmental Effects) Regulations.* Statutory Instrument No.1199. HMSO, London.
    (b) Scotland (1988). *Environmental Assessment (Scotland) Regulations.* Statutory Instrument No.1221. HMSO, London.

40. (a) Department of the Environment (1988). *Environmental assessment.* DOE Circular 15/88. DOE, London.
    (b) Welsh Office (1988). *Environmental assessment.* Welsh Office Circular 23/88. Welsh Office, Cardiff.

41. (a) Department of the Environment (1992). *Consultation paper on waste disposal and planning under an Environment Agency.* DOE, London.
    (b) Welsh Office (1992). *Consultation paper on waste disposal and planning under an Environment Agency.* Welsh Office, Cardiff.

42. Great Britain (1974). *Control of Pollution Act.* HMSO, London.

43. Royal Commission on Environmental Pollution (1985). See reference 2 (paragraphs 9.8–9.9).

44. Great Britain (1991). *Planning and Compensation Act.* HMSO, London.

45. Department of the Environment (1992). See reference 6.

46. Department of the Environment (1992). See reference 41.

47. Barton, J. R. (1992). *Reduction and recycling in general industrial waste streams.* WSL Paper W92065. Warren Spring Laboratory, Stevenage.

48. Her Majesty's Government (1992). *This common inheritance: the second year report.* Cm 2068. HMSO, London.

49. Department of the Environment (1991). *Recycling.* Waste Management Paper No.28. HMSO, London.

50. Department of the Environment (1992). *The UK environment*. HMSO, London.

51. Clayton P. et al. (1991). *Review of municipal solid waste incineration in the UK*. WSL Report LR 776 (PA). Warren Spring Laboratory, Stevenage.

52. Organisation for Economic Co-operation and Development (1991). *Environmental indicators: a preliminary set*. OECD, Paris.

53. Her Majesty's Inspectorate of Pollution (1992). *Waste disposal and recycling: sewage sludge incineration*. Process Guidance Note IPR 5/11. HMSO, London.

54. Department of the Environment (1992). See reference 50.

55. Department of the Environment (1991). *Digest of environmental protection and water statistics* No.14. HMSO, London.

56. Warren Spring Laboratory (1992). A review of incineration technology and of the pollution arising from the incineration of wastes: prepared at the request of the Royal Commission.

57. Department of the Environment. *Clinical wastes: a technical memorandum on arisings, treatment and disposal*. Waste Management Paper No.25. (In preparation).

58. England and Wales (1988). *The Control of Pollution (Special Waste) (Amendment) Regulations*. Statutory Instrument No.1790. HMSO, London.

59. Department of the Environment (1992). See reference 50.

60. Commission of the European Communities (1992). See reference 25.

61. O'Connor, D.G. (1991). Options for the disposal of chemical wastes and the duty of care. *Environmental Pollution Bulletin* (9) 30–40.

62. (a) Department of the Environment (1992). See reference 50.

    (b) Warren Spring Laboratory (1992). See reference 56.

63. Warren Spring Laboratory (1992). See reference 56.

64. Department of the Environment (1992). See reference 50.

65. Department of the Environment (Northern Ireland). Communication with the Royal Commission.

66. *ENDS Report* (1991). Government put on the spot by clinical waste imports. (197) p.10.

67. Warren Spring Laboratory (1992). See reference 56.

68. Department of the Environment (1991). See reference 55 (table 6.3).

69. Mitchell, D.J. and Scott, D.W. (1991). *Survey of waste disposal options*. Warren Spring Laboratory, Stevenage.

70. *ENDS Report* (1992). Subsidising the dash to burn trash. (211) p.12.

71. Woodfield, M. (1987). *The environmental impact of refuse incineration in the UK*. Warren Spring Laboratory, Stevenage.

72. Scottish Office. Communication with the Royal Commission

73. Council of the Isles of Scilly. Communication with the Royal Commission.

74. Department of the Environment (Northern Ireland). Communication with the Royal Commission.

75. Water Services Association. Evidence to the Royal Commission.

76 & 77. Department of the Environment (1991). See reference 55.

78. *ENDS Report* (1991). New emission data stir controversy over hospital incinerators. (196) 10–11.

79 & 80. Mitchell, D.J. and Scott, D.W. (1991). See reference 69.

81. Chemical Industries Association. Evidence to the Royal Commission.

82. Operators of the merchant special waste incinerators. Communications with the Royal Commission.

83. Mitchell, D.J. and Scott, D.W. (1991). See reference 69.

84. Warren Spring Laboratory (1992). See reference 56.

85. National Farmers' Union of England and Wales. Evidence to the Royal Commission.

86. FEC Consultants (1988). *Straw firing of industrial boilers*. Energy Technology Support Unit Report B1158. ETSU, Harwell.

87. *ENDS Report* (1992). See reference 70.

88. (a) *ENDS Report* (1992). See reference 70.

    (b) Clayton, P., et al. (1991). See reference 51.

89. Department of the Environment. Communication with the Royal Commission.

90. Warren Spring Laboratory (1992). See reference 56.

91. *The Observer* (1992). Dark days for clean power. (10492) p.33. (15 November 1992).

92. Her Majesty's Government (1990). *This common inheritance: Britain's environmental strategy*. Cm 1200. (See paragraph 12.35).

93 & 94. Department of the Environment (1992). See reference 50.

95. Mitchell, D.J. and Scott, D.W. (1992). *Investigations of emissions and pollutant pathways at a multiple hearth sewage sludge incinerator*. WSL Report LR 875. Warren Spring Laboratory, Stevenage.

96. Energy Technology Support Unit. Communication with the Royal Commission.

97. Warren Spring Laboratory (1992). See reference 56.

98. National Environment Protection Board, Sweden. Evidence to the Royal Commission.

99–106. International Solid Wastes Association Working Group on Waste Incineration (ISWA) (1991). *Energy from waste state-of-the-art report*. ISWA, Malmo.

107. Kiser J.V.L. (1991). Municipal waste combustion in the United States: an overview. *Waste Age* **22**, 27–30.

108. (a) *Chemical Engineer* (1993). Dioxin burn stalled. (534) p.6.

    (b) *Chemical Engineer* (1993). EPA snubs Gore on incinerator. (535) p.11.

109. Energy Technology Support Unit (1992). *Some observations on municipal solid waste management in Japan*. ETSU Report B00337. ETSU, Harwell.

110. Warren Spring Laboratory (1992). See reference 56.

111. European Communities (1989). See references 29 and 30.

112. Her Majesty's Inspectorate of Pollution (1992). *Municipal waste incineration*. Process Guidance Note IPR 5/3. HMSO, London.

113. Warren Spring Laboratory (1992). See reference 56.

114 & 115. Clayton P. et al. (1991). See reference 51.

116. Mitchell, D.J. and Scott, D. (1992). See reference 95.

117. Leonard, A., et al. (1992). *Investigation of emissions and pollutant pathways at an advanced fluidised bed sewage sludge incinerator*. WSL Report LR 843. Warren Spring Laboratory, Stevenage.

118. (a) Briscombe, C., Mitchell, D. and Scott, D. (1991). *An emission investigation at a small starved air clinical waste incinerator*. WSL Report LR 866. Warren Spring Laboratory, Stevenage;

    (b) Mitchell, D.J. (1991). *An emission investigation at a clinical waste incinerator*. WSL Report LR 766. Warren Spring Laboratory, Stevenage.

119. (a) Mitchell, D.J., Scott, D.W. and Briscombe, C. (1992). *Investigation of emissions and pollutant pathways at an advanced clinical waste incinerator*. WSL Report LR 870. Warren Spring Laboratory, Stevenage;

    (b) Mitchell, D.J. and Scott, D.W. (1992). *An emission investigation at an advanced rotary kiln clinical waste incinerator*. WSL Report L 897. Warren Spring Laboratory, Stevenage;

    (c) Loader, A. and Scott, D.W. (1992). *An emission investigation at an advanced starved air clinical waste incinerator*. WSL Report L 890. Warren Spring Laboratory, Stevenage.

120 –122. Warren Spring Laboratory (1992). See reference 56.

123. Great Britain (1960). *Radioactive Substances Act.* HMSO, London.

124. Commission of the European Communities (1991). Proposal for a Council Directive on the landfill of waste, COM (91) 102 final—SYN 335. *Official Journal of the European Communities* **C150**, 129–154.

125. (a) Environmental Safety Centre (1991). *Pollution control at chemical incineration works.* DOE Report No. DOE/HMIP/RR/91/055. DOE, London.

    (b) Cremer and Warner Ltd (1991). *Pollution control at hospital incinerators.* DOE Report No. DOE/HMIP/RR/91/041. DOE, London.

    (c) Ecotec Ltd (1991). *Pollution control for waste derived fuel processes.* DOE Report No. DOE/HMIP/RR/91/063. DOE, London.

    (d) Clayton Environmental Consultants (1991). *Pollution control at sewage sludge incineration works.* DOE Report No. DOE/HMIP/RR/91/040. DOE, London.

    (e) Warren Spring Laboratory (1991). *Review of pollution control at municipal waste incineration works.* DOE Report No. DOE/HMIP/RR/91/039. DOE, London.

126. Commission of the European Communities (1992). See reference 25.

127. Germany (1990). See reference 24.

128. R J Wheatley (1991). Getting a project up and running, in, *Energy from Waste: papers from a conference, London, 9 October 1991.* The Institute of Energy, London. pp.82–104.

129. National Environment Protection Board, Sweden. Evidence to the Royal Commission.

130. (a) Christmann A. and Schetter G. (1991). Future-orientated firing concept for refuse incineration plants as executed at the Ludwigshafen plant, in, *Proceedings of the Institution of Mechanical Engineers: engineering for profit from waste, Düsseldorf, 15–17 April 1991.* Mechanical Engineering Publications, Bury St Edmunds. pp. 13–20. (Municipal waste).

    (b) S. P. Dagnall and P. J. Scott (1991) Industrial and commercial wastes as fuel—a review of United Kingdom experience, in, *Proceedings of the Institution of Mechanical Engineers: engineering for profit from waste, Düsseldorf, 15–17 April 1991.* Mechanical Engineering Publications, Bury St Edmunds. pp.111–120. (Poultry litter; scrap tyres; typical industrial waste).

    (c) WRc (1991). *Selection of an alternative strategy for the disposal of sewage sludge from East London.* WRc Report No. UC1117. WRc, Swindon. (Sewage sludge).

    (d) Williams D. B. and Leech D.J. (1991). The manufacture of refuse derived fuel and plant modifications needed to make a competitive product, in, *Proceedings of the Institution of Mechanical Engineers: engineering for profit from waste, Düsseldorf, 15–17 April 1991.* Mechanical Engineering Publications, Bury St Edmunds. pp.79–84. (Open-cast coal).

    (e) Chappell, P. (1991). A review of municipal waste combustion technology, in, *Energy from waste: papers from a conference, London, 9 October 1991.* The Institute of Energy, London. pp.9–22. (Mined coal).

131. Dagnall S.P. and Scott P.J. (1991). See reference 130b.

132. Energy Technology Support Unit. Communication with the Royal Commission.

133. (a) Ottinger R. et al. (1990). *Environmental costs of electricity.* Oceana Publications, New York. p.456.

    (b) Chappell P. (1991). See reference 130e.

134. Department of the Environment (1992). *A review of options.* Waste Management Paper No.1. Second edition. HMSO, London. (See paragraph 7.1)

135. Department of the Environment (1992). See reference 50 (paragraphs 15.30–15.31).

136. Energy Technology Support Unit. Communication with the Royal Commission.

137. (a) Chappell P. (1991). See reference 130e.

    (b) Scragg D.M. (1991). An operator's perspective, in, *Energy from Waste: papers from a conference, London, 9 October 1991.* The Institute of Energy, London. pp.63–79.

    (c) Department of the Environment (1992) . See reference 134. p.39.

138. England and Wales (1991). *The Electricity (Non-Fossil Fuel Sources) Order*. Statutory Instrument No.2490. HMSO, London.

139. Department of the Environment (1992). See reference 134 (table 8.2).

140. National Environment Protection Board, Sweden. Evidence to the Royal Commission.

141 & 142. ISWA (1991). See reference 99.

143. United States Government (1991). *National energy strategy: powerful ideas for America*. First edition. GPO, Washington.

144. Department of the Environment (1992). See reference 134 (paragraph 8.17).

145. P. Chappell (1991). See reference 130e.

146. Energy Technology Support Unit (1990). *A review of mass burn incineration as an energy source*. ETSU Report R-57. ETSU, Harwell. (See p.44).

147. Williams D.B. and Leech D.J. (1991). See reference 130d.

148. Lelieveld, J. and Crutzen P.J. (1992). Indirect chemical effects of methane on climate warming. *Nature* **355**, 339–341.

149. Department of the Environment. Communication with the Royal Commission.

150. Department of the Environment (1992). See reference 50 (paragraph 3.16).

151. (a) Creaser C.S. et al. (1989). Survey of background levels of PCDDs & PCDFs in UK soils. *Chemosphere* **18**, 767–776.

    (b) Creaser C.S. et al. (1990). Levels and sources of PCDDs and PCDFs in urban British soils. *Chemosphere* **21**, 931–938.

    (c) Startin J.R., Rose M. and Offen C. (1989). Survey of background levels of PCDDs and PCDFs in UK vegetation. *Chemosphere* **19**, 531–534.

152. (a) Kjeller L. et al. (1991). Increases in the polychlorinated dibenzo-p-dioxin and dibenzofuran content of soils and vegetation since the 1840's. *Environmental Science and Technology* **25**, 1619–1627.

    (b) Stanley J.S. et al. (1990). Polychlorinated dibenzo-p-dioxin and dibenzofuran concentration levels in human adipose tissue samples from the continental United States collected from 1971 through 1987. *Chemosphere* **20**, 895–901.

153. Department of the Environment (1989). *Dioxins in the environment*. Pollution Paper No.27. HMSO, London. (See paragraph 3.29).

154. Department of the Environment (1989). See reference 153. (paragraph 2.4—The weighting scheme used in UK and European regulations is the International Toxicity Factor, *I-TEF*, adopted in 1988 by the North Atlantic Treaty Organisation Committee on the Challenges of Modern Society, *NATO-CCMS*).

155. Department of the Environment (1989). See reference 153 (paragraph 3.29).

156. Department of the Environment (1989). See reference 153 (paragraph 7.17).

157 & 158. Ministry of Agriculture, Fisheries and Food (1992). *Dioxins in food*. Food Surveillance Paper No.31. HMSO, London. (paragraph 40).

159. Committee on Toxicity of Chemicals in Food, Consumer Products and the Environment (1992). Appendix 1, in, *Dioxins in food*. Food Surveillance Paper No.31. HMSO, London.

160. Ministry of Agriculture, Fisheries and Food (1992). See reference 157 (paragraph 63).

161. Liem A.K.D. et al. (1992). Occurrence of dioxins in cow's milk in the vicinity of municipal waste incinerators and a metal reclamation plant in the Netherlands. *Chemosphere* **23**, 1675–1684.

162. Ball D. et al. (1991). *Panteg monitoring project: first interim report*. Welsh Office, Cardiff.

163. Ministry of Agriculture, Fisheries and Food (1992). See reference 157 (paragraph 64).

164. *ENDS Report* (1992). Coalite faces a second liability claim over dioxins. (215) p.9.

165. Ministry of Agriculture, Fisheries and Food (1992). *Studies on dioxins in Derbyshire: third report*. MAFF, London.

166. Berryman R. J. et al. (1991). *HMIP investigations into the emissions of dioxins and furans from the smokeless fuel plant and chemical waste incinerator at the Coalite works near Bolsover, Derbyshire.* DOE Report No. DOE/HMIP/RR/91/066. DOE, London.

167. *ENDS Report* (1992). See reference 164.

168. *ENDS Report* (1992). Coalite faces unprecedented clean up claim. (215) p.5.

169. (a) Fingerhut M.A. et al. (1991). Cancer mortality in workers exposed to 2,3,7,8-Tetra-chlorodibenzodioxin. *New England Journal of Medicine* **324**, 212–218.

    (b) Manz A. et al. (1991). Cancer mortality among workers in chemical plant contaminated with dioxins. *Lancet* **338**, 959–964.

170. Saracci R. et al. (1992). Cancer mortality in workers exposed to chlorophenoxy herbicides and chlorophenols. *Lancet* **338,** 1027–1032.

171. International Agency for Research on Cancer (1987). *IARC monographs on the evaluation of carcinogenic risks to humans: overall evaluations of carcinogenicity: an updating of IARC monographs Volumes 1 to 42.* Supplement 7. IARC, Lyon.

172. Committee on the Toxicity of Chemicals in Food, Consumer Products and the Environment (1989). Appendix 1, in, *Dioxins in the environment.* Pollution Paper No.27. London, HMSO.

173. Department of the Environment (1989). See reference 153 (paragraph 10.1).

174 & 175. Committee on the Toxicity of Chemicals in Food, Consumer Products and the Environment (1992). See reference 159.

176. Nuclear Research Institute, Karlsruhe. Evidence to the Royal Commission.

177. Greenpeace. Evidence to the Royal Commission.

178. Cory Environmental Ltd (1988). Environmental assessment submitted as part of a planning application for an industrial waste incinerator at Seal Sands, Billingham, Cleveland.

179. Department of the Environment (1992). *Reducing emissions of volatile organic compounds and levels of ground level ozone, a UK strategy.* A consultation paper. DOE, London.

180. Gauglhofer J. and Bianchi V. (1991). Chromium, in, Merian E. (ed.) *Metals and their compounds in the environment: occurrence, analysis and biological relevance.* VCH, Wennheim. pp.854–878.

181. Ministry of Agriculture, Fisheries and Food (1983). *Survey of cadmium in food: first supplementary report.* Food Surveillance Paper 12. HMSO, London.

182. Advisory Group on the Effects of Lead and Neuropsychological Effects in Children (1988). *Neuropsychological effects of lead in children: a review of research 1984–1988.* Medical Research Council, London.

183. Osborne J.M. (1992). Hazardous waste incinerator stack emission risks, in, *Proceedings of the 1992 Incineration Conference, Albuquerque, May 11–15, 1992.* Edited by M. E. Wacks. University of California, Irvine, 1992. pp. 237–244.

184. (a) Elliott P. et al. (1992). Incidence of cancers of the larynx and lung near incinerators of waste solvents and oils in Great Britain. *Lancet* **339**, 854–857.

    (b) Small Area Health Statistics Unit (1992). *An analysis of the incidence of cancers of the larynx and lung near incinerators of waste solvents and oils in Great Britain.* SAHSU Report No.4. SAHSU, London.

185. Lloyd O.L. et al. (1988). Twinning in human populations and in cattle exposed to air pollution from incinerators. *British Journal of Industrial Medicine* **45**, 556–560.

186. Scottish Home and Health Department (1988). *Report of a working party on microphthalmos in the Forth Valley Health Board area.* SHHD, Edinburgh.

187. Scottish Home and Health Department (1985). *Bonnybridge/ Denny morbidity review: report of an independent review group.* SHHD, Edinburgh.

188. (a) Welsh Office (1985). *The incidence of congenital malformations in Wales, with particular reference to the district of Torfaen, Gwent.* Welsh Office, Cardiff.

(b) Welsh Office (1987). *The incidence of congenital malformations in Wales, with particular reference to the District of Torfaen, Gwent: an updated analysis.* Welsh Office, Cardiff.

(c) Laurence K. (1987). *Neural tube defect and polydactyly in Gwent: an independent study on behalf of the Welsh Office.* Welsh Office, Cardiff.

189. Gustavsson P. (1989). Mortality among workers at a municipal waste incinerator. *American Journal of Industrial Medicine* **15**, 245–253.

190. *Irish Law Reports Monthly* (1988). Hanrahan v Merck Sharp and Dohme **8,** 629–646.

191. Cory Environmental Ltd. (1988). See reference 178.

192. Yorkshire Water Services Ltd. (1991). Environmental statement submitted as part of a planning application for a sewage sludge incinerator at Knostrop, West Yorkshire.

193. Clarke R. (1992). Radiation protection standards: a practical exercise in risk assessment. Paper delivered at *Risk Assessment, London, 5–9 October 1992,* a conference organised by the Health and Safety Executive.

194. Cleverly D. et al. (1991). Regulatory analysis of pollutant emissions, including polychlorinated dibenzo-p-dioxins (CDDs) and dibenzofurans (CDFs), from the stacks of municipal waste combustors, in, Hattemer-Frey, H. and Travis C. (eds.) *Health effects of the incineration of municipal waste.* CRC Press, Boca Raton. pp.47–63.

195. Bayer AG. Communication with the Royal Commission.

196. Mason D. (1992). DoE turns down Warwick clinical waste incinerator. *Surveyor* **178** (5205) p.5.

197. International Technology Europe plc. Evidence to the Royal Commission.

198. World Health Organisation (1987). *Air quality guidelines for Europe.* European Series No.23. WHO Regional Publications, Copenhagen.

199. Hampshire County Council. Evidence to the Royal Commission.

200. (a) Great Britain (1992). *Road Traffic (Carriage of Dangerous Substances in Road Tankers and Tank Containers) Regulations.* Statutory Instrument No.743. HMSO, London

(b) Great Britain (1992). *Road Traffic (Carriage of Dangerous Substances in Packages etc.) Regulations.* Statutory Instrument No.742. HMSO, London.

(c) Health and Safety Commission (1992). *The safe disposal of clinical waste.* HMSO, London.

201. C. de Wit et al. (1992). Polychlorinated dibenzo-p-dioxin and polychlorinated dibenzofuran levels in wildlife and patterns in fish and fish-eating wildlife in the Baltic Sea. *Chemosphere* **25**, 185–188.

202. Simmonds M.P., Johnston P.A. and French M.C. (1993). Organochlorine and mercury contamination in United Kingdom seals. *Veterinary Record* **132,** 291–295.

203. International Technology Europe plc. Evidence to the Royal Commission.

204. ORATE (Oswaldtwistle residents against toxic waste). Evidence to the Royal Commission.

205. Howlett S.P., Timothy S.P. and Vaughan D. (1992). *Industrial plasma: focusing UK skills on global opportunities.* Centre for Exploitation of Science and Technology, London.

206. Funfschilling M.R. and Eschenbach R.C. (1992). *A plasma centrifugal furnace for treating hazardous waste, Muttenz, Switzerland.* Paper delivered at *Electrotech 92, Montreal, 15–18 June 1992.*

207. Souet P. (1992). Waste management in France: the current situation and new objectives set by the national plan for the environment. Paper delivered at *Waste Collecting and Management: the French Approach, London, 28 April 1992,* a conference organised by the French Centre for Overseas Trade (CFCE), Paris.

208. Blue Circle Technical Centre. Communication with the Royal Commission.

209. Steele D.F., Wilks J.P. and Batey W. (1992). The electrochemical destruction of waste reprocessing solvent and ion exchange resins, in, *Proceedings of the 1992 Incineration*

*Conference, Albuquerque, 11–15 May, 1992.* Edited by M. E. Wacks. University of California, Irvine. pp.167–174.

210. Wessex Waste Management Ltd. Communication with the Royal Commission

211. Dumbleton B. (1993). Vegetarian tigers. *Surveyor* **179,** (5231) 10–11.

212. Independent Panel on Intractable Waste (1992). *A cleaner Australia.* Scheduled Wastes Working Group, Sydney.

213. Commission of the European Communities (1992). See reference 25.

214. Commission of the European Communities, Directorate General XI (Environment). Evidence to the Royal Commission.

215. European Communities (1989). See references 29 and 30.

216. Warren Spring Laboratory (1992). See reference 56.

217. Commission of the European Communities (1992). See reference 25.

218. British Standards Institute (1987). *Quality systems.* **BS 5750** (ISO 9000). BSI, London.

219. Durkee K.R and Eddinger J.A. (1992). Certification of medical waste incinerator operators and operator supervisors, in, *Proceedings of the 1992 Incineration Conference, Albuquerque, 11–15 May, 1992.* Edited by M. E. Wacks. University of California, Irvine. pp.443–446.

220. Royal Commission on Environmental Pollution (1985). See reference 2.

221. Waste Management Industry Training and Advisory Board. Evidence to the Royal Commission.

222. National Association of Waste Disposal Contractors. Evidence to the Royal Commission.

223. Gibson M. (1993). Institute of Wastes Management structured education and training scheme. *Wastes Management* (February) 36–37.

224. (a) Warren Spring Laboratory (1992). See reference 56.

    (b) Harrad S. and Jones K. (1992). Dioxins at large. *Chemistry in Britain* **28,** 1110–1112.

    (c) *ENDS Report* (1993). Catalyst cuts dioxin emissions from incinerators. (216) pp. 9–10.

225. Greenpeace. Evidence to the Royal Commission.

226. Royal Commission on Environmental Pollution (1985). See reference 2.

227. Greenpeace. Evidence to the Royal Commission.

228. *ENDS Report* (1993). ICI makes progress on waste, less on energy efficiency. (218) p. 3.

229. Greenpeace International (1991). *In-plant process changes to eliminate chlorinated solvents in various industrial sectors.* Greenpeace International, Amsterdam.

230. Advisory Committee on Business and the Environment (1991). *First progress report to the Secretaries of State for the Environment and for Trade and Industry.* Department of Trade and Industry, London.

231. Her Majesty's Government (1992). See reference 48 (paragraph 13.3).

232. Her Majesty's Government (1990). See reference 92 (paragraph 14.23).

233. (a) Reiter P. (1991). *Recycling potential assessment.* Seattle Solid Waste Utility, Seattle.

    (b) Morris J. (1991). Mixed paper recycling practices in North America. *Resource Recycling.* **10,** 84–91.

234. European Communities (1986). Directive on the protection of the environment and in particular of the soil, when sewage sludge is used in agriculture, 86/278/EEC. *Official Journal of the European Communities* **L181,** 6–12.

235. Wessex Waste Management Ltd. Communication with the Royal Commission.

236. Department of the Environment (1992). See reference 55 for source data.

237. European Communities (1991). Council Directive on batteries and accumulators containing certain dangerous substances, 91/157/EEC. *Official Journal of the European Communities* **L78,** 38–40.

238. Advisory Committee on Hazardous Substances. *First annual report 1991–1992.* HMSO, London. (Regulations are required to supplement the 10th amendment to the EC Directive on marketing and use—91/338/EEC).

239. Royal Commission on Environmental Pollution (1988). See reference 20.

240. European Communities (1989). See references 29 and 30.

241. Commission of the European Communities (1992). See reference 25.

242. Harrad S. and Jones K. (1992). See reference 224b.

243. Coopers & Lybrand Ltd (1993). *Landfill pricing: correcting possible market distortions.* HMSO, London.

244. Advisory Committee on Business and the Environment (1992). *First progress report: update: a note by the President of the Board of Trade and the Secretary of State for the Environment.* Department of Trade and Industry, London.

245. Her Majesty's Government (1992). See reference 48 (paragraph 13.6).

246. Environmental Resources Ltd (1992). *Economic instruments and recovery of resources from waste: a report prepared for the Department of Trade and Industry and the Department of the Environment.* ERL, London.

247. Coopers & Lybrand Ltd (1993). See reference 243.

248. Renewable Energy Advisory Group (1992). *Report to the President of the Board of Trade.* DTI Energy Paper No.60. HMSO, London.

249. Warren Spring Laboratory (1992). See reference 56.

250. Department of the Environment (1992). See reference 6.

251. WRc (1991). See reference 130c.

252. Royal Commission on Environmental Pollution (1992). *Freshwater quality.* Sixteenth Report. Cm 1966. HMSO, London.

253. Great Britain (1985). *Food and Environment Protection Act.* HMSO, London.

# APPENDIX A

# COMBUSTION SYSTEMS USED FOR WASTE INCINERATION

## Ashing Rotary Kiln

A.1  Ashing rotary kiln incinerators are used primarily to burn chemical waste. They are also suitable for the combustion of clinical waste and municipal solid waste, but are not used in the UK for municipal solid waste. Incinerators of this type are particularly efficient at destroying organic compounds. Most clinical waste units burn about one tonne of waste an hour but for municipal solid waste up to 20 tonnes an hour is possible.

A.2  Waste is fed downwards into a refractory-lined drum which acts as the grate surface in the primary combustion stage. The waste is ignited and the rotating action of the drum mixes it with air supplied through the walls. The separate secondary combustion chamber is fitted with air intakes and after-burners which complete the combustion of gases. Ash residues fall into a quench tank and are removed.

A.3  The refractory linings and drum seals are prone to damage. The concentrations of carbon monoxide and hydrocarbons emitted by incinerators of this type in the USA show considerable variability. The introduction of volatile wastes can also lead to "puffing" (escapes of unburnt gases through the end plates). Oxygen enrichment has been used to overcome these problems; but, as well as increasing running costs, it increases emissions of nitrogen oxides.

## Fluidised Bed

A.4  Fluidised bed incinerators are used in the UK mainly to burn dewatered sewage sludge cake at a rate of 3 tonnes an hour. They are also suitable for burning clinical waste; some types of chemical waste; and municipal waste that has been sorted and shredded. They are not used in the UK to incinerate municipal solid waste.

A.5  The solid, liquid or gaseous waste is injected onto a bed of sand or similar inert material which is agitated or 'fluidised' by an upward flow of air through a porous plate below it. Combustion occurs within the bed, which is maintained at 800–900°C. There are three types of fluidised bed incinerators: atmospheric, circulating and pressurised, which differ in respect of air velocity and pressure in the combustion chamber.

A.6  Emissions of sulphur oxides can be reduced by adding calcium compounds to the bed. In order to achieve the new HMIP standards however, acid gas removal systems would also need to be installed.

## Liquid Injection

A.7  Liquid injection incinerators are used most commonly for chemical waste such as oils and solvents. They can also be used to burn gases and sewage slurries.

A.8  Liquid waste is pumped from storage tanks and injected through an atomiser into one end of a refractory-lined cylinder. This may have a single combustion chamber with several zones or multiple chambers. Highly combustible liquids are fired into the first zone or chamber, together with waste gases. Incombustible liquids containing solids, for example sewage slurries can be injected into subsequent zones or chambers, where the liquid evaporates and the solid content burns.

A.9  Incinerators of this type achieve nearly total combustion of the waste, without leaving any ash. Carbon monoxide emissions are variable but, in the USA, generally exceed the limit of 50 mg/Nm³ proposed in the draft EC Directive on the incineration of hazardous waste (2.33 and table 2.3). The absence of moving parts leads to high reliability, although the atomisers are prone to block.

## Mass Burn with Excess Air Combustion

A.10   Mass burn incinerators are used to burn municipal solid waste. The capacity of existing plants in the UK is normally about 10 tonnes of waste an hour, although they can burn waste at a rate of 30 tonnes an hour.

A.11   The waste is fed by crane from storage bunkers to the feed hopper, from where it flows down, usually aided by a mechanical stoker, into the combustion chamber. Air is introduced through a moving grate in the chamber which agitates the waste and promotes thorough distribution of the air. Waste is fed onto the grate and passes first through a drying stage at 50–100°C, during which volatile compounds are released. These burn above the grate, where secondary air is introduced to facilitate complete gas phase combustion. The remaining waste moves down the grate and continues to burn slowly, and eventually the ash is discharged from the end of the grate.

A.12   Although there are a variety of designs for mass burn incinerators, the most efficient appear to be those with reciprocating or roller grates and the combustion chamber in the form of a vertical shaft.

## Multiple Hearth

A.13   Multiple hearth incinerators are an old design used to burn chemical waste and sewage sludge.

A.14   They consist usually of six to eight circular grates arranged in a cascade formation around a central shaft in a vertical cylinder with a refractory lining. Waste is introduced onto the top grate and moved down the cascade by rabble arms which help to expose fresh surfaces of the waste. Air is supplied to the grates. The middle grates represent the main combustion zone and temperatures there range from 750 to 1000°C. Final combustion and cooling of the ash residues occur on the lower grates. The ash may be discharged to a quench bath or removed after air cooling.

A.15   There is evidence that, although burnout is generally good, there can be poor gas phase combustion and very high carbon monoxide levels. There are high maintenance costs because of the number of moving parts.

## Pulsed Hearth

A.16   Pulsed hearth incinerators are used mainly to burn clinical waste.

A.17   The waste and ash are moved through the incinerator by the pulsing action of one or more refractory hearths, stepped at each side to form a U shape. Support burners ensure minimum furnace temperatures are maintained. Combustion air is supplied in excess through vertically positioned ports.

A.18   Very few data on the performance of this type of incinerator have been published. The absence of moving mechanical parts and the vertical positioning of the air ports in the hearths should make for good reliability. However the distribution of waste and heat might become uneven because of blockages.

## Slagging Rotary Kiln

A.19   Slagging rotary kiln incinerators are suitable mainly for chemical waste. They produce a vitrified slag which has a very low leaching rate for heavy metals and organic compounds and is therefore more amenable to landfilling than solid residues from other types of incinerator.

A.20   The slagging rotary kiln incinerator is similar to the ashing rotary kiln, but uses a higher combustion temperature (1400°C). This melts inorganic waste and ash and produces a liquid slag with a low organics content. The liquid slag is retained in the kiln to trap particulate matter before being solidified in a quench tank.

A.21   There are few published data on the performance of this type of incinerator.

**Starved air**

A.22   Starved air incinerators are most commonly used in the UK to burn clinical waste but they can also be used for sewage screenings and packaging materials. Most plants are small, burning 0.5 to 3 tonnes of waste an hour, and operate on a daily batch basis. The waste is fed manually onto a single fixed grate and the plant is de-ashed manually the next day.

A.23   Starved air incinerators consist of a primary ignition chamber, into which the waste is fed, and a secondary combustion chamber preheated to 1000°C. The temperature in the primary chamber is increased gradually (to 900°C) causing the release of volatile compounds in a limited supply of air which inhibits full combustion. Complete gas-phase combustion takes place in the high temperature, air-rich secondary chamber.

A.24   Some starved air incinerators have experienced considerable difficulties in achieving effective gas-phase combustion, resulting in short-term peaks of carbon monoxide, hydrocarbons and dark smoke in their emissions. Many plants have had to make semi-routine use of a dump stack. Equipment to deal with these problems is now available, and where fitted has reduced emissions considerably.

# APPENDIX B

# RELATIVE COSTS OF WASTE DISPOSAL BY INCINERATION AND LANDFILL

## Report by Aspinwall & Co Ltd on a study carried out for the Royal Commission

## 1. INTRODUCTION

B1.1   In support of the study by the Royal Commission on Environmental Pollution on the incineration of waste, Aspinwall & Co were retained to prepare this analysis of the comparative economics of landfill and incineration as waste disposal methods.

B1.2   The analysis of waste management practices involves a number of complex inter-relationships, and a comparative cost study of this nature must be framed along very strict guidelines in order to ensure that the conclusions reached are fair, i.e. that the comparisons match up directly and without prejudice to one option or the other.

*Sources*

B1.3   There is limited published information on the costs of either incineration or landfill. Further, the commercialisation of waste management activities has made much information commercially sensitive in the eyes of operators. However, a full literature search has been undertaken, and the noteworthy points of view have been duly referenced.

B1.4   The primary source of cost information for state of the art facilities is the waste management industry itself. Landfill costs have been derived from a few private sector and local authority (LAWDC) operators; incineration costs have been derived from engineering contractors.

B1.5   Traditionally, the Chartered Institute of Public Finance and Accountancy (CIPFA) has collated expenditure data on waste collection and disposal within local authorities, primarily for statistical comparison between authorities. However, this information has not been publicly available for three years now and in any event was considered unsuitable for our purposes. Within the CIPFA statistics there are many variations due to local circumstances such as methods of accounting, transport, use of private contractors, etc. All of these can have a significant influence on the expenditure data, and we have therefore chosen to bypass this source.

*Operating Standards and Technology*

B1.6   The environmental standards for each method of disposal will be guided by UK and EC legislation: primarily the existing and draft EC Directives and the relevant guidance notes on the combustion of wastes from Her Majesty's Inspectorate of Pollution.

*Size and Scope of Services Analysed*

B1.7   The size of the facilities in question need to be stipulated, as the costs of either incineration or landfill will vary considerably with economies of scale. This is not a serious problem so long as similar waste throughputs are assumed for either option. We therefore established the baseline conditions to apply to facilities each handling 200,000 tonnes per annum. For each option, economies of scale are discussed later in the report.

B1.8   The baseline analysis is also limited to the facilities only; the costs of initial collection and transport are not considered directly, but the transport costs of collected waste to the disposal site are discussed later for their relative importance to both options.

*Costs versus Charges*

B1.9   It must be emphasised that this is a study of costs, as opposed to charges. There is no attempt to include aspects of profitability which are reflected in the costs of commercial disposal faced by waste producers. It is an analysis of the costs of service provision. Other financial considerations such as capital charges, development taxes etc. are omitted in the main study, but are raised in a general discussion which follows.

*Discounted Cash Flow Analysis*

B1.10   Discounted cash flow analysis (DCF) has been applied to arrive at unit costs per tonne for both options. DCF analysis is a widely-used technique for the appraisal of capital investment projects, measuring in terms of their present worth the value of revenue streams and costs which occur over a long time horizon. It permits a direct comparison of various plant designs or disposal alternatives which have different life-spans or capital expenditure schedules. It also provides a useful measure for prospective operators of the level of investment and likely profitability of disposal facilities.

B1.11   The discount rate of 10 per cent assumed in this analysis is a generalised social discount rate which is appropriate to public sector investments. The rate is based on what the money would earn if it were invested in the best available alternative use (i.e. it is an opportunity cost). It is also a real rate of return, that is it is net of the impact of inflation over the life of the facility. The return on investment required by commercial investors may be higher, depending on the level of financial risk which is perceived. The sensitivity of results to different discount rates is discussed towards the end of this study.

**Report Structure**

B1.12   Chapters 2 and 3 deal respectively with the costs of landfilling and incineration, including an assessment of the incremental costs involved in the handling of more difficult waste streams, and energy recovery. A review and comparison of results is in Chapter 4, as is a brief discussion on the possible impacts of economic instruments. Chapter 5 looks at the trends and influences upon the future development of both options.

## 2.   THE COSTS OF LANDFILLING

**Introduction**

B2.1   The analysis of landfill costs below is organised into six sections which conform to the generally accepted stages of landfill development and operation: acquisition, assessment, development, operation, restoration and aftercare. As is demonstrated below, modern landfill husbandry represents a considerable commitment of professional and financial resources for an operator if it is to be commercially successful and environmentally acceptable.

*Summary of Costs*

B2.2   **Table B1** summarises calculated landfill costs.

B2.3   A total expenditure of over £33 million is required for this 200,000 tonnes pa facility accepting only MSW. Over the full life of the site, these costs are equivalent to a discounted cost per tonne of £9.83. The discussion below analyses component costs in more detail.

*Distribution of Costs*

B2.4   Landfills of this size are typically operated in phases. Each phase would consist of about 12 months of infilling, supplemented by several months of development and restoration, giving an approximate timespan for each phase of eighteen months. This will imply a distribution of the development and

## Table B1 — Summary of Landfill Costs

| Stage | Total Expenditure | Cost per tonne (DCF) |
|---|---|---|
| Acquisition | £8,000,000 | £4.27 |
| Assessment | £159,000 | £0.08 |
| Development | £5,016,000 | £1.30 |
| Operation | £16,044,000 (£802,200 pa) | £3.30 |
| Restoration | £2,472,000 | £0.48 |
| Aftercare | £1,600,000 | £0.40 |
| Total | £33,291,000 | £9.83 |

restoration costs over the operational life of the facility. In our model site, we assumed that there are 12 phases of operation through the site's 20 year life, and we have distributed the costs accordingly.

B2.5   For each stage, a table is provided which indicates the component costs involved, and the total expenditure, regardless of when it occurs (only operating costs are given as annual amounts). At the foot of each table, a unit cost per tonne is calculated using the DCF method; the percentage contribution of each stage to the total (discounted) cost of landfilling is also provided.

### Site Acquisition Costs

B2.6   Each parcel of land will have its own particular attributes and drawbacks, not to mention the influence of regional differentiation in values throughout the country. In general, prospective operators are concerned with three main factors in valuing voidspace:

— the amount of voidspace involved
— the types and quantities of waste to be disposed
— location and accessibility relative to urban and industrial centres which generate the wastes in question.

B2.7   The density of wastes is assumed to be about 1 m$^3$ per tonne of input, in accordance with standard industry practice, meaning that a voidspace of 4 million m$^3$ is required. A rule of thumb for the purchase of landfill voidspace throughout most of the 1980s was £1.00 per m$^3$. Valuations obviously fluctuated considerably around this figure, depending on many variables, such as regional location, the types of wastes to be handled, proximity to major conurbations etc. However, the valuations over time did not change greatly since there was generally no shortage of landfill capacity.

B2.8   In recent years, this value has tended to rise rapidly due to the increased difficulties in establishing new landfills, and the increase in their strategic importance. As the waste management industry develops, the control over disposal capacity is increasingly recognised as a valuable asset. Also, the industry has been flooded recently by cash rich newcomers such as the water companies, power companies and foreign interests (primarily from the US and France). This has brought about the current period of acquisition and consolidation in waste management, and it has resulted in higher valuations.

```
┌────────────────────────────────────────────────────────────────────┐
│  ┌──────────────────────────────────────────────────────────────┐   │
│  │                                                                │   │
│  │  Table   B2  -    Landfill Site Acquisition Costs             │   │
│  │                                                                │   │
│  │  Item                Rate          Quantity          Amount    │   │
│  │  ────────────────────────────────────────────────────────     │   │
│  │                                                                │   │
│  │  Site Acquisition  £2.00/m³    4,000,000 m³     £8,000,000     │   │
│  │                                                                │   │
│  │  Cost per tonne                                     £4.27      │   │
│  │                                                                │   │
│  │  % of total discounted costs                       43.4%       │   │
│  │                                                                │   │
│  └──────────────────────────────────────────────────────────────┘   │
└────────────────────────────────────────────────────────────────────┘
```

| Table B2 – Landfill Site Acquisition Costs | | | |
|---|---|---|---|
| Item | Rate | Quantity | Amount |
| Site Acquisition | £2.00/m$^3$ | 4,000,000 m$^3$ | £8,000,000 |
| Cost per tonne | | | £4.27 |
| % of total discounted costs | | | 43.4% |

B2.9   Regional disparities are also beginning to show. The South East is the most expensive area for voidspace due to the shortage relative to arisings[1]. Given these recent trends, we have assumed a price here of £2.00 per m$^3$, which represents a reasonable average of prices throughout the urban and industrial centres of the country. On this basis, total acquisition costs are put at £8 million, or £4.27 per tonne in **Table B2**. This represents about 43% of total discounted landfill costs.

B2.10   The alternative to the capital purchase of the site is to lease it, in which case the payment of royalties on a regular basis throughout the life of the site would replace this single up front commitment. It is very difficult to generalise about the value of royalty payments in comparison to purchase prices; under a royalty scheme payment would likely escalate during the life of the site, but the commitment of capital up front for purchase would also incur financial (mortgage or interest) charges. The main difference is in the pattern of spending, and hence on average cash flow each year. For our purposes, we have assumed that the operator is also the owner of the site, so as not to complicate the question of his obligations after the site ceases operation.

## Assessment Costs

B2.11   The allowance for site assessment is very modest in comparison to other costs (less than 1% of total costs), but these exercises are vitally important to the overall costs of operation. Costs are shown in **Table B3**. Improperly conducted site investigations, including geological and hydrogeological surveys, can result in incomplete understanding of the environmental risks from operation and consequently in inadequate site design. Planning legislation now requires an environmental assessment for developments of this nature.

B2.12   An allowance of £15,000 is made within the planning costs for a public inquiry, which may or may not be required. If it is, it could also become much more expensive (over £100,000) if it is contentious and drawn out. Some operators may also voluntarily incur costs for public relations, regardless of whether an inquiry takes place.

B2.13   The impact of higher regulatory pressure and the increased risk of future liability is likely to force up the costs of this stage in the near future, but overall the effect on total landfill costs would apparently be negligible.

## Development Costs

B2.14   The development stage is when most of the capital expenditure is incurred, and hence it is by far the most costly. The major expenses during this stage are for site lining, leachate collection and treatment systems, and landfill gas management systems. These three areas account for nearly £4 million, or roughly 90% of total development costs shown in **Table B4**.

```
Table  B3  -    Landfill Assessment Costs

Item                              Rate          Amount


1     Reconnaissance             Sum          £  10,000
2     Market survey              Sum          £   6,000
3     Prelim. Site Investigation Sum          £   7,000
4     Site survey                Sum          £   6,000
5     Full Site Investigation    Sum          £  70,000
6     Planning (+ meetings)      Sum          £  25,000
7     Environ.Assessment         Sum          £  35,000


      Total                                   £ 159,000

      Cost per tonne                            £  0.08

      % of total discounted costs                  0.8%
```

B2.15   A composite liner consisting of natural clay and high density polyethylene is assumed, which would not be strictly required in every situation although it is increasingly the standard approach. In the course of the technical assessment (above), the risk to the local environment of liner failure has to be assessed, and the decision made on the liner system to be deployed. However, the proposed EC Landfill Directive specifies criteria for site containment which make composite liners a practical choice.

B2.16   As a consequence of having the site lining, leachate and gas generated within the site require removal. Leachate treatment is assumed to take place on site (with discharge to sewer). Gas collection and control is also assumed in this base case, but its utilisation is not. The effect of incorporating energy recovery is included.

**Operating Costs**

B2.17   Expenditure on daily operation, not surprisingly, is the largest cost incurred over the life of the landfill—about 48% of total expenditure (**Table B5**). In reality, operating costs will vary from year to year depending on fluctuations in waste intake rates and other local conditions. Also, these costs have a tendency to vary a great deal from situation to situation. We therefore counsel caution in taking these figures at face value; they represent the average of a short list of examples which are subject to wide variation.

B2.18   All major components of plant and equipment are assumed to be leased, and appear here as operating items instead of capital outlays. Maintenance of the equipment is treated separately. The other major expense is on personnel (manager, foreman, weighbridge operator, machine operatives, labourers). An allowance of 20% is added to total operating costs to cover administration and other overheads.

**Restoration Costs**

B2.19   The cost of restoration is primarily the cost of capping the site, in this case with an underlayer of clay and a top layer of soil a total of 2 metres thick. No specific land use after restoration is assumed. The contribution of restoration expenditure to discounted costs is small at 5%. This is partly due to the discounting effect of these costs well in the future; the proportion of un-discounted expenditure is just under 8%. Costs of restoration are summarised in **Table B6**.

**Table B4 – Landfill Development Costs**
**Site Development**

| Item | | Rate | Quantity | Amount |
|---|---|---|---|---|
| 1 | Surf.water interception | £25/m | 1800 m | £45,000 |
| 2 | Lining (Composite): | | | |
| | – 2 mm HDPE                    ) | | | |
| | – 1 m clay (& geotextile) | £12.50/m² | 220,000m² | £2,750,000 |
| 3 | Leachate collection | | | |
| | – drainage blanket, geo-textile and manholes | £74,000 | 12 | £888,000 |
| 4 | Leachate removal (pumps and pipe network) | Sum | | £150,000 |
| 5 | Leachate treatment plant | ` Sum | | £250,000 |
| 6 | Effluent outfall | £25/m | 1000 m | £25,000 |
| 7 | Screening bunds | £35/m | 1800 m | £63,000 |
| 8 | Excavation (Soil strip to stockpile) | £0.4/m³ | 220,000m³ | £88,000 |
| 9 | Access (roads and parking) | Sum | | £100,000 |
| 10 | Security Fencing | £20/m | 1800 m | £36,000 |
| 11 | Tree planting | Sum | | £10,000 |
| 12 | Offices | Sum | | £35,000 |
| 13 | Wheel-cleaner | Sum | | £25,000 |
| 14 | Weighbridge(computerised) | Sum | | £50,000 |
| 15 | Garages/etc | Sum | | £25,000 |
| 16 | Utilities (water, elect.etc.) | Sum | | £20,000 |
| 17 | Gas management | | | |
| | – Monitoring Boreholes | £1000 | 28 | £28,000 |
| | – Wells @ 50 m spacing | £2000 | 36 | £72,000 |
| | – Well head (chambers) | £1000 | 36 | £36,000 |
| | – Extraction Pipe | £25/m | 4000m | £100,000 |
| | – Compound (M + E) | Sum | | £150,000 |
| | Total | | | £386,000 |
| 18 | Design (fees and management) | Sum | | £70,000 |

| | | |
|---|---|---|
| **Total** | | **£5,016,000** |
| **Cost per tonne** | | **£ 1.30** |
| **% of total discounted costs** | | **13.2%** |

**Aftercare Costs**

B2.20   Proper site development and operation should minimise the need for aftercare expenditure, but a certain amount of monitoring will always be required. Under conditions established in the Environmental Protection Act 1990, licensing authorities are under no obligation to issue a certificate of landfill completion until they are satisfied that there is no further threat to the local environment. This has

```
   Table   B5  -  Landfill Operating Costs

   Item                              Rate    Quantity(pa)      Amount


   1    Wages & salaries            £12,500   10 staff        £125,000
   2    Plant & Equipment (leased)
     -  Compactor                   £40,000        2      £80,000
     -  Loader                      £14,000        2      £28,000
     -  Scraper                     £45,000        1      £45,000
     -  other (screens,pumps,etc)                         £10,000
        Total                                             £163,000
   3    Equip. Maintenance            Sum                  £14,500
   4    Fuel                        £0.25/t   200,000t      £50,000
   5    Cover material (on site)    £1.50/m³  60,000m³      £90,000
             -Internal Bunds        £10/m     2,000m        £20,000
   6    Site maintenance              Sum                  £30,000
   7    Env. monitoring & control     Sum                  £30,000
   8    Surveying                   £400/ha   20 ha         £38,000
   9    Leachate treatment            Sum                  £40,000
   10   Rates (per tonne)           £0.4/t    200,000t      £80,000
   11   Systems maintenance (LFG, leachate)  (sum)         £20,000


   Sub total (annual)                                     £668,500

   Overheads (20%)                                        £133,700

                 Total (annual)                           £802,200

   Cost per tonne                                         £  3.30

   % of total discounted costs                            33.6%
```

brought concerns about the long term impact of landfilling on the environment to the heart of the debate about its true social cost.

B2.21   We have assumed an aftercare period lasting 30 years in this example, but it should be recognised that there is no agreement on the precise time that would be required before leachate (in particular) and gas were satisfactorily controlled. The latest (seventh) draft of the EC Landfill Directive is calling for a 50 year monitoring period; 30 years under the care of the operator and a further 20 years under the supervision of the licensing authority. The effect of extending the aftercare period does little to alter discounted costs since these are incurred well into the future.

B2.22   What is more important to the operator—and indeed to the licensing authority—is having to ensure that the funds are available at the time they are required. **Table B7** lists the expenditure requirements through two stages of aftercare: a first stage covering the first five years of intensive monitoring, followed by a second stage of 25 years during which activities can be stepped down. The total expenditure required over the whole period is estimated at over £1.6 million.

B2.23   To ensure that the funds are available, the licensing authority is likely to require that a fund be

**Table B6 – Landfill Restoration Costs**

| Item | | Rate | Quantity | Amount |
|------|--|------|----------|--------|
| 1 | Capping | | | |
| | – 1 m clay | £6/m$^3$ | 220,000 m$^3$ | £1,320,000 |
| | – 0.7 m subsoil | £4/m$^3$ | 147,000 m$^3$ | £588,000 |
| | – 0.3 m topsoil | £6/m$^3$ | 63,000 m$^3$ | £378,000 |
| 2 | Seeding | 30p/m$^2$ | 220,000 m$^2$ | £66,000 |
| 3 | Field drainage | £6000/ha | 20 ha | £120,000 |
| 4 | Landscaping | Sum | | £100,000 |
| | **Total** | | | **£2,472,000** |
| | **Cost per tonne** | | | **£ 0.48** |
| | **% of total discounted costs** | | | **4.9%** |

established and contributed to during the operational life of the facility. On the assumption that future costs would be estimated in the same way as they are here, the authority could require a contribution of 40 pence for every tonne of waste deposited, such that £1.6 million would be available at the beginning of the aftercare period. This transfers the timing of the operator's expense forward to the period of operation, with the funds collected offsetting the future obligation[2].

B2.24    This method provides the operator with a realistic present day cost of his aftercare commitment which remains relatively modest (4.8%) as a fraction of total costs.

**The Landfilling of Difficult Wastes**

B2.25    For the purposes of this research, difficult wastes are those materials, often liquid, which present special problems in waste disposal, **and** which can be either landfilled or incinerated. This refers primarily to sewage sludge and certain hazardous and/or special wastes.

B2.26    Co-disposal of these wastes with MSW is common practice in the UK. Although it is recognised as environmentally safe in Government circles (Waste Management Paper 26), the draft EC Landfill Directive confirms the likely future requirement strictly to segregate hazardous and non hazardous wastes in separate disposal sites.

B2.27    Despite the trend towards segregation, the operational standards for both types of landfill have been converging recently, and the incremental requirements (and costs) for landfilling difficult wastes are not substantially above those for MSW.

*Sewage Sludge*

B2.28 Despite the clear need to find land based alternatives to sewage sludge disposal at sea, landfilling is not perceived as the most practical choice. Such is the pressure on the landfill market from household, commercial and industrial wastes that suitable locations for sewage sludge are more and more difficult to find. The pathogens typically found in sludge exclude it from consideration at most locations which accept other household organic wastes. However, the potential for sludge to act as a catalyst in the production of landfill gas is not lost on operators of sites where this is applicable. There is no question of having landfill sites dedicated solely to sludge disposal.

## Table B7 – Landfill Aftercare Costs

| Item | Rate | Quantity | Amount |
|---|---|---|---|
| **Period 1: 5 years** | | | |
| 1  Maintenance | Sum | | £5,000 |
| 2  Settlement maintenance | Sum | | £10,000 |
| 3  Leachate treat.& disp. | Sum | | £50,000 |
| 4  Gas management | Sum | | £15,000 |
| 5  Environment monitoring | Sum | | £15,000 |
| Sub total (annual) | | | **£95,000** |
| **Period 2 : 25 years** | | | |
| 6)  Maintenance | Sum | | £1,000 |
| 7)  Leachate treat.& disp. | Sum | | £25,000 |
| 8)  Gas management | Sum | | £8,000 |
| 9)  Env. monitoring | Sum | | £15,000 |
| Sub total (annual) | | | **£49,000** |
| Total Expenditure | | | **£1,700,000** |
| Total Aftercare Fund (200,000 tonnes pa @ 40p/t = £80,000 pa) | | | £1,600,000 |
| Cost per tonne | | | £ 0.40 |
| % of total discounted costs | | | 4.1 % |

B2.29   The volume limits placed on sludge co-disposal at sites where it is permitted reduce the need for special consideration in site design and operation. The other costs of pre-treatment (drying) are typically not borne by the landfill operator.

*Hazardous and Special Wastes*

B2.30   Disposing of hazardous and special wastes will require extra considerations at most stages of landfill management. Table B8 below summarises the incremental items involved, following the arrangement of costs described above.

B2.31   The effect of placing these costs into the DCF table is to raise the total cost per tonne by 14% to £11.18. Total expenditure (not discounted) is increased by 17% (**Table B8**).

B2.32   The relatively modest increase in costs arguably does not reflect the increased risk inherent in handling hazardous and special wastes, but operators will usually seek to have this reflected in the charges for disposal. The costs of pre-treatment, increasingly required by regulations, are also not covered here.

```
┌─────────────────────────────────────────────────────────────────┐
│                                                                   │
│  Table B8                                                          │
│  Incremental Landfill Costs for Hazardous & Special Wastes³       │
│                                                                   │
│  Item        and       Notes              Incremental Cost        │
│  ───────────────────────────────────────────────────────         │
│                                                                   │
│  Assessment                                                       │
│  Site Investigation - add 20%                        £14,000      │
│  Planning           - greater preparation & PR       £25,000      │
│  Environmental Assessment - more detail              £15,000      │
│                                                                   │
│  Development                                                      │
│  Lining - added layer of clay, geogrid                            │
│           @ £20 per m² (increment over £12.50)    £1,650,000      │
│  Access Roads    - better surfacing, if required     (small)      │
│  Storage areas   - tankers, emergency storage       £30,000       │
│  Laboratory      - on site sampling                 £50,000       │
│  Security Fencing - internal                        £10,000       │
│  Offices         - additional services, first aid    £5,000       │
│  Design          - add 10%                           £7,000       │
│                                                                   │
│  Operation (annual)                                               │
│  Personnel - 2 add. operatives, 2 lab technicians   £50,000       │
│  Equipment - excavator, sweeper                                   │
│              (inc. fuel & maintenance)              £55,000        │
│  Leachate Treatment - depends on amount, say        £10,000       │
│  Environmental monitoring                            £5,000       │
│                                                                   │
│  Restoration                                                      │
│  Capping  -  HDPE cap 200,000m² @ £5/m²          £1,000,000       │
│              (additional to standard clay cap)                    │
│                                                                   │
│  Aftercare                                                        │
│  General  -  add 20%(primarily leachate                           │
│              treatment & disposal)                 £320,000       │
│                                                                   │
│  Total Increment to Expenditure                  £5,526,000       │
│  % Increase                                        + 16.6%        │
│                                                                   │
└─────────────────────────────────────────────────────────────────┘
```

## The Economics of Energy Recovery

B2.33   A recent report prepared for the former Department of Energy indicated that there are 453 landfill sites in the UK capable of generating large, utilisable quantities of landfill gas (LFG)[4]; but there are only 27 working schemes in the UK at present. That figure is likely to increase substantially in the coming years as a direct result of the Non Fossil Fuel Obligation (NFFO), whereby site operators generating electricity are eligible (subject to approval by the Office of Electricity Regulation) to receive a fee for their power which is well above the pool price (5.7p/kwh, as opposed to 2.5p/kwh).

B2.34   Our model site is easily of sufficient scale to generate utilisable quantities of gas, provided that there is a sufficient mixture of biodegradable wastes. There are three basic options for the gas after it is recovered:

— direct application for industrial use

```
┌─────────────────────────────────────────────────────────────┐
│  ┌───────────────────────────────────────────────────────┐  │
│  │                                                         │  │
│  │  Table  B9  -  Economics of LFG Utilisation            │  │
│  │  ──────────────────────────────────────────────────    │  │
│  │                                                         │  │
│  │  Power Output                                    2 MW   │  │
│  │                                                         │  │
│  │  Capital Costs                            £1,500,000    │  │
│  │  Annual Operating Costs                      £50,000    │  │
│  │                                                         │  │
│  │  Annual Revenue (pool price = 2.5p/kwh      £350,000    │  │
│  │  Simple Payback Period                       5 years    │  │
│  │                                                         │  │
│  │  Annual Revenue (NFFO price = 5.7p/kwh)     £798,000    │  │
│  │  Simple Payback Period                       2 years    │  │
│  │                                                         │  │
│  └───────────────────────────────────────────────────────┘  │
└─────────────────────────────────────────────────────────────┘
```

— upgrading to a proper fuel for market sale

— generation of electricity for sale to the national grid

B2.35   The direct application of gas for industrial use (e.g in firing cement or brick-making kilns) is possible in selected locations, but each scheme will be unique in terms of its costs and characteristics. Also, the upgrading of the mixed gases into a high concentration of methane gas for sale has not yet proven to be commercially viable in the UK. The primary and most pertinent application is the generation of electricity.

B2.36   Before generating equipment is purchased, the operators will have determined the volume of gas arising from the site as well as its composition, in order to estimate the amount of power that could be generated. Capital costs for equipment (collection system, compressors, engines etc.) tend to be in the range of £0.5–1 million per megawatt of power output. Our estimate below takes the midpoint of this range. Further, the system would be highly automated, but would require an estimated £50,000 of annual operational maintenance. On this basis, the assumed characteristics of the system are shown in **Table B9**.

B2.37   The system could be installed after five years of infilling, and continue for 10 years after final closure, giving a full operational life of 25 years. When the LFG recovery system is incorporated into the baseline DCF analysis at the electricity pool price of 2.5p/kwh, the unit cost of landfill declines from £9.83 to £9.55, a drop of just 3%. In cash flow terms, it would take five years for gas recovery to pay for itself, but the net benefits overall appear small.

B2.38   A second scenario would have the NFFO price apply for the first seven years of operation[5]. This has the effect of dropping overall costs to £8.82 per tonne (a drop of 10%), with the scheme paying for itself in two years. According to this analysis, the impact of the NFFO is clearly important, but gas utilisation overall does not have a profound effect economically on the costs of a site of this size.

**Summary**

B2.39   Single point estimates have been collated for landfill under various scenarios, which are summarised in **Table B10**.

B2.40   The most striking result of our calculations is the low variability in unit costs under different scenarios. In reality, there will clearly be variations in costs at each site depending on a host of variables, such that it is much more realistic to talk of a cost range rather than single point estimates. Allowing

Table B10 – Summary of Landfill Costs per Tonne

| Scenario | Cost per tonne |
|---|---|
| MSW Landfill | £ 9.83 |
| MSW Landfill with Energy Recovery | £ 8.82 - 9.55 |
| Hazardous Waste Landfill | £ 11.18 |

for a 20% variation either side of our calculation would put the range of costs for a MSW landfill site of 200,000 tonnes a year capacity at £8.20 to £11.80 a tonne.

B2.41   One of the most important variables in site costs will be the size of the site itself, and the inherent economies of scale in operation. Our model site is a relatively large site, consistent with recent trends in development towards fewer, larger facilities. It has not been possible within the scope of this research to assess other model sites of different size. An indication of cost sensitivity to facility size is found in Waste Management Paper 26, and suggests that unit costs—in particular unit operating costs—would rise gradually as the design capacity of sites decreases. The increase becomes more prominent when throughputs get below 50,000 tonnes per annum. **Figure 1** shows the WMP 26 costs alongside hypothetical costings for the present day.

B2.42   An historical perspective is also offered by the WMP 26 figures. This review, in 1984 costs, implied that the cost per tonne of a 200,000 tpa facility would be £2.70[6]. If engineering price indices of about 52%[7] are applied to this figure to bring it to £4.10 in 1992 costs, then improved technical standards must explain most (around 80%) of the increase up to £9.50.

## Figure 1

### Economies of Scale in Landfill Costs

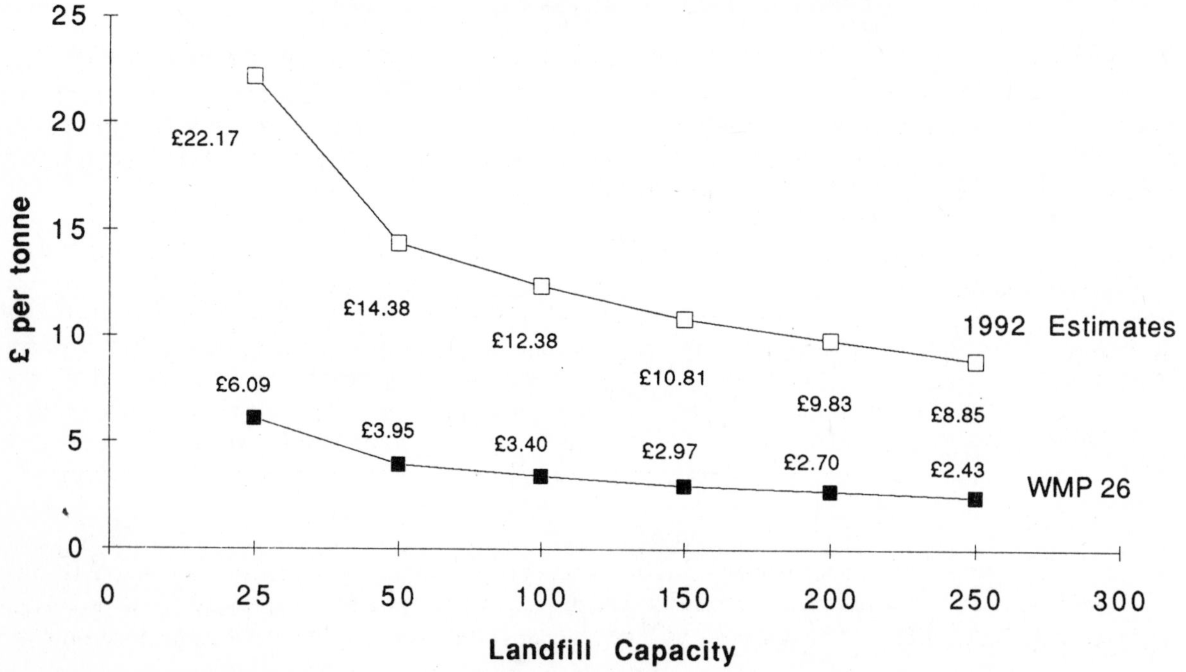

## 3. THE COSTS OF INCINERATION

### Introduction

B3.1    Incineration, usually with heat or energy recovery, is common practice in Europe but is much less so in this country. The major thrust behind the successful advance of the technologies and processes in Europe is the shortage of landfill sites and the higher environmental constraints upon their development. Equally severe environmental constraints (primarily emission abatement) are operated on incineration plants, but current technology has developed successfully to meet these challenges, albeit at great expense to plant operators.

B3.2    The decision to pursue incineration as a waste disposal option in the UK is typically a difficult one for local authorities, not least because of the high costs (capital intensity) relative to landfill. The constraints upon local authority borrowing and spending mean that private capital must almost always be involved in project development. The poor past public perception of UK incinerators complicates the choice further.

B3.3    Our baseline analysis below is of a mass burn incineration plant for MSW without resource recovery. However, it should be noted that such a configuration is increasingly untenable in the UK, even though the majority of plants still operating lack resource recovery. Mass burn incineration typically reduces the volume of waste by up to 90%, but only reduces the weight by about 70 to 75%. One significant cost factor is therefore the cost of residue disposal to landfill. The best way for incineration to assert a competitive advantage is by incorporating energy recovery, or at least some form of materials recycling. This is increasingly the only practical way to market this option. Therefore, in terms of a direct comparison with landfill, incineration with energy recovery is the most viable alternative.

B3.4    Gaining an appreciation of incineration costs has been decidedly more difficult than research into landfill. Much of this can be explained by the proprietary nature of most incineration technologies and the reluctance of engineering contractors to share cost information which they feel is commercially sensitive. By contrast, there is very little proprietary technology involved in landfill design and operation. A further difficulty lies in the fact that all of the most prominent exponents of waste combustion technology are outside of the UK and do not have working examples in this country that they can refer to. The result is that the costs presented here are necessarily more vague and less detailed than for landfill, but they are still a fair representation of the range of total costs involved for the purposes of the comparative analysis.

B3.5    There are five stages to mass burn incineration listed below: acquisition, assessment, development, operation and decommissioning. As in the previous chapter, a table is provided in each section outlining the component costs in each stage, as well as a discounted cost per tonne and the proportion each contributes to overall costs. Costs of incineration are summarised in **Table B11**.

B3.6    A total expenditure of £112 million is required for this 200,000 tonnes pa incineration facility, 3.5 times greater than the expenditure on landfill. Over the full life of the site, costs are equivalent to discounted cost per tonne of £37.15. (Note that this is without resource recovery).

### *The Impact of Different Technologies*

B3.7    There are essentially two types of combustion technology used commonly today to deal with mixed municipal solid wastes: rotary kiln systems and reciprocating (agitating) grate systems. The former are very popular in the US and are being marketed increasingly in Europe. Reciprocating grate technology still tends to be more popular in Europe since it is promoted by many of the leading engineering firms located here. In broad terms, there is very little to choose between the two in terms of costs. Different contractors can quote varying costs for the same plant design and technology.

B3.8    A plant of this capacity will typically have two input streams to provide greater flexibility in operation. It is vital to maintain a consistent feed of fuel to optimise the system's economic performance[8]. Achieving an availability of 85% throughout the operating life of the plant means that rigid specifications must be met, which will keep costs high.

| Table B11 – Summary of Incineration Costs | | |
|---|---|---|
| Stage | Total Expenditure | Cost per tonne (DCF) |
| Acquisition | £500,000 | £0.27 |
| Assessment | £155,000 | £0.08 |
| Development | £38,850,000 | £20.74 |
| Operation | £69,300,000 (£3,465,000 pa) | £14.32 |
| Decommissioning | £3,250,000 | £1.74 |
| Total | £112,055,000 | £37.15 |

B3.9   Gas cleaning can be based on a range of different technologies, the most costly being the "wet system" whereby pollutants are removed in scrubbers incorporating large volumes of liquid cleaners, mostly slaked lime. This is an effective way of achieving the emission limits specified in EC Directives, although the less costly "semi-dry" method (absorbents are sprayed into the gases) would also be suitable. Capital costs can vary by £2–3 million depending on the choice, but operating costs will vary inversely. The overall difference to expenditure is therefore slight.

*Distribution of Costs*

B3.10   Over half of the expenditure outlined above is incurred as operating expenses throughout the life of the facility, which is assumed to be twenty years. However, except for £3.25 million decommissioning costs at the end of its economic life, the incineration plant consumes the rest of the expenditure "up front" in terms of engineering and capital costs.

B3.11   Importantly, there is no aftercare period required and combustion plants therefore typically have an economic life which corresponds closely to their operational life. Two years of construction and preparation are assumed (as for landfill) but only one year post operation for decommissioning.

**Site Acquisition Costs**

B3.12   Acquisition costs are sometimes not included in assessments of combustion plant; the land is assumed to be available in principle, perhaps owned by the local authority or fallen into disuse. However the question of land use is important in the comparison with landfill, and an estimate is therefore required for consistency.

B3.13   The smaller parcel of land required relative to landfill means that incineration plant can be located more flexibly and ideally closer to the sources of waste arisings. However, stringent planning conditions usually restrict the options quite severely. Where energy or heat distribution is part of the intended design, proximity to these customers will be another determining factor. There must also be ready access to a secure, long term landfill to accept the residues from incineration.

B3.14   Our assumptions for plant location are that it would take up an area of about 10 hectares in or near a built up environment with relatively high industrial land values, say £50,000 per hectare. This yields an acquisition cost of £500,000 which clearly is only indicative (**Table B12**). In any event, its

```
Table  B12  –  Incineration Site Acquisition Costs

Item                        Rate            Quantity          Amount

Site Acquisition        £50,000/ha         10 ha           £500,000

Cost per tonne                                              £  0.27

% of total discounted costs                                  0.7%
```

contribution to total costs is usually modest, and it is more important to make the general point about the relative influence of acquisition costs on both disposal options.

**Assessment Costs**

B3.15   The assessment stage represents an extremely small fraction of overall costs but, as with landfill, it is vitally important (**Table B13**). Site investigations in this case will include several management-related functions: all aspects of the plant's operation, including the choice of technology, the securing of waste inputs, the securing of residue disposal capacity, etc. Financing will also need to be arranged for the high capital costs just ahead. Proper management of these issues would need to be demonstrated to the local authority.

B3.16   The experience in the UK over the last 10 years points to a public antipathy to developments of this kind. The allowance of £50,000 made for planning and public relations is twice that for landfill to reflect the relative difficulties that such a development could usually expect. It can easily get much higher than this, but the impact on overall costs is once again small.

```
Table  B13  –  Incineration Assessment Costs

Item                      Rate  &  Quantity              Amount

Site Assessment

1   Full Site Investigation      Sum                    £30,000
2   Planning (+ meetings)        Sum                    £50,000
3   Environ.Assessment           Sum                    £75,000

    Total                                              £155,000

    Cost per tonne                                       £0.08

    % of total discounted costs                          0.2%
```

```
┌──────────────────────────────────────────────────────────────────────┐
│                                                                        │
│   Table B14   -   Incineration Development Costs                        │
│                                                                        │
│   Item                       Rate & Quantity            Amount          │
│   ──────────────────────────────────────────────────────────────────  │
│                                                                        │
│   Site Development                                                     │
│   1  Capital Costs                                                     │
│    -  Civil & Building           Sum              £8,000,000            │
│    -  Mechanical & Electrical    Sum             £24,500,000            │
│   2  Mobile Plant (loading                                             │
│         shovels, containers)     Sum                £400,000            │
│   3  Strategic Spares            Sum              £1,200,000            │
│   4  Engineering Services        Sum              £1,850,000            │
│   5  Promotion, mgmt, legal      Sum              £2,900,000            │
│   ──────────────────────────────────────────────────────────────────  │
│                                                                        │
│   Total                                          £38,850,000           │
│                                                                        │
│   Cost per tonne                                  £ 20.74              │
│                                                                        │
│   % of total discounted costs                       55.8%             │
│                                                                        │
└──────────────────────────────────────────────────────────────────────┘
```

## Development Costs

B3.17   All development (capital) costs are assumed to be incurred prior to operation, although in reality, they may be spread out over a longer timeframe according to predetermined financing schedules. Regardless of the timing, this is by far the dominant phase of spending (**Table B14**).

B3.18   Total capital costs are estimated at £38.85 million, broken down as indicated in Table B14. The cost of engineering services are included as quoted costs are usually integrated into a single figure for turnkey services. These costs will include the agitating grate combustion system and gas cleaning technology indicated above.

## Operating Costs

B3.19   There are several factors which are costly in terms of annual cash flow (**Table B15**). Nearly £3.5 million is required annually, £1.1 million of which is concerned with the monitoring and disposal of about 60,000 tonnes of residues from the plant (50,000 tonnes of bottom ash and 10,000 tonnes of fly ash and residues). Disposal costs are assumed to be £15 per tonne for residue disposal, but transport costs to the landfill are not included.

B3.20   Wages and salary costs are high, and the average salary of £18,000 (compared to £12,500 for landfill) reflects the need for more skilled personnel. Maintenance expenses are approximated as functions either of capital expenditure or tonnage throughput.

## Decommissioning Costs

B3.21   All quotations on decommissioning costs were given as a proportion of the capital costs for all main engineering works, usually in the range of 10%. There is no assumption about salvaging equipment for sale at a discounted price, but this could reduce costs slightly. Due to discounting, the relative contribution of this stage to present day costs shown in **Table B16** is small at 5%.

```
Table  B15  -  Incineration Operating Costs

Item                          Rate      Quantity (pa)        Amount


1  Wages + salaries          various      26 staff         £480,000
2  Maintenance
 - Civil & Building            1% of capital               £80,000
 - Mechanical & Electrical    £5/t       200,000 t       £1,000,000
3  Mobile Plant               Sum                           £20,000
4  Fuel                       £0.2/t     200,000 t          £40,000
5  Combustion Additives       Sum                          £350,000
6  Env. monitoring (sample)  £3/t        60,000 t          £180,000
7  Residue Disposal           £15/t       60,000 t         £900,000
8  Rates (per tonne)·         £0.5/t     200,000 t         £100,000


   sub total (annual)                                    £3,150,000
   contingency (10%)                                       £315,000
   Total (annual)                                        £3,465,000

   Cost per tonne                                          £ 14.32
   % of total discounted costs                              38.5%
```

## The Incineration of Difficult Wastes

B3.22   For the combustion of more specialised wastes such as sewage sludge and hazardous wastes, it is not just a matter of adding special features to existing MSW incinerators; an entirely different technology is needed. Furthermore, hazardous (and clinical) waste incinerators in particular are usually smaller in scale than 200,000 tonnes pa to better suit their more specialised markets.

*Sewage Sludge*

B3.23   Incineration of sewage sludge is undergoing a strong revival, clearly prompted by the commitment by the UK government to phase out the disposal of sewage sludge to sea by 1998. The most practical land based alternative is the spreading of sludge on agricultural land, but the National Code of

```
Table  B16  -  Incineration Decommissioning Costs

Item                     Rate           Quantity           Amount


Site Decommissioning   10% of capital                    £3,250,000

Cost per tonne                                             £ 1.74

% of total discounted costs                                 4.7%
```

Practice for spreading, underpinned by the EC Nitrate Directive, will restrict the amounts that may be applied and where.

B3.24    Very few incineration plants are presently in operation in the UK, although several are being planned. Since most of them require a supplementary fuel to maintain combustion , average operating costs have been very high in practice—indeed the plants that survived through the 1980s did so despite high costs only because there were no practical disposal alternatives in those areas (Sheffield, Birmingham, Wigan).

B3.25    The first new sewage sludge incinerator in over a decade was built in Bradford for Yorkshire Water in 1988. The plant has a design capacity of 18,000 tonnes per annum. Performance tests were undertaken between December 1988 and April 1989 and yielded the unit operating costs shown in **Table B17**.

B3.26    This is consistent with earlier quotations derived by the Water Research Council in 1988. The WRC figures relate to facility with a capacity of 80,000 dry tonnes comprising the specialised functions of such plants; centrifugation (direct drying), indirect drying, fluidised bed incineration (with heat recovery) and gas scrubbing to meet the German TA Luft standards. Total capital costs were estimated at £16.8 million with annual operating costs of £3.2 million, equivalent to just over £40 per tonne[9].

B3.27    Older facilities, such as that operating at Coleshill (Severn Trent) have been quoted to be incurring costs of £70 per dry tonne, the difference being in the dewatering stage, where the Coleshill plant still relies on older more labour intensive techniques, and in the lack of energy or heat recovery[11].

B3.28    Economies of scale will be harder to achieve with sewage sludge incineration because of the need to supplement the sludge with other fuel inputs. This particular cost would rise in proportion to the size of the unit, offsetting the economies gained.

*Hazardous and Special Wastes*

B3.29    According to the DoE Digest of Environmental Protection and Water Statistics, only 5% of hazardous waste arisings in the UK were sent to incineration in 1989. However, interest in this option is increasing steadily, reinforced by the EC's waste strategy which gives priority to treatment and incineration over landfill. Clinical and certain special wastes are already incinerated in accordance with standard best practice.

B3.30    Most merchant hazardous waste incinerators operating in Europe are in the range of 20,000 to 60,000 tonnes pa throughput (2.5–8 tonnes per hour, based on 85% availability). Quotations for turnkey capital and installation costs are in the range of £20–60 million, or approximately £7–10 million per tonne-hour of throughput. This compares with about £1.4 million per tonne-hour for the model MSW incinerator.

B3.31    The combination of greater technical requirements, higher performance standards and reduced economies of scale conspire to push unit costs up to a range of £120–150 per tonne. This is an indicative range based on our own extrapolation of limited information from contractors.

B3.32    Clinical waste incineration is yet another technology and yet another set of operational variables. Usually, on-site combustion will be an integrated function within the broader operation of the hospital, and operating costs are therefore hard to distinguish. More recently, opportunities are growing for the private sector to invest in merchant facilities which service a wide area. These plants are relatively small in capacity—necessarily so, since the total amount of UK clinical waste arisings is in the range of 250–300,000 tonnes per annum. Capital costs range from £750,000 for new installation of small on-site incinerators up to £7 million for larger merchant facilities. For the latter, returns on investment tend to be favourable because of the high charges made for the service (£250–500 tonne).

**Table B17 – Unit Operating Costs Reported for Yorkshire Water's Bradford Incinerator (Lurgi), Dec 1988 – Apr 1989**

| Item | Costs (£/dry tonne)[10] |
|---|---|
| Labour | £ 11.40 – 17.78 |
| Rates | £ 2.10 – 3.28 |
| Power | £ 8.70 – 13.57 |
| Chemicals | £ 11.00 – 17.16 |
| Ash Disposal | £ 2.80 – 4.37 |
| Contract Maintenance | £ 6.50 – 10.14 |
| **TOTAL** | £ 42.50 – 66.30 |

**Table B18 – Economics of Incineration with Energy Recovery**

| | |
|---|---|
| Calorific Value of MSW | 8.5 GJ / tonne |
| Additional Capital (turbines, grid connection) | £8,000,000 |
| Additional Operating Costs (annual) | £80,000 |
| Incinerator Utilisation | 85% |
| Boiler Efficiency | 70% |
| Turbine Efficiency | 30% |
| Annual Gross Power Output | 99.2m kwh (13.2 MW) |
| In house consumption | 65 kwh/t = 13m kwh |
| Annual Power Exported | 86.2m kwh (11.6 MW) |
| Annual Revenue (pool price = 2.5 p /kwh) | £2,154,100 |
| Annual Revenue (NFFO price = 4.5 p /kwh) | £3,877,400 |
| Annual Revenue (NFFO price = 6.55 p /kwh) | £5,643,700 |

**The Economics of Energy Recovery from Incineration**

B3.33 With so much capital needed for incineration generally, the incremental effort to recover heat or energy for use is not that onerous. The majority of plants in Continental Europe incorporate municipal waste incineration with district heating requirements. Such plants are usually small in scale and generally rely on government assistance, but overall costs are kept down in any event by the existence of the necessary infrastructure for heating distribution.

B3.34 A facility of this capacity in the UK more realistically will be based on electricity generation, perhaps with co-generated heat if suitable industrial customers were nearby. The operating characteristics are set out in **Table B18**.

B3.35 The specific equipment needed which would not form part of the original plant design relates specifically to heat and power generation and connection, costing about £8 million. Boilers for heat recovery would be incorporated, but unless there are conveniently located customers nearby, the benefit

| Table B19 - Summary of Incineration Costs per Tonne | |
|---|---|
| Scenario | Cost per tonne |
| MSW Incineration | £ 37.15 |
| Incineration with Energy Recovery | £20.84 - 29.08 |
| Sewage Sludge Incineration | £40 - 70 |
| Hazardous Waste Incineration | £120 - 150 |

(revenue) of distributing waste heat for use elsewhere will seldom be attractive relative to the costs. The NFFO boost to electricity prices reinforces the commercial advantages of focusing on power generation exclusively. With the operating characteristics set out, plant output is estimated at 11.6 megawatts.

B3.36    Plugging in the additional cost and revenue figures for power generation reduces the overall facility cost by 22% to £29.08 per tonne, assuming normal pool prices (2.5p/kwh) would apply.

B3.37    Incorporating the assumption that the model plant has been granted a NFFO contract in the second tranche of 1991 (NFFO II) , i.e electricity purchased at a premium price of 6.55p/kwh for the initial seven years of operation, unit costs fall by 44% to £20.84.

B3.38    Preliminary indications are that any future NFFO awards may be granted for a fixed period from the start of generation for every plant, say 10 years, but at a lower strike price. For a hypothetical NFFO III, we have modelled 10 year of income at 4.5p/kwh. Estimated costs in this situation are £23.94 per tonne, 36% below costs without the NFFO.

B3.39    In all cases, it is usually feasible to recover scrap metal (at least) from the waste stream for additional revenue, but this will vary with throughputs in a highly unpredictable manner.

**Summary**

B3.40    The estimates for the costs of waste incineration under various scenarios are summarised in **Table B19**.

B3.41    Allowing a 10% variation either side of our calculations gives a range of costs for a 200,000 tpa MSW incinerator of £34–£41 per tonne, for incineration with energy recovery (normal prices) of £26–£32 per tonne. These are the guideline ranges which allow for variation in any of a number of operating variables.

**Economies of Scale**

B3.42    Economies of scale in MSW incineration are implicitly strong for such capital intensive facilities. In the US, local authorities have pooled their wastes and resources to support facilities which are of sufficient size to keep unit costs at a manageable level. The addition of power generation reinforces the economies.

B3.43    **Figure 2** presents an indication of possible scale effects for incineration with energy recovery

## Figure 2

## Economies of Scale with Incineration Plant

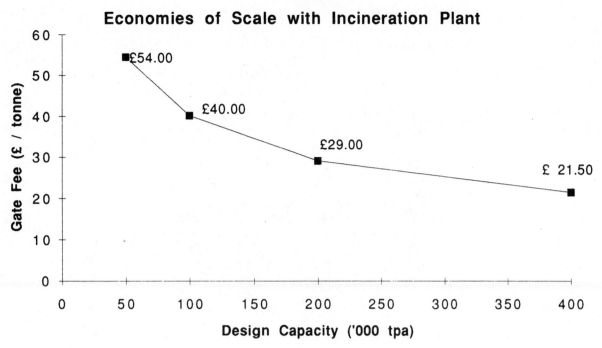

based on limited published information on European facilities. It should be remembered that there will be variation in design specifications and technologies as well as size in different facilities, such that this graph should only be viewed as guidance.

B3.44   As with landfill, there are significant diseconomies observed in small facilities capable of handling around 50—100,000 tpa. Beyond our base case example at 200,000 tpa, the benefits of scale are still prominent; a doubling of design capacity leads to a 26% decline in average unit costs. Much larger plants are yet being planned; Cory's planned development at Belvedere would be handling around 1.2 million tonnes a year. Extrapolating from this graph would suggest that unit costs for a plant of this size might be of the order of £15 per tonne.

## 4.   COMPARATIVE ANALYSIS

### Analysis of Direct Costs

B4.1   Landfill and incineration are completely different concepts from an engineering standpoint, and the direct comparison of the two must be subject to the appropriate caveats. Just the same, we have provided a visual comparison of the distribution of discounted costs in **Figures 3a and 3b**.

B4.2   Clearly, the most important comparison is between the *total* costs of each as options in waste disposal, since the individual stages contrast strongly in their orientation to the technical issues of each, and therefore are not strictly comparable.

B4.3   The previous two chapters have highlighted respectively the present day costs of landfill and incineration. These are summarised in **Table B20**.

B4.4   At face value, the decision on which to employ from a cost standpoint is straightforward. There is little prospect of direct incineration, either for MSW or more difficult wastes, being able to compete

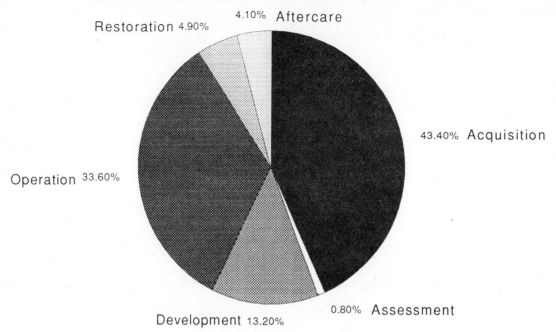

### Figure 3a
### Distribution of Landfill Costs

4.10% Aftercare

Restoration 4.90%

43.40% Acquisition

Operation 33.60%

0.80% Assessment

Development 13.20%

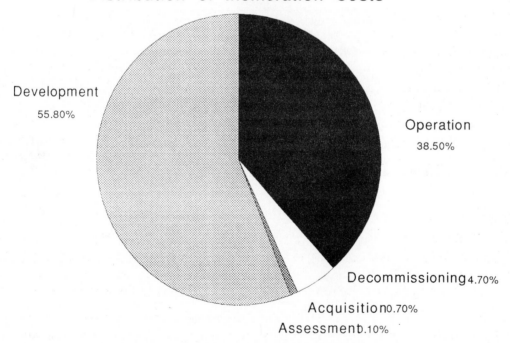

### Figure 3b
### Distribution of Incineration Costs

Development
55.80%

Operation
38.50%

Decommissioning 4.70%

Acquisition 0.70%

Assessment 0.10%

economically with direct landfilling now or in the near future. However, incineration with energy recovery on this scale can be competitive with long range landfill (with transfer), depending on a number of site specific variables.

B4.5    Many of these other variables are not quantifiable. Political judgements will also need to be made about the acceptability of each method locally. The factors influencing such a judgement would include:

— waste market profile; population size, industrial activity and likely trends in both
— waste collection and recycling activities

Table B20 – Comparative Analysis of Landfill & Incineration Costs (£/tonne)

| Description | Landfill | Incineration |
|---|---|---|
| MSW | £9.83 | £37.15 |
| With Energy Recovery | £8.82 – 9.55 | £20.84 – 29.08 |
| Difficult Wastes | £11.18 | £40 – 150 |

— existing transport infrastructure
— markets for electricity or heat
— availability of public funding to offset capital expenditure

B4.6 Below is a brief summary of two primary considerations not included in the direct cost analysis, transport and environmental impairment.

**Analysis of Implied Costs**

*Transport Costs*

B4.7 The lower cost of landfilling means that it will tolerate greater transport costs and be attractive over greater distances. However, the ability of incineration plants to be located in closer proximity to centres of population, and hence to the point of waste arisings, implies that the cost of transport associated with incineration is typically lower than it would be for landfill. Indeed, the investment decision can often be simplified down to the choice between an incinerator and a transfer station on a

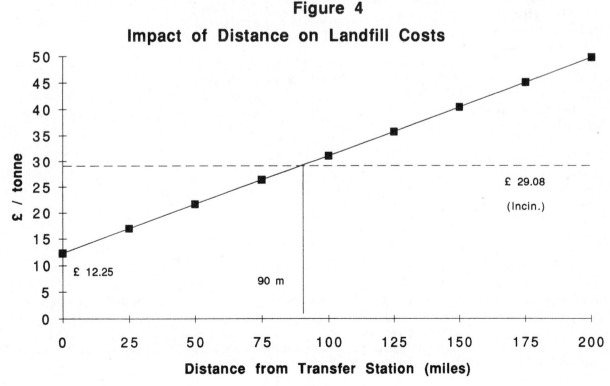

## Figure 4

## Impact of Distance on Landfill Costs

## Figure 5

## Sensitivity to Purchase Value

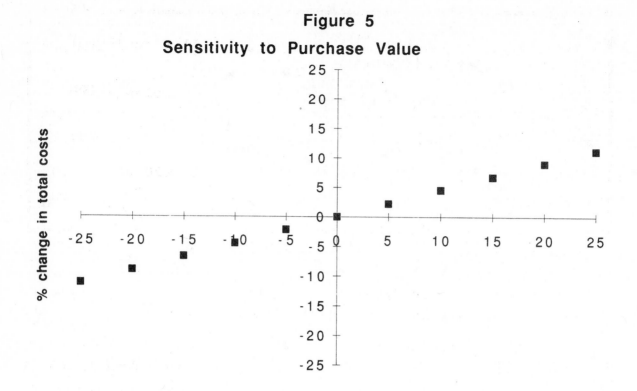

given site with onward transport to the landfill for final disposal in both instances. The key considerations are therefore the relative cost of transfer facilities, and consequently at what distance landfill becomes more expensive than incineration.

B4.8    The vast majority of wastes (over 70%) sent to landfill in the UK are collected and transported there directly, but the remainder must be batched and forwarded through transfer stations. As local landfills are completed, the need to travel longer distances is increasing the need for transfer and long haulage of wastes from the country's larger urban centres. Incineration plants, by contrast, typically receive all of their wastes directly. The impact of adding a road transfer station and further rolling stock at a capital cost of, say £3 million, plus operating costs of £200,000 per annum, would add about £2.42 per tonne by itself to the cost of landfill disposal. The combined cost of transfer and disposal (excluding transport) is therefore £12.25 per tonne.

B4.9    Estimating the cost of transport is notoriously difficult. Until recently, the National Association of Waste Disposal Contractors (NAWDC) published cost tables for various types of collection vehicles[12]. On the basis of 1990 cost data for a roll-on roll-off vehicle (£2.44 per mile), and assuming that this vehicle has a fully loaded capacity of 13 tonnes (compacted), the cost of waste transport can be inferred to be just over 19 pence per tonne-mile.

B4.10    Given the differential in estimated costs between transfer/landfill and incineration with energy recovery (£12.25 v £29.08), an incremental distance of 90 miles (146 kilometres) to and from the landfill (45 mile one way distance) would be needed to make the integrated cost of collection and disposal to both options equal (**Figure 4**)[13]. This is illustrative only—distance itself will be a function of the quality of road access and any other route restrictions.

*Environmental Impairment*

B4.11    In terms of their impact on the environment, incineration has in the past been perceived to be more harmful than landfill, mostly by virtue of the emissions and residues created. However, the potential long term risks associated with landfill are now becoming more fully understood and there is growing pressure for operators to take account of this risk through dedicated aftercare management funds (see Chapter 3). A lengthy aftercare period is not required with combustion plants, if only because the problem is transferred to the landfill through the disposal of residues.

B4.12   Below, we list the primary impacts of both disposal methods:

| Landfill | Incineration |
| --- | --- |
| Landscape & visual amenity | Visual amenity (stack height) |
| Nature conservation | Road traffic |
| Road traffic | Noise and vibration |
| Noise and vibration | Odour and dust |
| Odour and dust | Waste water disposal |
| Litter and vermin | Gaseous emissions |
| Gas migration | Residue (ash) disposal |
| Leachate migration | Water usage |

B4.13   With landfill, proper on site management will prevent leachate from percolating through to groundwaters, but the control of landfill gas can never reach a reasonable level until the site is near completion and properly engineered to gather the gas (60% methane). Escaping gases have a significant greenhouse effect in the atmosphere[14]. The other factors will clearly vary according to site conditions, but there will likely be at least some small measure of environmental impairment from all of them.

B4.14   The major pollutants from MSW incinerators include acid gases, heavy metals and dioxins. Modern gas cleaning technologies are able to control these emissions at or below the levels required by law. Properly engineered incinerators may still be expected to create minor nuisances with dust, noise and odour which, although probably less than that experienced at landfills, will be more apparent if the plant is located closer to centres of population. The incinerator plant can also face problems for itself and its designated ash landfill if heavy metal concentrations in the ash are above acceptable limits.

B4.15   No judgement can readily be made about the comparative impact of these options on the environment since the cost of that impact will vary from person to person, from site to site. What we do believe is that these costs are potentially high. Where the perceived impairment "threatened" by one option is considered to be well above the other, it can tip the balance in the choice of options.

**The Impact of Economic Instruments**

B4.16   The potential to influence behaviour in waste markets through economic means is increasingly seen as a viable alternative to the traditional reliance on command and control regulations. Direct subsidies, or allowances, are available under a variety of government schemes,such as those to support novel technologies (DEMOS, DTI) or encourage the growth of new markets (NFFO).

B4.17   Ultimately the intention of such economic instruments is to influence the choice of disposal route, but this is done by influencing either the availability of different options (i.e. reducing the costs of development) or the relative charges made for those services. We have been dealing with costs throughout this study, and therefore stick to the question of enhancing availability. Both methods are discussed below in terms of their power to shift the balance of waste movements away from landfill.

B4.18   Capital allowances are a direct tool which might be used in this situation where the relative capital costs of incineration are significantly greater than landfill. Every £1 million reduction in capital costs for combustion plant reduces the cost per tonne by about 50 pence. Thus a 20% capital allowance for our model incinerator with energy recovery would allow unit costs to drop below £20 per tonne. This would make waste combustion competitive with long range landfill and transfer.

B4.19   The willingness of government to assist directly in this manner depends on support for the development of incineration, possibly within the context of national objectives for (e.g.) resource recovery. This is what has occurred in European countries such as Denmark and Holland where there are stated goals for energy from wastes within a broader strategy.

B4.20   Fiscal policy can take a number of forms, the main headings of which are:

— product based charges; including landfill taxes, deposit/refund schemes, etc

— administrative charges, licence fees, recycling credits, etc

— tradeable permits; with specific application to increasing recycling of certain materials.

B4.21   Product based charges such as landfill taxes may be intended to influence the pace of waste minimisation and recycling more than influence the choice of final disposal. However, they might assist other disposal options indirectly. The main impact would likely be to reduce the amount of waste sent to final disposal of any kind, packaging materials in particular. Tradeable permits would have much the same effect.

B4.22   Administrative charges, such as an increase in the licence fee for landfill operators, would have a minimal effect on reducing landfill development, since these costs are such a small amount of total expenditure.

## 5   COST INFLUENCES AND SENSITIVITIES

B5.1   The various pressures operating on both landfill and incineration have been alluded to in the previous chapters. Notably, legislative changes have been fairly persistent in forcing up design standards and the attendant costs. However, there are forces at work within the broader field of waste management, such as pressures on waste minimisation and recycling, which will bring their own influences to bear on the final disposal options.

B5.2   Five important issues are analysed here for their impact on one or both options and hence on relative costs:

— the availability of land for the development of landfill sites;

— changes in the volume of waste (i.e. the flexibility of either option to cope with volume changes and the viability of different sizes of operation);

— changes in waste composition (affecting energy output);

— changes in energy prices (affecting the value of energy produced); and

— alternative disposal technologies.

B5.3   Where it is feasible, the impact of the influences is quantified with reference to the cost analyses in Chapters 3 and 4.

### The Availability of Land

B5.4   The siting of a landfill site is already a complicated process but it is bound to become even more difficult in the future. The latest draft of the EC Landfill Directive proposes to include restrictions in terms of proximity (not less than 500 metres) to roads, recreational areas, houses, waterways or agricultural sites[15]. Clearly this doesn't leave much room for new development, especially for sites of the size described in this study which can occupy around 50 hectares of land.

B5.5   The UK tradition of refilling voidspace left by quarrying works may ease the impact of these new restrictions, but in the long term the consequence will be that landfills become fewer, and subsequently more valuable.

B5.6   The two primary effects are therefore:

— higher valuations of voidspace

— longer distances from source, probably including more use of transfer stations.

B5.7   There is already evidence of the first effect as a result of higher valuations being placed on voidspace. The sensitivity of landfill costs to higher transaction values is shown graphically in **Figure 5**. Changes in total costs are measured on the Y axis as a function of changes in the variable on the X axis. The sensitivity to transfer and transport costs was discussed previously.

B5.8   Not surprisingly, costs are reasonably sensitive to transaction values, since they comprise a large proportion of the baseline unit costs (Chapter 3). A 25% increase in land values would result in an 11% increase in total unit costs. Changing land values would have only a small direct impact on incineration costs.

## Waste Volumes

B5.9   The volume of wastes generated by households and business is coming under increasing pressure:

— the European Commission's waste management strategy places waste minimisation, reduction and recycling as priorities over final disposal;

— in the UK, the Duty of Care is already leading to an internal review by many producers of industrial and commercial wastes of their waste generation and disposal arrangements;

— Integrated Pollution Control (EPA 1990) will lead to process changes with a consequent reduction in waste generation;

— an EC Packaging Directive is forthcoming, likely based at least in part on stringent German regulations which force materials back through the distribution chain; and

— greater recycling of household wastes following the preparation of formal recycling plans by UK local authorities.

B5.10   Reduced waste volumes from these initiatives will be widespread, although the pace of change is difficult to gauge. The impact on the overall waste industry will be to force a certain amount of structural change upon it. Waste companies will need to follow the wastes as they are diverted from the traditional disposal routes and become engaged more directly in recycling. At the same time, companies in other trades may seek to gain greater control over waste movements in order to feed their own requirements. Recent moves of this nature have been undertaken by members of the paper industry and the water industry.

B5.11   The effects on individual facilities would in theory be more pronounced on incineration plants than on landfill. The efficiency of the combustion process tails off dramatically when a constant throughput rate is not maintained. Indeed, ensuring that sufficient long term inputs are committed to the plant is a key prerequisite to project viability, especially to support energy recovery. Operators could be expected to move to attract additional streams if the contracted amounts were to start dwindling. Landfills, by contrast, are easily adaptable to slower throughputs; operating costs could be stepped down on several fronts, and the value of the site arguably is enhanced by its greater longevity.

## Waste Composition

B5.12   Changes in waste composition will occur as a direct result of changes in volume. The focus of current recycling activities on paper, board, plastics and textiles (among other materials) has the potential to compromise the value of municipal solid waste as a feedstock for combustion, as measured by aggregate calorific value. **Table B21** outlines typical MSW composition and the contribution of various materials to energy potential.

B5.13   The weighted average calorific value of the waste stream is 8.5 MJ/kg, or 8.5 GJ/tonne. Greater recycling would alter the percentage by weight of each material and might lower gross calorific value. The sensitivity of incineration/ energy recovery costs to changes in CV is shown in **Figure 6**.

B5.14   It can be seen from this graph that calorific value needs to change substantially before it has a significant effect on overall costs. However, such a substantial change is not out of the question, if the high recovery targets in the EC packaging directive are to be achieved. A 25% decrease in calorific value would increase costs by 11.5%.

## Energy Prices

B5.15   The analysis in Chapter 4 highlighted the importance of the NFFO in enhancing overall combustion plant economics. Indeed including revenue based on the programme price of 6.55p/kwh

## Figure 6

### Sensitivity to Calorific Value

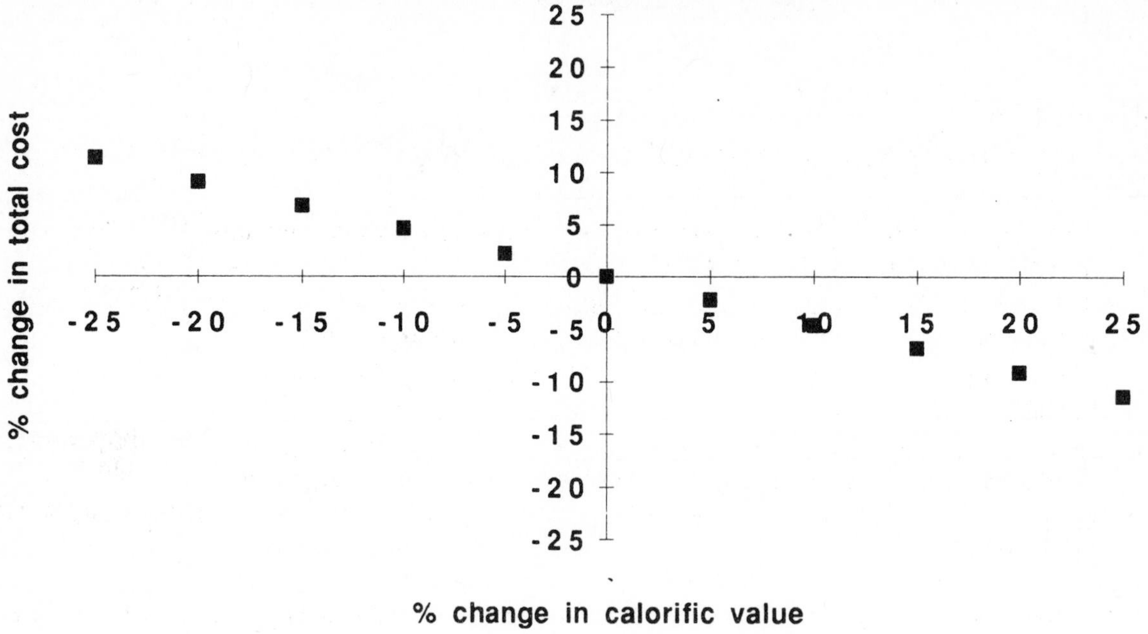

% change in total cost (y-axis)

% change in calorific value (x-axis)

created positive cash flow during the operating period. The NFFO is a fixed price programme, but the number of years that it applies would clearly affect plant viability. Many of the large EFW programmes currently under development in the South East are only still going because of their NFFO awards in the last tranche (1991).

B5.16   Sensitivity to the pool price is more muted, as demonstrated in **Figure 7**, but it still has a clear impact on costs. A 25% change in energy prices leads to a 10% drop in total costs.

**Table B21 – Typical MSW Composition and Calorific Value[16]**

| Waste Type | % weight | Gross CV (MJ/kg) |
|---|---|---|
| Paper,  board | 33 | 12 |
| Plastic film | 3 | 27 |
| Dense plastic | 3 | 30 |
| Textile | 4 | 15 |
| misc. combustible | 5 | 13.5 |
| Putrescible | 20 | 5.6 |
| Fines (<10mm) | 10 | 3.6 |
| Glass | 9 | – |
| Metals | 8 | – |
| misc. non combustible | 5 | – |
| **TOTAL** | **100** | **8.5** |

142

## Figure 7
## Sensitivity to Energy Prices

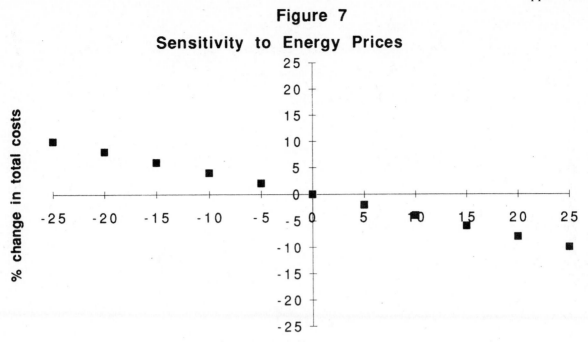

**% change in total costs** (y-axis)

**% change in energy prices**

### Landfill Disposal Charges

B5.17    In chapter 3, it was noted that rising landfill charges have a dual effect on incineration; they naturally favour the competitive position of this option, but they also force up the costs of disposal of ash, residues and rejected materials. **Figure 8** below demonstrates the sensitivity of total incineration costs to changing landfill charges.

B5.18    A 20% increase in our assumed base estimate of £15 per tonne landfill charge to £18 forces up the unit cost of incineration by around 3%. This shows the economic links between landfill and incineration, and it helps to illustrate that incineration can be defined equally well as a method of treatment as opposed to a competitive disposal option.

### The Choice of Discount Rate

B5.19    The 10% discount rate applied to our DCF calculations has been chosen by Aspinwall as an appropriate rate on which to measure public sector investments. However, it is clear, especially with regards to incineration, that private capital would likely be involved in investments of this size. Private interests may look for higher rates of return. A higher discount rate reflects a greater emphasis on the costs incurred in the first years of the project. Therefore, not surprisingly, incineration costs are much more susceptible to different discount rates than landfill costs which are more evenly spread. **Figure 9** shows this graphically.

B5.20    Assuming a very high required rate of return of 20%, landfill disposal costs are increased 21% to £11.90 per tonne; incineration costs are increased 34% to £38.90.

### Alternative Disposal Technologies

B5.21    At present, there are no practical disposal techniques besides landfill and incineration which can satisfactorily handle the range and volume of wastes to be dealt with. Certain wastes may be subject to pre-treatment, recycling or composting depending on suitability or need, but these applications are best used in conjunction with one of the two main disposal options.

## Figure 8
## Sensitivity to Landfill Charges

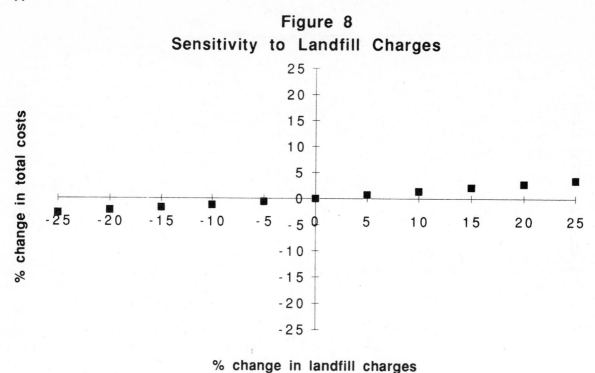

% change in landfill charges

B5.22 The longer term view of disposal technology includes new thermal, chemical or biological systems which aim to reduce and neutralise wastes. About the only thing that is certain about the new techniques is that they will leave residues requiring further disposal. Significant changes in technology are likely to be far in the future; in the meantime the technology of waste disposal will be mostly about staying abreast of ever changing standards and minimising the impact on the environment.

## Figure 9
## Sensitivity to Discount Rate

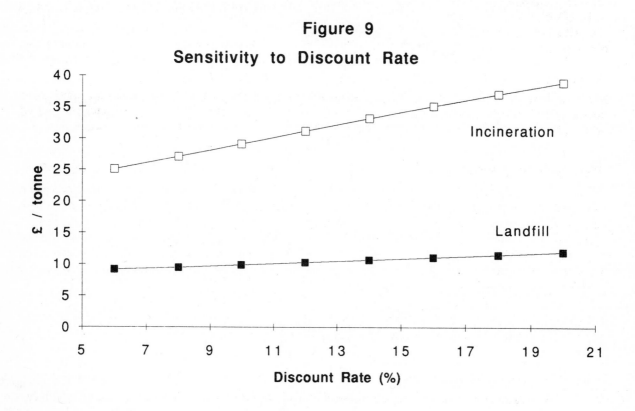

Discount Rate (%)

**Notes:**

1  A recent article by John Holmes in Industrial Waste Management (May issue) indicates that transaction values in the South East have reached £5.00 per m$^3$ on occasion—more likely the average would be around £3.00. In the Midlands and further north, valuations fall off, averaging £1.50 to £2.00.

2  This does not result in a precise match between the fund and the calculated obligation, which is actually £1.7 million, but there are other interest and tax considerations which could allow the gap to be made up or surpassed. In any event, the aftercare costs are subject to several variables which make these guidance figures only.

3  Items and costs have been estimated based on Waste Management Paper 26 (Table 17, Appendix 4) and updated for contemporary practice.

4  Environmental Resources Ltd., National Assessment of Landfill Gas Production, Report B1192 for the Energy Technology Support Unit, Harwell, 1990.

5  This is the length of time that schemes approved under last year's second tranche of NFFO schemes would be eligible for.

6  The cost is implied because estimates were only given for a 150,000 tonnes pa facility at £2.97 and a 250,000 tonnes pa facility at £2.43, of which the mid point is £2.70.

7  BEAMA Ltd., part of the CPA Advisory group, publish a regular list of engineering price indices.

8  It is a requirement of EC Directive (89/369/EEC) that the gases are at a temperature of minimum 850$^0$C for 2 sec. To ensure these conditions are maintained at all times an auxiliary burner is included.

9  R. C. Frost, Developments in Sewage Sludge Incineration, J. of the Institute of Water and Environmental Management, no.2, October 1988.

10  P. Lowe and G Groeger, The Revival of Incineration in the UK, in Water Science & Technology 1991, pp.1803–10.

11  Water Bulletin, 406, April 1990, p8–9.

12  Their publication has been ceased due to concern over commercial sensitivity.

13  This estimate is reasonably consistent with the perspective of J. R. Holmes in The United Kingdom Waste Management Industry, (IWM, 1992).

14  A. Porteous suggests that the greenhouse effect from escaping landfill gases in the UK is equivalent to that caused by the $CO_2$ gases from all coal fired power stations in the country, in Municipal Solid Waste Management in the UK—Time for a Reappraisal ?, Harwell, 1991.

15  In addition, hazardous waste landfills are to be located not less than 2000 m from residential areas.

16  Source: Warren Spring Laboratory.

# APPENDIX C

# WASTE MANAGEMENT POLICY IN THE NETHERLANDS

*This appendix contains an extract from the summary of the Ten-Year Programme on Waste Management (TJP.A) published in August 1992 by Afval Overleg Orgaan (AOO), the Dutch Waste Management Council.*

*AOO is responsible for organising waste management on a national scale. It consists of representatives of the Ministry for Housing, Regional Development and the Environment (VROM), the Association of Provincial Authorities and the Association of Netherlands Municipalities. It was established in 1990 when these three bodies entered into a joint agreement on waste disposal. Representatives of environmental and consumer organizations and trade, industrial and scientific bodies are advisers to the Council. Regional Waste Management Councils (RAOOs) have been established in each province or group of provinces. The Ten-Year Programme will be rolled forward every three years, after consultations with the relevant interests.*

## Policy and starting-points

C.1   In this first TJP.A the AOO makes a proposal to manage waste disposal in the Netherlands in accordance with the responsibilities described in the National Environmental Policy Plan (NMP) and NMP-plus, supplemented with the accentuated goals that were recently announced as a reaction to the adjusted figures on waste volume included in the National Environment Survey 2 1990–2010.

C.2   The TJP.A is based on the following starting-points:

— **Maximum stimulation of prevention and recovery** Responsibilities with regard to waste prevention and recovery were derived from the NMP and NMP-plus and elaborated into a policy scenario. This scenario provides an estimate of the capacity required for final waste treatment in 2002, subdivided into combustible and non-combustible waste.
The measures presented in the TJP.A have been tested for the consequences of prevention and recovery. The programme is flexible; if prevention and recovery are successful, no excess capacity for incineration will occur.

— **Drastic decrease of landfill disposal** Landfill disposal is an irreversible burden on physical structure and the environment. It should be limited as much as possible, firstly by means of intensified prevention and recovery and secondly by realizing sufficient incineration capacity, in combination with a policy on acceptance of wastes (see section 4.5).

— **Continuity in waste disposal** The TJP.A specifies the composting and landfill capacity for each region. It also provides the basis for decisions about incineration capacity to be taken within the next three years. These decisions lead to a step-by-step expansion of treatment capacity. This will, however, not be realized until 1998. In order to guarantee continuity in the short term, agreements have been made or are being made between the RAOOs about the processing of waste residues. This temporary solution should, however, fit within the long-term perspective.

— **An efficient approach to waste disposal** Within the context of a regional approach, the goal is scaling up final waste treatment in comparison with the present situation [in order to achieve economies of scale].

— **Regional and national self-sufficiency** The TJP.A emphasizes the responsibility of the regional for waste management. Shifting the responsibility for environmental problems to other regions or other countries should be prevented. The regional approach is also preferred in order to create an

146

adequate basis for the necessary alternative methods of waste processing and integral management of the waste chain within each region.

— **Waste disposal in accordance with existing regional and transport policies** The TJP.A provides a framework for the regional development of processing capacity and the building of transfer stations, and consequently a framework for increasing waste transport by train and by ship.

— **Minimizing environmental effects** Incineration plants, landfill sites, processing plants and other facilities for waste disposal must comply with the requirements of the legislation relating to the environment. This is also a pre-limiting condition for the recovery of waste substances.

# Development of waste disposal

## The waste volume

C.3   Precise details about waste volume cannot be provided until a national, uniform registration system for waste substances has been realized. An attempt was made to give an accurate overview of the quantity of waste processed in 1990. On the instructions of the AOO landfilled and incinerated waste was inventorized. Moreover, use was made of the information provided by the RIVM (National Institute of Public Health and Environment) in the National Environment Survey 2 1990–2010.

C.4   The TJP.A involves the following eight categories of waste ("the AOO wastes"):

— domestic waste;
— industrial container waste;
— construction and demolition waste;
— office, shop and service waste;
— waste from sanitation departments;
— coarse domestic waste;
— shredder waste;
— non-specific hospital waste.

C.5   By far the biggest proportion of these wastes is disposed of by landfill, although they contain components that are suitable for recovery and, as soon as recovery is impossible, for incineration.

C.6   Because of their influence on the waste volume to be landfilled, polluted soil and sewage sludge have also been included.

C.7   The three main components of the AOO wastes by weight are:

— paper, approx. 15%;
— vegetable, fruit-and garden-waste (GFT-waste) and "other organic waste", approx. 28%;
— stony material, approx. 20%.

The proportion of non-combustible material in the AOO wastes is approx. 30% of the total. In 1990, the potential quantity of combustible waste was approx. 9.5 million tonnes.

### Final waste treatment and GFT-waste treatment

C.8   Notwithstanding maximum efforts with regard to prevention and recovery it is obvious that part of the waste must be landfilled or incinerated. According to the policy combustible waste should be incinerated. Only non-combustible and non-recoverable waste would have to be landfilled. In the present situation incineration capacity in the Netherlands is, however, most inadequate, so that this objective cannot be met.

C.9   Of the total waste volume for final treatment in the eight AOO waste categories of 14.3 million tonnes in 1990, 2.8 million tonnes were incinerated and 11.5 million tonnes were landfilled. Of the waste volume landfilled in 1990, 6.7 million tonnes consisted of combustible waste. The residual capacity of

**Figure S.2    The expansion of the incineration capacity in the Netherlands based on hard and soft initiatives**

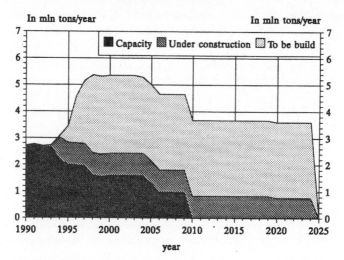

(Source: Waste Information System, AOO, 1992)

the existing landfill sites was approx. 57 million tonnes; inclusive of the capacity to be added, the excess capacity was approx. 146 million tonnes. The capacity differs from region to region.

C.10    The present incineration capacity is approx. 2.8 million tonnes on a yearly basis. The majority of this capacity can be found in the province of South Holland. Presently there are about 10 initiatives for new incineration plants. Estimates of the expansion of incineration capacity should, however, take into account the closure of (parts of) existing plants as well as the plants to be built. Decisions regarding investment in these initiatives, in various stages of planning, will have to be taken in the next few years. After these initiatives have been realized, incineration capacity in the Netherlands will be about 5.3 million tonnes in the year 2000. After 2010 the capacity may decrease to 3.6 million tonnes due to economic depreciation. Due to shortage of incineration capacity about 6.7 million tonnes of combustible waste (exclusive of sewage sludge) is landfilled each year. Figure S.2 shows the expected expansion of incineration capacity in the Netherlands.

C.11    In the present situation the treatment capacity for GFT-waste is approx. 360k tonnes a year. Investment decisions have been made about future capacity of 185k tonnes a year. Without taking into account plans which are not yet firm, the total capacity will be about 550k tonnes in 1996. By 1995 about 1000 to 1360k tonnes of separately collected GFT-waste is expected (depending on the number of households receiving separate collection and the response of citizens). Separate collection will be implemented before processing capacity has been expanded [to the same extent]; it is essential that decisions about investments with regard to the expansion of processing capacity are made as soon as possible.

**Administrative organization**

C.12    The organization of waste disposal is developing rapidly. At a policy level the waste Management Council (AOO) and the Regional Waste Management Councils (RAOOs) have been established. At an executive level the waste processing and treatment market is not developing according to plan and there is a lack of steering and adjustment. As a result, the steering of wastes, as well as initiatives for processing and final treatment, are developing unsatisfactorily. In several provinces organizations engaged in waste management (steering organizations) have been established to manage waste-processing (brokerage function) and take initiatives for waste treatment and processing (initiative function).

**Market**

C.13   The market for final waste treatment consists of the demand for processing capacity (from waste collectors and waste producers) and the supply of processing capacity. In this market the following bottlenecks occur:

— the demand for and supply of processing capacity is not clear;

— the operation of the market is surrounded with, on the one hand, investment risks and, on the other hand, doubts about technical developments and government policies anticipating these developments;

— the current waste processing tariffs are not in accordance with a balance between demand and supply. Large difference in tariffs occur and these have an undesired effect on the movement toward a reduction of landfilling and on the stimulation of waste prevention, the waste treatment market, waste recovery and useful application, and regional self-sufficiency;

— a number of international developments become relevant to our national market. Waste processing is in the hands of an increasingly smaller number of firms. These businesses keep an increasing number of links in the chain under their own control. Another development is the EC regulation on international transport of waste between member states. Moreover, the development of the European Single Market may have consequences for the national processing and treatment market. In border areas municipalities have the opportunity to cooperate [across frontiers] in the field of waste policy.

**Physical planning**

C.14   One of the main problems experienced in the realization of waste processing plants seems to be the lack of a solid basis with respect to physical planning. Moreover, there is often some administrative opposition. These problems are intensified because no suitable provisions have been made about co-ordination between environmental policy and town and country planning. The designation procedure is not used frequently either. Moreover, it is obvious that at an early stage of decision-making non-environmental aspects are decisive.

**Waste transport development**

C.15   Due to the increasing complexity and scale of waste disposal, the number of transport movements will increase. In order to avoid environmental problems a shift in the mode of transport from road to railway and waterway will be required. There is only a slight chance that such a shift will develop autonomously. As a result, an approach aimed at integration and the best possible adjustment of all the links in the chain, from the source of the waste until final treatment, will be necessary.

**Environmental problems**

C.16   During the preparation of the TJP.A an environmental impact assessment was drawn up (see paras C.26–C.28 below). This is aimed at comparison of the various alternatives for treatment and particularly at the decision between incineration and landfilling.

C.17   From an environmental point of view a technique involving anaerobic composting seems to be promising; waste is separated into an organic part for anaerobic composting and a dry residue for incineration. This technique should be tested as soon as possible on the specific composition of Dutch waste for reliability, costs and environmental effects. The next TJP.A will provide more details on this technique and the contribution of anaerobic composting to environmentally acceptable final waste treatment.

**Questions about social acceptance**

C.18   Social acceptance of the waste policy and the initiatives regarding waste disposal is not a matter of course. The realization of new waste processing plants usually appears to encounter much opposition, in spite of the improved decision-making procedure via environmental impact assessment. Presently, this opposition goes beyond the "not in my back garden" syndrome.

**Figure S.3: Policy scenario**

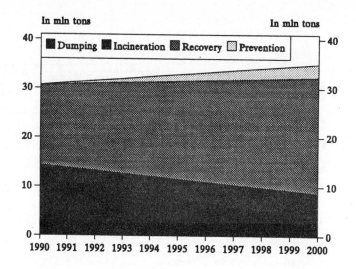

(Source: Waste Information System, AOO, 1992)

C.19    Processing waste more thoroughly leads to higher costs, and it remains to be seen if the higher costs will be accepted.

C.20    The producer is now responsible for waste. This starting-point, included in a letter of 19 October 1990 written by the Minister of VROM to the Lower Chamber, leads to restrictive requirements about products, the obligation to return packaging etc. and to volume-restricting measures.

# Programme

[The actions required to implement the programme were itemised in an appendix to the summary.]

### Scenarios for increase in waste volume

C.21    Two scenarios have been worked out for the period to 2000 in order to be able to make valid statements on the increase in waste volume and the processing capacity to be realized:

— the **policy scenario,** which is based on the increase in waste volume, and the realization of the aims and objectives, laid down in the NMP-plus, the accentuated goals drawn up in connection with the National Environment Survey 2 1990–2010, and the stepping up of the collection, recycling and processing of GFT-waste.

— the **head wind scenario,** which takes into account practical problems experienced in stimulating waste prevention and recovery. In this scenario, which is very similar to the figures provided by the National Environment Survey 2 written by the RIVM, the tasks specified in the NMP-plus are not achieved, at least not in time.

C.22    [Figures S.3 and S.4 illustrated these two scenarios.] In the policy scenario the demand for final waste treatment decreases from 14.3 million tonnes in 1990 to 8.7 million tonnes in 2000. Due to prevention and recovery, the relative contribution of final waste treatment decreases from 45% to 25% and is therefore almost halved. The head wind scenario also shows a decrease in demand for final waste treatment, but a less pronounced one, namely to 13 million tonnes in 2000.

C.23    There are two possible directions of development after the year 2000:

**Figure S.4: Head wind scenario**

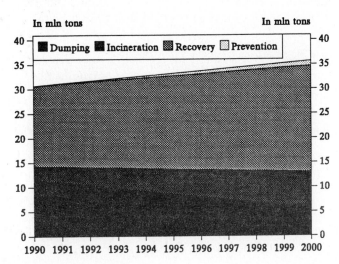

(Source: Waste Information System, AOO, 1992)

— an increase in waste volume of 1.3% a year;

— a long-term perspective scenario, which is optimistic about progress and results in the field of prevention and recovery.

C.24  For programming incineration capacity the AOO prefers to use the policy scenario as the basis, in order to prevent a situation of excess capacity.

C.25  The head wind scenario has been used as the basis for programming landfill capacity. The next TJP.A (in three years time) will be adapted to the actual expansion experienced in waste volume.

**Comparing alternative forms of waste processing in the EIA**

C.26  The EIA examined the environmental consequences and the burden on physical structure of a number of possible alternative policies:

— the reference variant (minimal landfill);

— the policy variant (minimal landfill plus pre-separation);

— minimal incineration (alternative 1);

— maximum pre-separation, anaerobic composting and minimal landfill (alternative 2);

— maximum pre-separation, minimal incineration (alternative 3).

C.27  Alternatives 1 and 3 are inconsistent with the starting-point of environmental policy but they indicate the consequences of a situation in which existing incineration capacity is not expanded (alternative 1 = no action) or only waste separation and digestion plants are built (alternative 3). Alternative 3, originally called the most environmentally acceptable alternative, can, however, hardly be called that, considering the enormous quantity of wastes to be landfilled, which would occupy a lot of space; a relatively low recovery of energy; and as a result a limited contribution to the $CO_2$ objective.

C.28  Compared to alternative 3, the combination of maximum pre-separation/digestion and minimal landfill (alternative 2) is more acceptable: energy production is considerably more extensive and considerably less space will be used. Considering the pre-separation and composting capacity required this alternative would not be realized quickly. However, it can be considered a direction for future consideration. The digestion technique cannot yet be considered a proven technique for the wet fraction from pre-separation. It is advisable to arrange practical trials in the near future.

**Promotion of prevention and recovery**

C.29  In late 1991 the Minister of VROM gave further impetus to the policy objectives regarding prevention and recovery, at a time when waste volume appeared to exceed expectations. This implied that prevention and recovery will have to contribute more in order to meet the objectives specified by the NMP-plus. The relative contribution of prevention should increase from 0% to 10% in 2000. The contribution of recovery should increase from 53% to 67% in 2000.

C.30    The role of the AOO in this field is focused on consultation and adjustment between government, provinces and municipalities. At present the AOO is preparing a number of programmes on prevention and recovery:

— a programme "organization structure, prevention and recovery", aimed at adjustment and consultation between the Ministry of VROM, provinces and municipalities with regard to prevention and recovery;
— a programme for planning processing capacity for GFT-waste;
— a programme aimed at co-ordination of waste prevention within companies;
— a programme for organizing the separate collection of the dry components in waste.

From the beginning of 1992 an Information centre for prevention and recovery has operated at AOO's offices. This centre is especially directed at the contributions of provinces and municipalities.

## Composting/digestion of GFT-waste

C.31    Presently, less than 50% of the waste processing capacity for GFT-waste required by 1 January 1995 is available or in an advanced stage of decision-making. In accordance with the GFT Regulations extra composting capacity must therefore be provided by 1 January 1995 at the very latest, but preferably before that date, [in all regions except the northern region]. For the year 2000 the TJP.A includes an accentuated goal for processing capacity, as used in the policy scenario.

## Programming final waste treatment

C.32    The AOO has organized the programming of treatment capacity in such a way that:

— each region will have sufficient waste processing capacity;
— if the policy scenario correctly represent the situation that will exist in the year 2000, there will be no excess capacity for incineration;
— if events follow the head wind scenario there will be enough flexibility to prevent the landfilling of combustible waste for a long period of time;
— the required incineration capacity will be established as soon as possible in order to limit the demand on scarce landfill capacity.

C.33    The expected expansion of incineration capacity in the Netherlands (Figure S.2) almost corresponds with the capacity required according to the policy scenario; see Figure S.5.

[Calculations about incineration and landfill capacity have been made for individual regions.]

C.34    Provinces and municipalities will create the administrative conditions for, and take initiatives for realizing, incineration capacity. Less incineration capacity needs to be realized than was expected earlier. This makes it possible to develop existing plants in the province of Gelderland rather than building new plants in the Central Netherlands. In the province of South Holland the more limited extra capacity may also be realized in existing plants, as an alternative to a new plant at Ypenburg. All of the other initiatives must be realized according to plan.

C.35    The required landfill capacity for the period 1992–2002 is determined by the volume of residual waste in accordance with the head wind scenario, minus the incineration capacity in this period. In 1990 11.5 million tonnes of the AOO wastes were landfilled. Provinces and municipalities should realize, as soon as possible, 23 million tonnes of extra landfill capacity. This capacity is needed for the period

**Figure S.5    The expansion of the waste volume for final waste treatment in accordance with the policy scenario.**

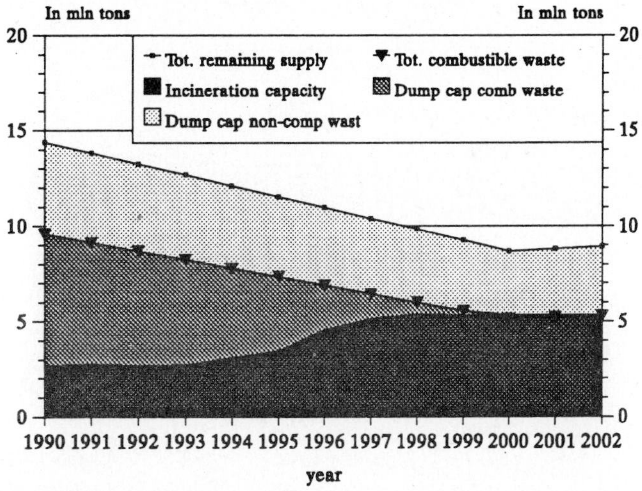

(Source: Waste Information System, AOO, 1992)

1991–1996. In order to provide enough capacity for the period till 2002, another 20.8 million tonnes of landfill capacity has to be authorised.

C.36    A considerable increase in prevention and recovery and the realization of sufficient incineration capacity should enable landfilling of combustible waste and recoverable waste to be ended. In addition a policy on acceptance of waste and on charging must be adopted for landfill. This implies that the provinces should enforce bans on the landfilling of combustible waste and unseparated construction and demolition waste. The provinces should also include environmental costs in tariffs by changing the conditions for permits.

C.36 *[bis]*    The AOO will support and coordinate initiatives at a regional level so as to encourage tariff harmonization. The Minister of VROM will be asked to support the policy on acceptance of waste and on charging by means of Regulations.

**Measures regarding waste processing in accordance with programming**

C.37    With regard to treatment capacity the AOO aims at self-sufficiency for each region. This should be laid down in provincial plans and in the relevant permits.

*Restructuring of interregional contracts*

C.38    In order to achieve a regional approach a number of interregional contracts should be terminated. The AOO will also determine which attribution of costs justifies the responsibility of the parties involved in the restructuring of these wastes.

*Emergency regulations and organization*

C.39    In mid-1993 the AOO will make a proposal to put an end to the (temporary) regional shortages of suitable treatment capacity. The AOO will also make a proposal with regard to the organizational design of implementation of this regulation.

**Implementing a programme in accordance with town and country planning**

C.40    In order to find suitable locations for waste disposal a physical structure for waste disposal should be developed. In accordance with government policy the TJP.A provides a physical selection and evaluation framework. The AOO will elaborate this framework to cover specific types of waste disposal facility.

C.41    The object is that provinces and municipalities will realize the necessary capacity, in accordance with this framework. Provinces are responsible for the incorporation of locations for waste disposal facilities in plans on waste management and regional development plans. Municipalities are responsible for regulations in zoning plans. Wherever necessary the provinces and subsequently the Minister of VROM should use their statutory authority to remove any existing barriers in relation to the realization of waste disposal plants.

## Implementing environmentally acceptable transport

C.42　From considerations of environmental hygiene and traffic management waste substances should be transported by ship and by train as much as possible. Due to the narrow economic margins this will not be easy. The AOO will stimulate discussion and co-operation between waste transporters, suppliers, processors and final processors, their ultimate objective being:

— to create standardization, which is necessary if there is to be a good connection between stages;
— to tackle the logistic aspect of disposing of waste systematically.

Simultaneously, provinces and municipalities must integrate the optimal features of logistic structure into the regional waste disposal framework.

## NOTE ON TERMINOLOGY

*This is an edited version prepared by the Commission's Secretariat from the English language summary: detailed information about wastes and waste disposal facilities at the regional level has been omitted.*

*To match the normal English usage, the term "effluents", which appears in the original, has been replaced here by "wastes"; and "dumping", "dumped" and "dump" have been replaced by "landfill", "landfilled" and "landfill site". The term "final treatment" is used a number of times for what is normally called in the UK "disposal".*

| | |
|---|---|
| *AOO* | *Waste Management Council* |
| *AOO wastes* | *see definition in para C.4* |
| *EIA* | *environmental impact assessment* |
| *GFT-waste* | *vegetable, fruit and garden waste* |
| *NMP* | *National Environmental Policy Plan* |
| *NMP-plus* | *Update of NMP* |
| *RAOO* | *Regional Waste Management Council* |
| *RIVM* | *National Institute of Public Health and the Environment* |
| *TJP.A* | *Ten-Year Programme on Waste Management* |
| *VROM* | *Ministry for Housing, Regional Development and the Environment* |

# APPENDIX D

# INVITATION TO SUBMIT EVIDENCE

In September 1991 the Royal Commission issued a press release in the following terms:

**STUDY ON INCINERATION**

The Royal Commission on Environmental Pollution has decided to carry out a study on pollution arising from the incineration of wastes.

The study will be concerned with the environmental impact of land-based incineration, including emissions to air and disposal of residues. It will take account of the design and operation of plant and of regulatory issues and cost. It is likely to cover the incineration of most kinds of waste, including municipal, clinical, toxic and other chemical wastes, sewage and agricultural sludge and animal remains. It will focus on the following questions:-

What is the impact of pollution from the incineration of wastes on human health and the wider environment?

For what kinds of waste is incineration an appropriate method of treatment, assuming that all reasonable steps have been taken to minimise the production of waste?

What should be required of a incinerator? What designs and operational procedures are at present available and what additional features would be desirable?

Are the present or proposed regulatory frameworks and enforcement procedures for waste incineration satisfactory? If not, what changes should be made?

What public concerns have arisen from the incineration of wastes? How should they be addressed?

The Commission has invited evidence from a number of organisations but would welcome evidence from any organisation or individual that wishes to express a view.

# APPENDIX E

# ORGANISATIONS AND INDIVIDUALS CONTRIBUTING
# TO THE STUDY

An asterisk (*) indicates that members of the Commission had discussions with representatives of the organisation.

## Government Bodies

*United Kingdom*
Department of Energy
Department of the Environment*
Department of the Environment for Northern Ireland
Department of Health
Department of Trade and Industry
Ministry of Agriculture Fisheries and Food
Scottish Office Environment Department
Welsh Office

Alkali and Radiochemical Inspectorate (Northern Ireland)
Health and Safety Commission
Her Majesty's Inspectorate of Pollution*
Her Majesty's Industrial Pollution Inspectorate (Scotland)

*Denmark*
National Agency for Environmental Protection

*Germany*
Council of Environmental Advisers
Federal Environmental Agency*
Federal Ministry of the Environment*

*Netherlands*
Netherlands Agency for Energy and the Environment*
National Institute for Public Health and Environment*

*Sweden*
National Chemical Inspectorate
National Environment Protection Board

*USA*
Environmental Protection Agency

*European Community*
Commission of the European Communities, Directorate-General XI (Environment, consumer protection and nuclear safety)

**Other Organisations**
AEA Technology
Alliance for Beverage Cartons and the Environment
Association of County Councils
Association of Metropolitan Authorities
Association of the British Pharmaceutical Industry
BADCAP Campaign (Belvedere, Kent)
BASF plc
Bayer AG
Belco Technologies Corporation
Best Global Ltd
BETTER Campaign (Belvedere, Kent)
Bexley Health Authority
Biffa Waste Services Ltd
Binnie and Partners
Birwelco Ltd
Blue Circle Technical Centre
BP International Ltd
British Cement Association
British Medical Association
Brooke Bond Foods Ltd
Buckinghamshire County Council
BUPA Hospitals Ltd
Campaign against the Clydeside Incinerator
Centre for Exploitation of Science and Technology
Cerestar UK Ltd
Chematics International Co Ltd
Chemical Industries Association
City of Glasgow District Council
Cleanaway Ltd*
Combined Heat and Power Association
Communities against Toxics
Confederation of British Industry
Convention of Scottish Local Authorities
Cory Environmental Municipal Services Ltd
Country Landowners Association
County Planning Officers Society*
Cremer and Warner
Dairy Trade Federation
Dames and Moore
Davyhulme Residents Action Committee
Degussa Ltd
Ebara UK Ltd
Energy Technology Support Unit
Environment and Health Working Group, Glasgow
Environmental Toxicology International Inc
Envirorisk
ERL Ltd
Evans Universal Ltd
Fläkt Industriella Processor AB
Food and Drink Federation
GEC Alsthom Ltd
Greenpeace*
Haden Drysys Ltd
Hampshire County Council
Highland Regional Council
Humberside County Council
Independent Panel on Intractable Wastes, Australia

Industry and Environment Associates
Institute of Energy
Institute of Wastes Management
Institution of Plant Engineers
Institution of Water and Environmental Management
Institution of Chemical Engineers
Institution of Mechanical Engineers
Institution of Civil Engineers
International Technology Europe Ltd
John Brown Engineering Ltd
KC Process Ltd
Kellogg Co (UK) Ltd
Kernforschungszentrum Karlsruhe GmbH
Kirkcaldy District Council
Laboratory of the Government Chemist
Leverkusen Municipal Waste Management Company*
London Waste Regulation Authority
Lurgi Energie- und Umwelttechnik GmbH
Marine Conservation Society
Martin GmbH
Medical Research Council
Middlesbrough Borough Council
Milk Marketing Board
Motherwell Bridge Projects Ltd
National Association of Waste Disposal Contractors*
National Power plc
National Starch and Chemical Co Ltd
National Farmers Union
National Society for Clean Air and Environmental Protection
National Physical Laboratory
Natural Environment Research Council
NHS Estates
North London Waste Authority
North Humberside Campaign against Toxics
Northern Foods plc
ORATE (Oswaldtwistle Residents Against Toxic Waste)
Pedigree Pet Foods plc
Process Plant Association
Rank Hovis Ltd
Rechem Environmental Services plc
Retech Ltd
Royal Town Planning Institute*
Royal Society of Chemistry
Royal College of Veterinary Surgeons
S Grundon (Waste) Ltd
Severn Trent Water Ltd
Slough Trading Estate Ltd
Small Area Health Statistics Unit*
Sound Resources Management Group, USA
South East London Combined Heat and Power Ltd
Soya Health Foods Ltd
Stuttgart Municipal Utilities Company*
Tate and Lyle Sugars Ltd
Thames Water Utilities Ltd
Tiru SA
Trafford Edible Oil Refiners Ltd
Travers Morgan Ltd

Ulster Farmers Union
W L Gore Ltd
WARMER Campaign (World Action for Recycling Materials and Energy from Rubbish)
Warren Spring Laboratory*
Waste Management International Inc
Waste Management Industry Training and Advisory Board
Watson Hawksley Ltd
Wessex Waste Management Ltd
Wimpey Environmental Ltd
Women's Environmental Network
WRc plc
Yorkshire Water Services Ltd*

## Individuals

| | |
|---|---|
| Dr C S Creaser, | University of East Anglia |
| Professor F A Fairweather, | Unilever plc |
| Dr K C Jones, | University of Lancaster |
| Dr F D Mole, | University of Surrey |
| Dr J Nash, | Massachusetts Institute of Technology |
| Mr V Patel, | London Borough of Sutton |
| Dr J Petts, | Loughborough University of Technology |
| Professor A Porteous, | The Open University |
| Mr B Price | |
| Mr N Semple | |
| Professor J Swithinbank, | University of Sheffield |
| Dr P T Williams, | University of Leeds |

**The Commission also received representations from the following Portsmouth residents about a proposal for a new incinerator:**

Mr J S Barrand
Mr M S Garlick
Mr and Mrs G Hopwood
Mr E Lane
Mr P W Lyons
Mr A Slack
Mrs M Smith

Mr R E Shenton
Mr L R Stubbington
Mrs M Richardson
Mr L E Wake
Mr and Mrs D Wiggins
Captain and Mrs J Wilson

These representations were passed to the Department of the Environment.

## Visits

Members of the Commission made visits in order to meet representatives of the organisations listed below, and, where relevant, see the incinerators operated by them:

19–21 February 1992   *Germany*
　　Bayer AG, Leverkusen.
　　Leverkusen Municipal Waste Management Company
　　Federal Environmental Agency
　　Federal Ministry of the Environment

23–24 March 1992   *Germany*
   Stuttgart Municipal Utilities Company
   Nuclear Research Centre, Karlsruhe

20–21 May 1992   *United Kingdom*
   Yorkshire Water Services Ltd, Esholt, Bradford.
   Cleanaway Ltd., Ellesmere Port, Cheshire.

3 July 1992   *Netherlands*
   Netherlands Agency for Energy and the Environment
   National Institute for Public Health and Environment

# APPENDIX F

# MEMBERS OF THE ROYAL COMMISSION

## CHAIRMAN

SIR JOHN HOUGHTON CBE FRS

    Chairman of the Scientific Assessment Working Group of the Intergovernmental Panel on Climate Change

    Chief Executive (formerly Director-General) of the Meteorological Office 1983–91

    Formerly Deputy Director of the Rutherford-Appleton Laboratory, Science and Engineering Research Council

    Professor of Atmospheric Physics, Oxford University 1976–83

    President of the Royal Meteorological Society 1976–78

    Vice-President of World Meteorological Organisation 1987–91

## MEMBERS

SIR GEOFFREY ALLEN PhD FRS FIC FIM FRSC FInstP HonFIChemE HonFCGI CEng

    Executive Adviser to Kobe Steel Ltd

    A Vice-President of the Royal Society

    Senior Vice-President of the Institute of Materials

    Chairman of the Council of Science and Technology Institutes

    Chairman of Cambridge Quantum Fund

PROFESSOR H CHARNOCK CBE FRS

    Visiting Fellow, Department of Oceanography, University of Southampton

    Senior Visiting Fellow, Institute of Oceanographic Sciences

    Past-Director of the Institute of Oceanographic Sciences

    President, International Union of Geodesy and Geophysics 1971–75

    President, Royal Meteorological Society 1982–84

PROFESSOR DAME BARBARA CLAYTON DBE MD PhD HonDSc(Edin and Southampton) FRCP FRCPE FRCPath

    Honorary Research Professor in Metabolism, University of Southampton

    Past-President, Royal College of Pathologists

    Chairman, Medical Research Council Committee on Toxic Hazards in the Environment and the Workplace

    Chairman, Health of the Nation Task Force on Nutrition

    Chairman, Standing Committee on Postgraduate Medical Education

    Chairman, Medical and Scientific Panel of Leukaemia Research Fund

    Honorary Member, British Paediatric Association

MR H R FELL FRAgS NDA MRAC

    Managing Director, H R Fell and Sons Ltd

    Council Member, Royal Agricultural Society of England

    Member, Minister of Agriculture's Advisory Council on Agriculture and Horticulture 1972–81

    Commissioner, Meat and Livestock Commission 1969–78

    Past-Chairman, Tenant Farmers Association

MR P R A JACQUES CBE BSc
> Head, Trades Union Congress Social Insurance and Industrial Welfare Department
> Secretary, TUC Social Insurance and Industrial Welfare Committee
> Secretary, TUC Health Services Committee
> Secretary, TUC Pensioners Committee
> TUC Representative, Health and Safety Commission
> TUC Representative, Social Security Advisory Committee

PROFESSOR J H LAWTON BSc PhD FRS
> Director, Natural Environment Research Council Interdisciplinary Research Centre for Population Biology
> Professor of Community Ecology, Imperial College of Science, Technology and Medicine
> Honorary Research Fellow, Natural History Museum, London
> Adjunct Scientist, Institute of Ecosystem Studies, New York
> Member, British Ecological Society
> Member, American Society of Naturalists
> Chairman-elect, Royal Society for the Protection of Birds

PROFESSOR R MACRORY Barrister MA(Oxon)
> Denton Hall Professor of Environmental Law, Imperial College of Science, Technology and Medicine
> Associate Director, Imperial College Centre for Environmental Technology
> First Chairman of the UK Environmental Law Association 1986–88
> Editor-in-Chief of the Journal of Environmental Law
> Specialist Adviser in environmental law to the House of Commons Select Committee on the Environment

PROFESSOR J G MORRIS BSc DPhil FIBiol FRS
> Professor of Microbiology, University College of Wales Aberystwyth
> Chairman, Biological Sciences Committee of the Science and Engineering Research Council 1978–81
> Chairman, Biological Sciences Committee of the University Grants Committee 1981–86
> Member, Society for General Microbiology

MR D A D REEVE CBE BSc FEng FICE FIWEM
> Deputy Chairman and Chief Executive, Severn Trent Water Authority 1983–85
> Past-President, Institute of Water Pollution Control
> Past-President, Institution of Civil Engineers
> Formerly Member, Advisory Council on Research and Development, Department of Energy
> Additional Member, Monopolies and Mergers Commission

EMMA ROTHSCHILD MA
> Senior Research Fellow, King's College, Cambridge
> Research Fellow, Sloan School of Management, Massachusetts Institute of Technology (MIT)
> Associate Professor of Science, Technology and Society, MIT 1978–88
> Member, OECD Group of Experts on Science and Technology in the New Socio-Economic Context 1976–80
> Board Member, Stockholm Environment Institute

PROFESSOR Z A SILBERSTON CBE MA
> Senior Research Fellow, Management School, Imperial College of Science, Technology and Medicine
> Professor Emeritus of Economics, University of London
> Past Secretary-General, Royal Economic Society
> Past Member, Restrictive Practices Court
> Past-President, Confederation of European Economic Associations
> Director, Brussels Office, London Economics
> Member, Biotechnology Advisory Commission, Stockholm Environment Institute
> Specialist Adviser, House of Lords Select Committee on the European Communities

# GENERAL INDEX

# INDEX OF PLACES

Printed in the United Kingdom for HMSO
Dd 5061325   9/93   C3   56219   51.0.0   ON 260139